Wild Plants and their Habitats in the North York Moors

A comprehensive flora of the North York Moors National Park

NAN SYKES

Published by

North York Moors National Park

ISBN 0 907480 42 X

Front Cover Photographs:

1. Kildale Moor – NYMNP
2. Wood vetch – Allan Drewitt
3. Harebell and Lady's bedstraw – Peter Roworth A.R.P.S.

The assistance of the Yorkshire Philosophical Society in the publication of this book is gratefully acknowledged by the National Park Committee.

Contents

FOREWORD

The management of a National Park involves making policies and taking decisions about the use of the Park for a wide variety of purposes. Always it is necessary to uphold the twin aims of conserving the landscape and promoting its enjoyment by all who wish to use it. A comprehensive and up-to-date data bank of the Park's natural resources is an essential requirement if decisions are to be soundly based.

Although a good deal of "botanising" has taken place in the Park since the Victorian era, it is only recently that attempts have been made to collect floral data in a systematic fashion. The publication of this Flora is a milestone in the development of our understanding of the environment of the North York Moors. The information in it will be useful to academic researchers, to the National Park Authority and other environmental agencies in their work and to all who wish to discover more about their local environment.

Nan Sykes is one of those dedicated and thoroughly professional voluntary researchers of our native flora that are the hallmark of British botany. She has produced a work of great value and in so doing has enthused a number of young botanists to become experts in fieldwork, an achievement of no less value. All those of us who love the North York Moors are indebted to her.

J. C. Statham

INTRODUCTION

For centuries, man has been intrigued by the variety of wild plants which spring up on any ground left to its own devices and, by the Victorian age, the careful study of plant whereabouts became an absorbing passion for many leisured persons – especially clerics. Undeterred by limited means of transport, they succeeded in documenting the wealth of wild flowers which at that time were commonplace – so common in fact, that many 19th century botanists quite shamelessly gathered every unusual specimen, either to be dried for an herbarium or to be bartered between collectors.

Resulting from this wave of natural history fervour, many floras came to be compiled for specific areas. The opening of the Whitby-Pickering railway in 1836 was accompanied by a list of plants in its vicinity. In 1863, one John Gilbert Baker had printed at Thirsk a treatise on *Botany, Geology, Climate and Physical Geography of North Yorkshire* – no small achievement. Tragically, a fire at his home destroyed the entire edition, and it was not until 1906 that a revised work was compiled and published. Frank Elgee's work in 1912 *The Moorlands of North-East Yorkshire* contains many references to plants, and in 1915 Bernard Reynolds published a neat resumé of wild flowers he had encountered in the Whitby district. Nearly 40 years later, in 1953, a group of enthusiasts in the Scarborough Field Naturalists' Society produced a two-volume guide to the flora and fauna of the countryside between Flamborough and Ravenscar and inland to Thornton-le-Dale.

Following the second World War and the dramatic changes to the rural environment then underway, the Botanical Society of the British Isles decided that it was essential to have an up-to-date record of the status of wildflowers throughout the country. Enlisting the voluntary help of hundreds of amateur botanists, the Society succeeded in producing distribution maps for every British vascular plant species. Based on 10km squares of the national grid, these distribution maps were published in 1963 as the first *Atlas of the British Flora.*

This work provided a valuable broad-based indication of native vegetation in the 1950s, but new technology was rapidly bringing far-reaching changes to natural ecosystems.

It soon became apparent that much more detailed information was required if effective strategies, based on sound knowledge, were to be developed to conserve our wildflower heritage for the future.

It was against this background of a need for precise data that in 1986 I set about compiling this flora. Keen amateur botanists in the area assisted with the collection of the records and many organisations provided valuable assistance and background information.

My grateful thanks go to the many people who have helped, particularly the National Park Authority which has supported the project from its early concept through to publication.

My sincere appreciation for his technical expertise and encouragement also go to Andrew Malloch, Director of Ecology at Lancaster University's Institute of Environmental and Biological Sciences, who compiled and made available the computer programme and arranged for initial printing of the distribution maps.

I am extremely grateful to the enthusiastic band of recorders who turned out in all weathers, trudged over most exacting terrain, dealt with aggressive dogs (and the occasional bull), searched in vain for vanished species and spent many hours assembling records ready for the computer – Margaret Atherden, Angela Clark, John Blackburn, Paul Harris, Vincent Jones, Ian Lawrence, Sheila Metcalfe, Brian Pickersgill, Gordon Simpson, Chris Wilson and Mike Yates, and also Eric Chicken for his helpful comments on the text.

I should like to thank, too, the following organisations and individuals who contributed records:

North York Moors Phase I Habitat Teams
North Yorkshire & Cleveland Heritage Coast Phase I Habitat Teams
Pteridological Society of the British Isles
Yorkshire Naturalists' Union
Scarborough Field Naturalists' Society
Ryedale Natural History Society
Whitby Naturalists' Club
C M Rob Natural History Society

P Abbott, M Anderson, S Arnold, P Barfoot, J Bolton, A Bowns, W Bramley, D Bramley, E Chicken, A Cooper, J Cooper, B Dickinson, J Dinwiddie, B Fewster, J Gatenby, K Gerhardsen, B Gilling, D Grant, F Gravestock, A GreatRex, M Gulliver, R Gulliver, J Hall, D Haythornthwaite, B Hurlock, C Jermy, J Lambert, H Mason, R Maycock, T Medd, G Milne, S Pashby, H Pellant, S Powell, E Preston, S Rees, J Renney, C Ridge, R Ridsdale, P Robinson, P Skelton, N Thompson, G Towle, M Usher, A Wallis, B Walker, J Williamson, H Wyett

and the following organisations for their assistance:

Agricultural Development and Advisory Service
Botanical Society of the British Isles
British Ecological Society
British Rail
English Heritage
English Nature
Forestry Commission
National Trust
North Yorkshire Moors Railway
RAF Fylingdales
Woodland Trust
Yorkshire Wildlife Trust

Finally, I should like to thank the many landowners who permitted access to their land. Without the co-operation of all these people this flora would not have been possible.

This project has been both absorbing and enjoyable to carry out and has, I think, engendered a good deal of thought and concern about the current status of local wildflowers. The overall picture is indeed grave and it was with sadness that several older recorders visited familiar haunts only to find their treasured plants had gone; many younger recorders read with envy accounts of how plant-rich our countryside used to be. However, there is a wind of change in the air, shown by the numerous incentives now available to land users to recreate some of the colourful flower-strewn waysides of yesteryear. All who have been involved in this survey earnestly hope that their efforts, and this resulting publication, will assist towards the rescue and reinstatement of our native flora before it is too late.

Nan Sykes
Thornton-le-Dale
1993

THE SCOPE OF THIS FLORA

Of the 2,000 or so plants that can be found throughout Britain, about 850 occur within the North York Moors National Park. Some of these are abundant, others are rare, but the wide range of plants which exists reflects the diversity of habitats and the fact that the Park lies in an intermediate zone between upland and lowland Britain.

This book describes the distribution and status of vascular plants within the National Park and in the area around Whitby, Sleights and Ruswarp which lies outside the Park boundary. It includes trees, shrubs, sedges, ferns and grasses as well as the obvious flowering plants. Mosses, lichens and fungi are not included. The area covered was divided into 396 tetrads (2 x 2 kilometre squares) based on the National Grid, thus covering a total area of 1584 sq km. The tetrads provided a basis for the survey work and, as far as possible, every different habitat in each tetrad was searched several times during the growing season. After six years, 120,000 records had been collected and processed to produce the distribution maps.

Wild Plants and their Habitats in the North York Moors should be regarded as a base-line flora of vascular plants known to occur in the North York Moors National Park as the 20th century draws to a close. It is the culmination of recording over a comparatively short six year span and inevitably there are still gaps to be filled. Further study is required, for example, on hybrids and subspecies, and on micro-species of groups such as eyebrights, hawkweeds, dandelions and brambles, whose ability for self-fertilisation has led to the development of local characteristics.

It is hoped that the publication of this book is just a beginning; plant population is never static. Any additional records of less common species, new sightings or information of plants recorded in this work but subsequently lost should be submitted to the National Park Office in Helmsley where the database will be constantly updated.

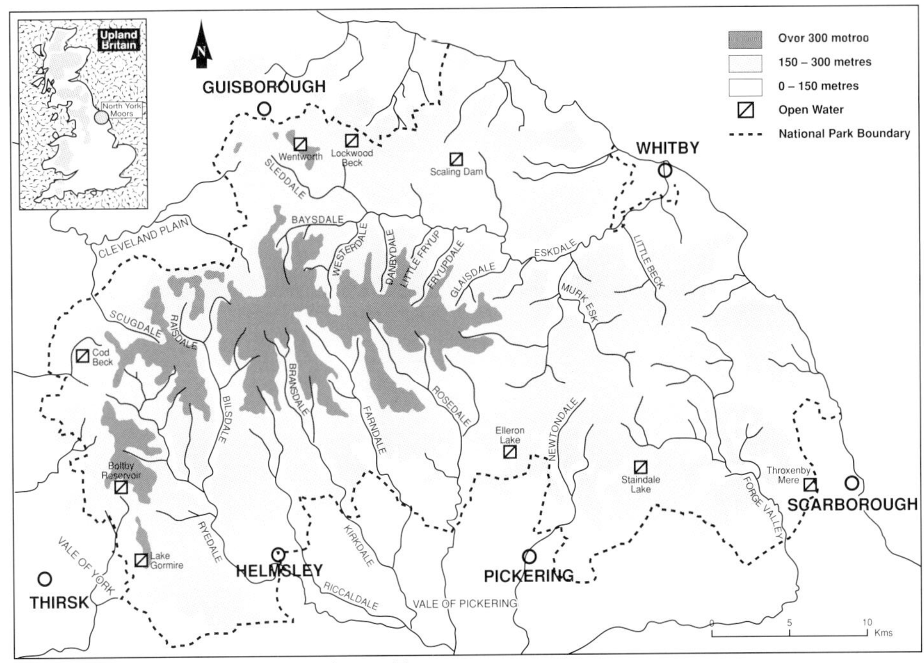

Map I – North York Moors – Landscape Features

The North York Moors National Park

Of the present 11 National Parks in England and Wales, the North York Moors, designated in 1952, was the sixth National Park to be created. It was chosen because of its extensive plateau of heather moorland – a habitat with limited distribution both in Britain and throughout Europe. Abruptly terminated by coastal cliffs to the north-east, rocky escarpments to the west and north, and sloping agricultural land to the south, the 1436 sq km (554 sq miles) of the Park form a distinct upland landscape reaching a maximum height of 545m (1490ft) on Urra Moor. Most of the heather-clad hills are above the 244m (800 ft) contour, the elevation decreasing towards the south and east.

Situated on the drier eastern side of Britain, the National Park has a congenial climate throughout its lower land. On the upland areas, however, annual rainfall may exceed 1000mm, often falling as snow. With low winter temperatures and strong winds, these exposed moorlands offer a harsh environment where only specialised plants survive. Over the centuries, normal vegetative decay was inhibited by such cold, wet conditions resulting in layers of waterlogged peat. This varies in depth across the moors reaching up to 3.5m deep on the central watershed.

The unique character of the National Park, with its windswept, flattish hills dissected by small steep-sided valleys is due mainly to its underlying geology (see Map II). The rocks of the North York Moors were laid down in the warm coral-laden seas of the Jurassic era (210-145 million years ago) and fluctuations in sea level during that time resulted in different types of rock being formed, ranging from limestones and sandstones to shales and mudstones. Subsequent uplifting and erosion followed by the scouring effects of several ice-ages formed the basis of the existing landscape. This variation in rock types has significantly influenced the vegetation. Acid sandstones support the true heather moorland with its blanket bogs, dry heath, shallow peaty slacks and constant water. To the south of the sandstone massif are the limestone and calcareous grits of the Tabular Hills which provide some of the richest plant habitats in the Park.

Following the deposition of these various rock strata came a sequence of ice ages. The last, retreating some 12,000 years ago, left extensive deposits of boulder clay along the coastal plain, as well as hummocks of sandy moraine in Eskdale and wetlands trapped among the hills. Meltwater from the glaciers etched the drainage pattern which exists today, although most streams and rivers are mere trickles compared with the raging torrents which originally cut the valleys.

Although a sparse tundra type vegetation survived on exposed summits after the last ice age, climatic improvement soon enabled plant colonisation of the barren landscape. Climate played a significant part in the ebb and flow of plant survival with arctic scrub replaced by pine, birch and juniper, then later elm, oak, hazel and alder moving in to create mixed woodland as the temperature increased. Wildwood, predominantly oak, birch and rowan,

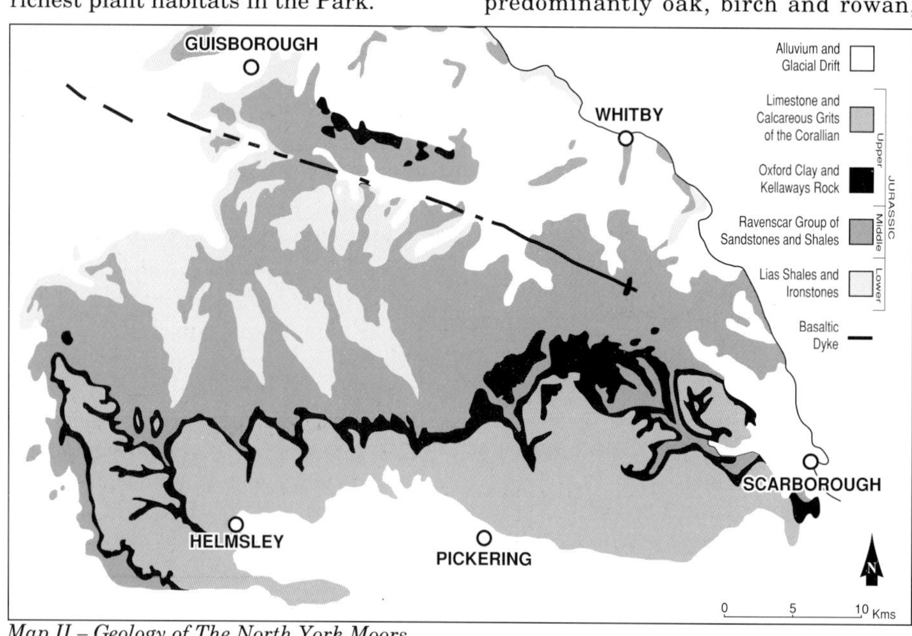

Map II – Geology of The North York Moors

virtually blanketed the uplands by 6,000 BC, spreading into the dales and lower land where swamps inhibited tree growth.

Plants spread here from further south in Europe but with the glaciers melted by warmer climate, the sea level rose and by 5,500 BC Britain was cut off from mainland Europe, preventing any further natural recolonisation by plants.

The geology and climate have not only affected the natural vegetation but they have influenced the way in which man has used the land. The plants growing here today are, therefore, a result of the complex interaction of geology, soils, climate and man's activities.

Indeed, from around 6,000 BC man started to influence the wildwood and its plants. Using primitive stone axes and fire, early settlers removed trees to create open glades, and introduced primitive wheat and barley with a few associated weeds. Food from hunted wild animals and fruits of the forest was increasingly augmented by farmed crops, grown on fresh clearings as nutrients declined. Each wave of immigrants, moving northwards from continental Europe, brought new plants and cultivation skills. Forest clearance accelerated with iron-age man's charcoal burning needs; Roman invaders, with their more sophisticated lifestyle, introduced numerous culinary herbs. But it was the large and prosperous monastic settlements of Rievaulx, Byland and Whitby, with their outlying granges and thousands-strong flocks of sheep, which completed the transformation of post-glacial forest to the treeless landscape of today's moorland. The monks did, however, like later herbalists, introduce various medicinal plants to the local flora.

After the dissolution of the monasteries in the 16th century, dales' farmers acquired common rights on the uplands, where grazing pressure was maintained by hill sheep and store cattle, with not a little help from an enormous rabbit population. Heather, a natural understorey shrub of the original oak and birch woodland, survived on the windswept and water-logged plateau, where it provides the principal food for red grouse. By the 19th century landowners realised that by "farming" heather they could increase the grouse population, a process which continues to this day, and explains the semi-natural purple expanse of moorland. Only in a few inaccessible gills are remnants of the original tree cover to be found.

Coincidental with man's transformation of the upland landscape, his wanderings brought in new plants to augment the existing flora. Explorers of the Elizabethan era returned with hitherto unknown plants from the New World; alchemists and wealthy men of property sent plant hunters far and wide to collect exotic species; as farming practice moved from open commons to enclosed fields, new crops were introduced together with associated weeds. Thus a succession of alien species reached these shores from Europe and beyond, and natural seed dispersal brought into the local flora those plants able to find a suitable habitat and survive the climate.

Today just over a third of the National Park is ericaceous moorland. This provides sparse grazing for up to 50,000 hill sheep. The coastal and Cleveland plains and the southern limestone are more fertile however, and they support a mixture of dairying, grazing and arable farms. In the dales traditional stock-rearing exists

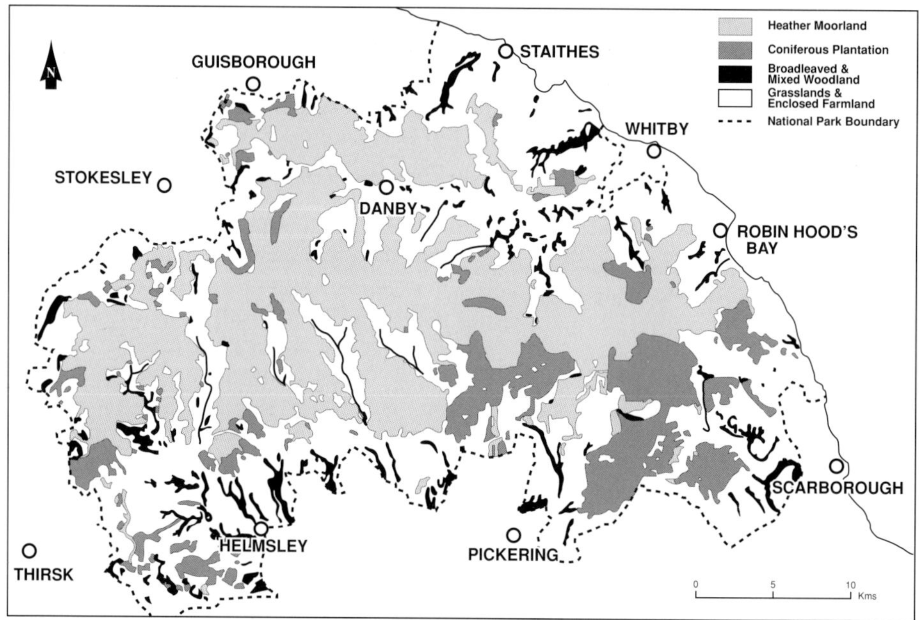

Map III – Vegetation and Land Use

although most of the pasture has been much "improved". Such varied agricultural land-use creates many different habitats and a correspondingly wide variety of plantlife. Woodlands range from ancient semi-natural deciduous woodland which clothes many coastal valleys to remnant oak and birch woodland in dale-heads and extensive conifer plantations. These offer different opportunities for plants to flourish.

The geology of the Park has also had a direct effect on man's activities as many of the hillsides contain valuable mineral deposits. The scars of past mining and quarrying are still evident with jet, alum, ironstone, coal and building stone having been extracted. Several disused quarry faces and spoil heaps which are now overgrown, are floristically rich.

The zenith for abundance and variety of the local flora was probably reached towards the end of the 19th century, when organic farming was the norm; lanes were earthen tracks, woodland usually meant native trees with lush ground flora; hedges, hedgerow trees, ponds and streams were needed for stock; and chemical sprays were unknown. Since the start of the 20th century man's influences have caused the decline both in abundance and variety of wildflowers. Rarer species with exacting requirements and those already at the limit of their natural range have been lost as land uses changed too quickly for them to adapt.

Modernisation of agriculture is undoubtedly the main factor in habitat loss although it is to traditional agriculture that many plants owe their survival. The North York Moors did not escape the post-war philosophy of increased intensity of food and timber production and all the associated detrimental effects. Sadly moorland has been ploughed and cultivated, old herb-rich meadows re-seeded, fields enlarged, wetlands drained and ancient woodlands felled. The habitats which are most depleted in the National Park are traditional hayfields, limestone pasture, marshy meadows, naturally regenerating deciduous woodland, unburnt moorland and cultivated ground free from chemical sprays. A significant length of hedgerow has been lost and young hedgerow trees are now a rarity.

Written accounts of the local flora 40 years ago are few but those that do exist are sufficient to indicate that more than 20 once familiar flowers have been lost from the National Park area and others which were plentiful are now reduced to a few isolated sites.

The following plants which are known to have grown within the National Park area were not found in this survey:

Marsh fern
Pillwort
Prickly headed poppy
Field pepperwort
Dittander
Corn gromwell
Vervain
Jacob's ladder
Bladderwort
Allseed
Dodder
Corncockle
Great sundew
Wild clary
Shepherd's needle
Autumn lady's tresses
Marsh gentian
Cornflower
Annual knawel
Round-leaved wintergreen
Trifid bur marigold

Many other species are at risk of being lost to the local flora unless positive action is taken (see Appendix 1).

In spite of these losses, the North York Moors National Park still has a very rich and interesting flora. This variety reflects not only the wide range of habitats within its boundary but also its unique position between the geographical spread of upland and montane plants typical of northern Britain, the less hardy species of the southern counties, the moisture-loving Atlantic types and the salt-tolerant and frost-sensitive maritime species. In fact, there are several plants that are scarce in Britain which can still be found locally, albeit in small numbers. These include:

Monkshood
Long stalked cranesbill
Narrow-leaved marsh orchid
Corn chamomile
Ramping fumitory
Small white fumitory
Flixweed
Wood cudweed
Wild pansy
Mountain St John's wort
Creeping forgetmenot
Baneberry
Green-winged orchid
Dwarf cornel
Wood barley
Tufted loosestrife
Fingered sedge
Marsh rosemary
Burnt-tip orchid
Yellow star of Bethlehem
Birdseye primrose
Mountain currant
Wintergreen
Bithynian vetch
Corn buttercup
Few-flowered sedge
Night-flowering catchfly
May lily
Tall broomrape

Alongside radical changes in the way agricultural land is managed, a number of other factors have affected the appearance of the National Park and its wealth of flora. A decline in resident populations has meant inadequate labour to maintain traditional walls and hedges and the large numbers of visitors has led to footpath erosion and road widening, surfacing and fencing, all of which have had detrimental effects on the natural environment.

It is, however, unhelpful to dwell on the gloomy side and now as the 21st century approaches, the general realisation of what we have lost is starting to generate positive benefits. Increased leisure time which has brought visitors into the National Park has stimulated interest in their environment. People are becoming increasingly aware of the wildlife around them and making demands for its protection. Many schemes and grants are now available to farmers and landowners to enable them to protect and manage semi-natural habitats and also to encourage more traditional management of farmland. The North York Moors National Park Authority offers help and support for this kind of work and the pioneering North York Moors Farm Scheme which helps farmers integrate conservation with farming has been met with national acclaim.

Threats of large-scale afforestation and agricultural reclamation of moorland are now in the past but there is still a need to increase awareness of the sensitivity of our countryside amongst the people who live and work here, as well as the people who visit and particularly amongst the people who make the decisions which will affect the future of the countryside. The National Park Authority is working closely with the farmers and landowners who manage and care for the land in the hope that further losses to our flora can be averted and the occurrence of our rarer species increased. So, despite the considerable losses in species which have occurred throughout the 20th century, future prospects are more optimistic and hopefully the 21st century will be one in which the importance of our natural flora is universally recognised and positive steps are taken to protect our valuable wildlife habitats for the future.

Plant Habitats of the North York Moors

Moorland

The expanse of heather-clad moorland, stretching almost unbroken from the coast to the western edge of the Hambleton Hills, was the main justification for establishment of the North York Moors National Park in 1952. At that time, the moorland covered some 678 sq km (260 sq miles). Although afforestation, drainage, liming and reseeding had by 1988 reduced that area to around 500 sq km (193 sq miles), it is still the largest single tract of heather moorland in England and Wales. Valued for the sense of wilderness it creates throughout the year and for its spectacular purple haze when in flower, the moorland provides an important habitat for upland birds and an economic resource for hill sheep farmers and grouse moor owners, as well as a specialised environment for plantlife. Harsh and forbidding for much of the year, it is a landscape which draws increasing numbers of visitors to relish its space and freedom.

The moorland covers most of the extensive plateau area, ranging in height from about 150 m (492 ft) to 442 m (1449 ft) and gradually sloping down towards the south-east. It is by no means a totally "natural" landscape, the vegetative cover which provides its unique appeal being maintained by a specialised management regime. Left to its own devices, much of the moorland would gradually revert to oak, birch and pine woodland and scrub, with bracken and heather dominating the ground flora. Evidence of this reversion may be seen in places such as Lowna, Bridestones and Westonby.

Whereas a century or two ago, the moorland was regarded by many as "wasteland", the situation is very different in the 1990s, with a good grouse moor changing ownership for upwards of £400 a hectare. Almost half of the moorland is subject to ancient common rights (three mediaeval-style courts leet still operate) and a complex system of land management has evolved which combines sporting interest, sheep grazing, public enjoyment and wildlife conservation. This has a direct effect upon the type and distribution of plants.

Dry Heath

The prime objective of moorland management is to provide sheep and grouse with food, cover and nesting sites, so most moorland is subjected to rotational burning every 10 to 15 years to provide a succession of young heather stands. In a few level areas, this practice has been supplemented in recent years by mechanical cutting. (In some cases, the resultant heather brash is baled and sold as a filter for effluent purification in Holland). Both systems have the effect of preventing shrub or tree growth, with any sapling surviving this treatment being quickly devoured by ever-searching sheep. Hence the scarcity of plants such as petty whin, which survives precariously on the moors of Levisham, .Goathland, Fylingdales and Spaunton. Juniper, an early post-glacial coloniser, is also on the brink of local extinction. Known to be unable to survive burning, the few remaining juniper bushes are either in very wet areas or on an inaccessible crag; no juvenile bushes have been found.

On an intensively managed moor where maximum grouse production is paramount, an almost total monoculture of ling (common heather) is the aim. Originally an understorey plant in upland forest, heather is well-adapted to survive even without tree cover on these wet and windswept hills and impoverished peaty soils. A fungal association in its roots helps the plant to make best use of scarce nutrients; its waxy leaves defy desiccation and it has a prolific seed production.

More often, moorland vegetation is a complex assembly of ericaceous shrubs, grasses, herbs and ferns. Cross-leaved heath is found on damper ground, with bell heather on drier sandy hummocks; bilberry, with its penetrating roots, on exposed north-facing slopes; and bracken exploiting deep well-drained soils away from the moor tops. All grow in ever-changing mosaics. Varying according to aspect, moisture, management and substrate, the shrub cover is interspersed with cowberry, crowberry, gorse, soft rush and wavy hairgrass. Heavy sheep grazing, often where winter feed is provided, opens the way for grasses to dominate. These may include matgrass, fescue, bents and sweet vernal grass. Early hairgrass quickly colonises bare ground, soon to be accompanied by sheep's sorrel with its scarlet leaves, clumps of pill sedge and, on more open areas, heath bedstraw and tormentil.

On parts of the moorland north of Castleton grasses dominate ericaceous plants. Purple moorgrass and soft rush occur in damp areas but matgrass is most abundant with its pale decaying leaves creating a "white moor". Extensive patches of heather on these northern hills have an unusual misty grey appearance due to excessive down on the foliage.

This rather limited flora typifies the drier moorland which occupies most of the uplands. Some botanical enrichment is to be found on the edges of roads and tracks, close-cropped by sheep but devoid of heather and colonised by numerous low-growing hardy plants. These may include:

Selfheal
Daisy
Pearlwort
Heath milkwort
Harebell
Eyebright
Lesser trefoil
Violet
Dovesfoot cranesbill
Mouse-ear
Dandelion
Foxglove

During the summer, roadside banks in these drier parts are often colourful with communities of bell heather, crowberry and cowberry. On adjacent sheep-grazed turf the tall purple musk thistle contrasts with low growing white-flowered knotted pearlwort and spikes of purplish felwort and pink centaury. It is on drier heath, amongst old bracken litter or hiding beneath unburnt heather, that the starry white flowers of chickweed wintergreen flourish – a legacy from early post-glacial pinewoods. The yellow-flowered semi-parasitic cow-wheat is a plant of acidic woodland which apparently survives long after the removal of its tree cover. It is occasionally seen in quantity on open dry moorland as near Parsley Beck. The moors do not easily yield their botanical gems and much searching is needed to find the diminutive lesser twayblade in damp heath and the elusive moonwort on moorland turf, both of which have been recorded in less than a dozen sites.

Wet Heath, Flushes, Mires and Bogs

Wet heath is found in areas where permanent waterlogging occurs. Superficially, it can look similar to grassy dry heath but closer inspection reveals a variety of habitats and vegetation. It is in the saturated peat, the seeping spring lines or flushes, the enclosed valley mires and the trickling rivulets criss-crossing the moors that botanical riches are to be found. Fylingdales Moor is an important example of extensive wet heath plant communities and many similar, if smaller, wetland mosaics are ranged across the moors.

Quickly recognisable by a preponderance of the pale mauve flowers of cross-leaved heath, a species-rich wet moor is likely to reveal purple moorgrass, cottongrasses, rushes, pondweed and marsh pennywort amongst ubiquitous heather and sedges. Interspersed will be acidic pools and runnels, possibly with a water crowfoot *(Ranunculus omiophyllus* or *R. hederaceus)*, blinks, starwort and rafts of sphagnum moss. On damp peaty turf are tufts of heath rush and, less commonly, heath grass and deergrass.

Like its drier counterpart, wet heath presents a complex gradation of plant communities but with a much wider range of species. The combination in each location is largely determined by nutrients and micro-climate. Where spring water seeps out from an impervious rock, it spreads to create either an acidic or a base-rich flush in which may grow some of the rare and interesting plants of the area, such as the insectivorous sundew and butterwort, the beautiful grass of Parnassus, and the diminutive cranberry and bog pimpernel, as well as:

Marsh arrowgrass
Spike rush
Lousewort
Heath milkwort
Bog asphodel
Pennywort
Water mints
and sedges – (*Carex dioica, C. lepidocarpa, C. demissa, C. echinata, C. flacca, C. panicea and C. nigra*)

Flushes in Wheeldale, Cold Keld, Crabdale, Bogmire Gill, Rudland and Scarth Wood Moor are typical of many found across the uplands, most frequently on a sloping moor edge or cleft in the moor plateau. Though often small in size, this in no way diminishes their importance as they are one of the richest botanical habitats within the National Park. It is on moorland flushes and in blanket bogs that rare plants such as white beak-sedge, marsh St John's wort, marsh rosemary, cloudberry, narrow-leaved marsh orchid and small white orchid are found.

On a larger scale are the valley and basin mires – boggy areas formed over thousands of years where glacial meltwater became trapped in enfolding hills. Deep peat is likely to have accumulated from abundant sphagnum and other wetland plants, the species varying according to available nutrients in the impeded drainage. In acidic mires, cottongrasses and rushes dominate with purple moorgrass and perhaps white sedge but, with more enrichment, the flora may include many of the flush species together with:

Bottle sedge
Tawny sedge
Bogbean

Sweet gale
Marsh orchids
Marsh cinquefoil
Lesser spearwort
Marsh violet
Valerian
Black bog rush
Devilsbit scabious
Spike rushes
Pondweed

Known locally as slacks or swangs, examples of these rich wetlands may be seen at Glaisdale Swang, Ewe Crag Slack, Goathland's Moss Dike and slacks in Biller Howe Dale.

Beware of bright green patches of sphagnum moss in such habitats – enticing they may look, entwined with sundew and bog pimpernel, but all too often they are floating mats suspended above a treacherous sinking morass. Sphagnum moss has in the past been collected for use as surgical dressings because of its absorbent capacity. Today, it could be threatened due in part to drier weather and also to illegal but substantial collecting for hanging baskets.

An ancient use of the term "Moss" describes the blanket bog areas, covering 15% of the moorland, where high rainfall and humidity combined with poor drainage induce the typical heather/rush/cottongrass vegetation of the high moors. May Moss was known by that name 700 years ago and it remains a wet and dangerous raised bog on the watershed between Ellerbeck and Grain Beck. Cottongrass in flower, resembling a distant covering of snow, reveals the location of other "mosses" on the moorland watershed. Some, like Yarsley Moss, still justify the name, while others have dried out to become species-poor dry heath.

Although thought by many to be a stark and unchanging environment, a moorland habitat is very fragile, and once damaged, takes a long time to recover. Uncontrolled fires, which sometimes burn the peat, can cause severe damage. Erosion is also very difficult to reverse. The loss of heather due to bracken invasion is another serious and widespread problem. Control of this aggressive plant and re-establishment of heather is proving both difficult and expensive. Continuing threats to the moorland environment include activities such as drainage (formerly widespread), creation of vehicle tracks, small-scale agricultural reclamation and tree planting.

Grassland and Farmland

Nearly half of the National Park is grassland and farmland, varying from scrubby moor-edge acid grassland on dalesides, through areas of unimproved old pasture, coastal cliffs, tracksides and verges, to recently ploughed and ryegrass-reseeded silage fields on dairy farms and arable land. It encompasses a wide variety of plant communities and is almost always a product of man's land management.

Least interesting botanically (though most profitable from an agricultural standpoint) is a ryegrass ley, cultivated and reseeded in rotation with cereal crops and offering next to no chance for native grasses or herbs to establish. A field of this nature may have no more than two or three plant species such as ryegrass, white clover and timothy grass. At the other end of the spectrum are the remaining fragments of unimproved limestone grassland which, over centuries of grazing and/or mowing without chemical inputs, have developed a rich and complex sward.

Natural Grassland

Only a small area of grassland can be regarded as truly "natural" vegetation. It occurs mainly on the coastal cliffs where strong winds and salt spray, combined with unstable boulder clay, prevent the succession to woodland which would normally occur on unmanaged grassland. Inland, fragments of near-natural grassland occur in the narrow gills of lower Ryedale and occasional daleheads, where thin soils and almost vertical valley sides prevent either sheep grazing or tree establishment. All other grassland in the Park is a legacy of man's long history of land management.

Calcareous Grassland

Herb-rich limestone grassland persists more by accident than design – on hillsides too steep for cultivation; on unstable screes where afforestation has failed; in disused quarries; and on roadside embankments. The Yorkshire Wildlife Trust reserve at Ellerburn Bank is a poignant reminder of the profusion of flowers which formerly coloured permanent grassland in the Tabular Hills. Over 150 species have been recorded on this 2.19 ha (7.19 acre) site. They include:

Bee orchid
Fly orchid
Greater butterfly orchid
Ploughman's spikenard
Rockrose
Felwort
Thyme
Fairy flax
Hairy oat grass
Greater knapweed
Bladder campion
Mullein
Purple milk vetch
Burnet saxifrage
Musk mallow
Viper's bugloss
Yellow oat grass
Marjoram
Dropwort
Long-stalked cranesbill
Woolly thistle
Kidney vetch
Hairy violet
Wild mignonette

Sadly, few such pieces of grassland remain, most having been ploughed up and reseeded to produce heavier, earlier maturing crops for silage or grazing.

Only a few scattered remnants of this rich habitat have been found – on south-facing slopes in valleys and old quarries on the corallian limestone between Helmsley and Hawnby; on the western escarpment north of Sutton Bank; and around Kepwick, Hutton-le-Hole, Thornton-le-Dale and Gillamoor. It is estimated that only 195 ha (482 acres) of unimproved herb-rich calcareous grassland now exist (0.14% of the Park). The fact that much of this fragmented habitat is relegated to so-called "wasteland" indicates that special protection will be needed to retain those species which are found almost exclusively on limestone grassland.

Acidic Grassland

Nutrient-poor acidic soils cover much of the upper dales and moorland fringe where centuries of sheep grazing have produced a distinctive sward of grasses, sedges and low-growing herbs. They are likely to include bent grasses, wavy hairgrass, matgrass and fescues with heath bedstraw, tormentil and harebell. Slightly enriched turf adjacent to moorland roads tends to have a wider range of species, though the harsh climate and constant nibbling cause plants to grow in such diminutive form as to be barely recognisable. In this turf additions to the above species are likely to be:

Selfheal
Barren strawberry
Wild thyme
Eyebright
Lesser trefoil
Sheep's sorrel
Ribwort plantain
Heath woodrush
Pill sedge
Creeping buttercup
White clover
Dandelion

In the wake of too many sheep grazing a sward, the unpalatable matgrass soon dominates, interspersed with heath rush and ribbed sedge. On poorly drained soils tufted hairgrass and rushes are abundant, with purple moorgrass indicating wetter conditions. Although species-poor in themselves, these fescue/bent hill grazings are frequently enhanced by base-rich flushes occurring above impervious bands of Oxford clay. They can be floristically rich with such species as white sedge, bogbean, marsh pennywort, ragged robin, marsh arrowgrass, sundew, bog pimpernel and sneezewort.

Hill grassland includes many old intakes which, in times of more profitable stock rearing, were enclosed from the moor but today their use and profitability are diminished by bracken encroachment. Its dense summer shade, deep litter and nutrient absorption eventually suppress most other vegetation, with one exception, chickweed wintergreen. Historically regarded as a rarity, this plant is now found plentifully in upland pasture, often thriving beneath bracken or heather. The invasion of bracken into moorland grasslands necessitates expensive and labour-intensive control measures. Reasons for encroachment of bracken into fields which, only a few decades ago, provided good hill grazing include changes in management and stocking practices, climatic variation and acid rain.

Neutral Grasslands

In the dales, on the coastal plain and on the north-west perimeter of the National Park, scattered unimproved neutral grasslands can still be found. A few old ridge and furrow pastures indicate where the grass sward is long established and, where less intensive farming prevails, plants such as pepper saxifrage, meadow saxifrage, green-winged orchid, dyer's greenweed, saw-wort, early purple orchid, adderstongue fern and salad burnet may be found, with very rare occurrences of lesser butterfly orchid and field gentian. As old pastures are drained and fertilised, their botanical diversity diminishes. For the most part this type of grassland is managed to produce heavier crops for grazing or silage but many fields remain with a sward containing:

Red clover
Crested dogstail
Cocksfoot
Ryegrass
Sweet vernal grass
Meadow foxtail
Red fescue
Timothy grass
Rough meadow grass
Cowslip
Meadow vetchling
Birdsfoot trefoil
Ribwort plantain
Meadow buttercup
Pignut
Yellow rattle
Harebell
Field thistle
Sorrel
Yarrow
Betony

Many of the neutral grasslands would once have been hay meadows with this range of plants. Today, few traditional hay meadows exist, many having been reseeded for more productive silage, while others are no longer managed for hay in summer. Continuous grazing can affect the species present, although it may still result in an interesting sward. Marshy grassland is often found in low-lying, wetter parts of fields and is distinguished by stands of soft rush and often dense meadowsweet. A distinctive community may also include:

Ragged robin
Large birdsfoot trefoil
Cuckoo flower
Marsh foxtail
Marsh valerian
Brown sedge
Sneezewort
Lesser stitchwort

Recent drainage has led to a reduction in the extent of this type of grassland and few extensive areas remain. However, failure of older field drains can result in the re-establishment of rushy vegetation.

Farmland

In the National Park there are approximately 620 full-time farmers whose holdings range from large arable farms and dairy units to small marginal hill farms. Farming practice is strongly influenced by soils, geology and drainage. Arable land covers about 300 sq km (116 sq miles) of the more fertile land on the fringes of the National Park. Most of this land is of limited value for wild plants due to intensive management and use of artificial fertilizers and herbicides to increase crop yields. Few arable weeds survive and shepherd's needle, cornflower and corncockle are now extinct in this locality, while many more once familiar cornfield weeds have all but disappeared. The recent concept of conservation headlands could rescue some of these colourful plants. That a seed resource still remains is apparent from the plants which emerge on newly set-aside land after more than 20 years under intensive production.

Although most cereal fields present a weed-free appearance, a limited range of native plants, more herbicide resistant, have survived and include:

Charlock
Field pennycress
Red dead nettle
Corn spurrey
Upright hedge parsley
Wild radish
Scentless mayweed
Scarlet pimpernel
Black bindweed
Wild oat
Field speedwell
Field poppy
Shepherd's purse
Pale persicaria
Field pansy
Fat hen
Fool's parsley
Fumitory
Redshank
Parsley piert
Sterile brome

From a botanical standpoint, fields of later harvested root crops are usually of more interest than intensively managed cereal fields. Under any crop, field corners which are inaccessible to modern farm machinery are most likely to retain a few wild plants. On upland farms, valuable plant habitats for diminishing grassland communities may still be found on unimproved pastures near the moorland edge.

Stackyards produce a range of waste-ground plants such as hedge garlic, white dead nettle, black horehound, stinging nettle, docks and hedge mustard, with unusual occurrences of celery-leaved buttercup in a Farndale farmyard, hairy buttercup on a Howdale farm and fragrant agrimony near Scalby. Red goosefoot is frequent on manure heaps, while in trampled gateways swinecress may be found amongst knotgrass and pineapple weed.

Farmland also provides a habitat for some unusual alien plants which have possibly been introduced in uncleaned seed or in bird droppings. For instance, two species of a yellow-flowered type of forgetmenot – *Amsinckia* – have established in fields from Bickley to Harwood Dale and near Ruswarp; pigweed appeared on farmland at Suffield; and gold of pleasure, treacle mustard, pepperwort, flixweed and caraway flowered for a season on arable fields.

Woodland and Forest

Ancient Woodland

More than 6,000 years ago native wildwood covered practically the whole area of the National Park but a continuous process of deforestation has left only fragments of natural forest vegetation. Ancient semi-natural woodland (land known to have had tree cover since 1600 and therefore likely to have been wooded since post-glacial colonisation many thousands of years ago) now covers only about 3.2% of the Park. Despite the term "ancient woodland", few woods contain massive old trees. The term refers to the continuity of a woodland habitat in one form or another.

The ancient woodland which has survived is largely on hillsides too steep to plough, in coastal inlets, on infertile exposed daleheads, on wet riverside areas difficult to drain and also on estates where natural woodland is an economic component of estate management and a valued amenity. Scattered throughout the Park, these woods are often small and isolated, such as in the steep gills in the Rye valley. Extensive tracts of ancient woodland have, however, survived at Mulgrave Woods near Sandsend, Arncliffe Woods in Glaisdale, at Ridge Lane, Roxby, in Forge Valley, Riccal Dale and Sinnington.

Management of ancient woodland over the centuries has involved selective felling and replanting; winter shelter and grazing for sheep, cattle and pigs; coppicing; charcoal burning; provision of fencing stakes, building timber and firewood; creation of fox coverts; and pheasant rearing. This has created wide diversity in tree canopy and ground flora. Nowadays, recreational activities including horse riding and motor cycling take place in some woods.

Depending upon the geology, the nature and depth of soil and the management history, the tree canopy shows wide variation. Hybrids of pedunculate and sessile oak, and of silver and downy birch, together with rowan, dominate upper dale woodlands; ash, wych elm and wild cherry are characteristic of woods on the southern limestone; alder is found in damp situations, particularly along riversides; Scots pine, although no longer a native tree in northern England, germinates freely from plantations; and sycamore thrives in coastal locations and establishes itself abundantly in inland woods. Associated species include field maple, hawthorn, bird cherry, crab apple, small-leaved lime and aspen.

The shrub layer is an important part of woodland structure. Typical species which occur are hazel, holly, elder, blackthorn, spindle, guelder rose, wild privet and sallows.

Introduced Softwoods

The most drastic alteration to native woodland has been extensive conversion to conifer plantations. Although on a few estates, exotic trees such as western hemlock and grand fir were introduced by 19th century landowners, their impact was minimal. From the 1950s, however, government grant-aid encouraged widespread replanting of ancient woodland with quick-growing softwoods. Much old oak and ash woodland with its rich ground flora disappeared. The policy continued for 30 years by which time only fragments of native woodland remained, often surrounded by conifer plantations, thus effectively isolating natural seed dispersal and regeneration. More enlightened government policy now provides financial incentives towards restoration of broadleaved woodland and new plantings of native hardwoods.

Woodland Ground Flora

Not surprisingly, this chequered history has produced botanical diversity ranging from grass-covered swards in old wood pasture to the spectacular display of spring flowers in wood coppice situated in sheltered limestone valleys, where a rich ground flora may include:
Early purple orchid
Ramsons
Wood anemone
Bluebell
Red campion
Primrose
Yellow archangel
Wood sorrel
Lily of the valley
Yellow star of Bethlehem
Baneberry
Wild daffodil

Woods in Thornton Dale have birdsnest orchid, green hellebore and monkshood. Forge Valley (a National Nature Reserve) has a wealth of less common woodland plants including columbine, gromwell and two rare sedges *Carex strigosa* and *Carex digitata*. Yedmandale, Sleightholmedale and several other valleys have remnants of ancient woodland with rich ground flora. Further west, oak and ash woodlands around Rievaulx and Helmsley are species-rich with mountain currant, spindle, wild privet, stone bramble, purging buckthorn and herb Paris. In Kirkdale and other wooded limestone dales may be found greater butterfly orchid, the rare mountain melick, wood barley and lesser or common wintergreen – a very uncommon plant today, despite its name.

Further north, woodland in upper Eskdale is sparse. Generally open to sheep grazing, birch woods such as Danby Park have little regeneration and limited ground flora but where grazing is minimal, as at Crag Wood, Danby, a more interesting plant community flourishes.

Further down Eskdale, dense deciduous woodland clothes the steep glacial meltwater channels of Stonegate Gill and Crunkly Gill where, despite some conifer and ornamental shrub planting, rarities such as oak fern and wood fescue survive. In woods around Glaisdale, Grosmont and Goathland, beneath regenerating oak, birch, holly, elm, hazel and small-leaved lime, a lush ground flora typical of more acid soils may have clumps of pendulous sedge growing amongst bilberry, ground ivy, violet, greater woodrush, male and broad buckler ferns, cow-wheat and soft shield fern. In wet areas the ground flora often includes large bittercress, opposite-leaved golden saxifrage, wood horsetail, water mint and marsh marigold.

Mulgrave Woods, flanking East Row Beck from Sandsend to Peel Wood, have a similar rich tapestry of vegetation with especially lush fern communities, including narrow buckler fern and common polypody. Soft shield fern occurs here and in other woods in the east of the Park.

Coastal valleys are often impenetrable with unmanaged woodland. Again, rich fern communities occur on steep banks, particularly noticeable in woodland behind Boggle Hole Youth Hostel. Occasionally trees have been removed leaving a shrub canopy of honeysuckle, wild rose, hazel and blackthorn, with rarely, a rich ground flora including lily of the valley.

Alder is abundant in linear woodland fringing many miles of streams and rivers and, infrequently, in alder carr woodland as at Greenhow. At Greencliff Hagg, Bilsdale, a formerly coppiced alder wood is believed to have been planted to supply clog soles. Coppicing has been re-introduced in another Bilsdale alder wood, and in hazel and oak woodland at Hawnby and Harwood Dale.

Natural regeneration of native woodland trees, especially oak, has for decades been prevented by sheep roaming freely over the uplands and their woods, but incentives to reduce grazing pressure by fencing will allow some of these woods to regenerate.

Forest

Although so little remains of the original native wildwood, trees of one sort or another occupy about 20% of ground in the Park. By far the most grow in coniferous plantations which cover more than 20,000 ha (49,420 acres). Semi-natural broadleaved woodland covers less than 5,000 ha (12,355 acres) and the remaining 3,300 ha (8,154 acres) comprise an assortment of scrub, mixed plantations and copses, many recently planted on farms and dalesides. Early forest plantations on the moorland, established from 1920 onwards, were frequently of Scots pine and larch, later superseded by higher yielding lodgepole pine and Sitka spruce, with frost resistant Norway spruce in the valley bottoms. Beech was planted extensively on shallow calcareous soils and sycamore on exposed sites. Small numbers of hemlock, grand fir and western red cedar were included in planting schemes.

Increasingly, the need for timber production is being linked with wildlife conservation and a much more varied structure is developing within the forests as a result of positive management. Streamsides are no longer planted; planned felling is creating a mosaic of forest structure; areas known to have retained valuable ground flora are left to natural regeneration; a conservation inventory influences work schedules; and funds are being diverted towards increasing public awareness of forest wildlife. This multi-purpose approach indicates that while forests continue to produce a valuable timber resource, they can, with sensitive management, provide habitats of varied botanical interest.

Forest Ground Flora

As the forests cover a range of soil types, altitude, aspect and gradient, wide diversity exists in the natural vegetation which has survived on compartment edges, forest rides and unplanted fringes. Of low botanical interest is a dense spruce plantation on acid heath, where light scarcely enters. In these limiting conditions only a few plants of broad buckler fern and heath bedstraw may struggle for survival in a thick mat of decaying needles. On a richer soil, a mixed plantation with dappled light is likely to maintain a more interesting ground flora but it is on the compartment edge, on firebreaks and tracks, where a whole range of species is found, especially at junctions where shading from the timber crop is reduced. While a narrow shady ride on nutrient poor ground may have little other than rank grasses, a wide ride on base-rich soil may be fringed with species such as:
Twayblade
Centaury
Marjoram
Sweet cicely
Hemp nettle

Fleabane
Salad burnet
Hemp agrimony
Cowslip
Toadflax
Comfrey
Giant bellflower
Golden rod
Early purple orchid
Common spotted orchid

These species are the remnants of the flora existing before planting occurred. Frequently pools form on track edges and a moister habitat supports sedges (*Carex flacca, C. panicea, C. demissa, C. nigra*) as well as:
Sweet grass
Mints
Cottongrasses
Bush grass
Lousewort
Ragged robin
Bristle scirpus
Sneezewort
Reedmace
Golden saxifrage
Meadowsweet
Marsh violet
Butterwort
Bog asphodel
Sweet gale

Forests planted in peaty soil and lashed by wind and rain have a grassy heath vegetation in firebreaks, with rushes, ribbed sedge and tufted hair-grass in damp furrows, interspersed with heather, bramble, bilberry and large ferns on better drained ridges. Firebreaks are subject to little disturbance and juvenile birches, rowan, hollies and hawthorns occasionally establish. On untrampled grassy tracks a local rarity, lesser wintergreen, may be found.

Some of the richest plant habitats in the forests occur on infrequently used rides, particularly where they have been made from locally quarried limestone. In Langdale Forest, small rose-pink flowers of locally rare sand spurrey share sandy pockets with myriads of eyebright flowers. Hedge bedstraw, uncommon hereabouts, flourishes in Harwood Dale Forest, where a colony of yellow-wort fringes a trackside. New Zealand willowherb, a comparative newcomer to local vegetation, spreads in the absence of competition and is often associated with slender St John's wort. The ground flora of former natural woodland can also survive on ride edges and may include chickweed wintergreen, wood anemone, cow-wheat and, more rarely, oak fern.

Ferns are a common component of open forest floor vegetation, where mixed planting has allowed some light penetration through gaps in the tree canopy. Fine shuttlecocks of male fern and broad buckler fern with fronds a metre high flourish in such conditions. Steep-sided rocky gills in the forests of Dalby and Ampleforth have rare colonies of black spleenwort and maidenhair spleenwort with, more frequently, hartstongue, hard shield fern and, in the east, soft shield fern.

Whereas some quarries in forested areas have shared the dismal fate of many on agricultural land and become rubbish dumps, fortunately a number have been left alone and have revegetated with several uncommon species such as barberry, kidney vetch, viper's bugloss, ploughman's spikenard, felwort and orchids.

In valleys where planting has been kept back or removed from the water's edge, natural vegetation flourishes.

Deepdale, Newtondale, Raindale, Mason Gill and Wheeldale are typical, and host such plants as devilsbit scabious, sawwort, herb Paris, guelder rose, aspen, primrose and dropwort. Grass of Parnassus flourishes in a few secluded forest gills.

The scarcity of open water habitats throughout the Park emphasises the value of those which exist within the forests. A few are bomb crater legacies from the last war; others such as Staindale, Keysbeck and several smaller ponds have been created primarily for conservation and have acquired a range of aquatic plants. Beulah pond in Newtondale has a rich vegetation attractive to dragonflies and other invertebrates.

As well as providing refuges for a variety of indigenous plants, forests in the North York Moors are home to some national rarities. May lily has a fragile colony north of Forge Valley, one of its few sites in Britain. Less critical is a population of yellow bird's nest on Sutherbuff Rigg. Both wood cudweed and dwarf spurge are scarce countrywide but survive in Wykeham Forest. Intermediate wintergreen is known locally only in an eastern plantation and nationally is virtually confined to Scottish mountains.

The explosion of wild flowers which occurs after clear felling indicates that a valuable seed resource still remains within the forested areas. Re-establishment of natural vegetation is part of modern forest management. Although conifer plantations can appear to be devoid of native plants, the network of rides and open spaces within the forests have retained much native flora which would undoubtedly have been destroyed if the land had undergone modern agricultural development.

The Coast

The coastal cliffs, extending some 48 kms (30 miles) between Scalby and Boulby, consist largely of unstable and somewhat calcareous boulder clay, shales and sandstones. Steep and lashed by salt-laden winds, with water-logged shelving and forever crumbling into the sea below, they provide a specialised shifting habitat, colonised chiefly by a range of grassland species.

The cliffs reach 200 m (650 ft) above sea level at Boulby and are incised by numerous wooded ravines such as Hayburn Wyke, Stoupe Beck and Overdale where sheltered micro-climates encourage lush fern communities under the woodland canopy. The shore is, for the most part, strewn with large boulders or lias shale with only small stretches of sand at Stoupe Beck, Boggle Hole, Saltwick, Whitby, Sandsend, Runswick and Staithes. Land above the cliffs is usually cultivated to the extreme edge where erosion causes continuing reduction in field size.

Cliff Plants

On the exposed sea-facing cliffs, bent/fescue grassland alternates with dense thickets of blackthorn and hawthorn. [See Natural Grassland]. Constant seepage of water encourages stands of great horsetail with tall fescue, coltsfoot, common reed and butterbur. Occasionally, however, more enriched flushes have a range of lime-loving plants including pyramidal orchid, fragrant orchid, butterwort and grass of Parnassus. At Cromer Point, just outside the Park boundary, a colony of yellow-wort grows with marjoram, centaury and carline thistle.

Tall melilot grows near Robin Hood's Bay, and dyer's greenweed near Runswick. Buckshorn plantain and sea plantain are abundant on well trodden path edges, while scurvy grass, bluebell and primrose inhabit much short grassland. Ling, bell heather and common spotted orchids thrive on heathy areas. Wet patches around Sycarham have water mint, marsh marigold, ragged robin and water parsnip, with swathes of wild daffodils on sheltered banks. A colony of northern marsh orchid occupies an exposed cliff ledge, while adderstongue fern and frog orchid appear spasmodically amongst cliff vegetation. Rare on eastern cliffs is the sea spleenwort which is known only on salt-sprayed rocks near Hundale Point.

Roger Trod, Beast Cliff and Common Cliff have unusual natural plant assemblies but Marnardale, near Robin Hood's Bay, once planted as a wild flower reserve, supports several British species not normally found in these parts. Sea buckthorn growing spasmodically from Hawsker northwards is likely to have been planted. Wood vetch and soft shield fern are more common along the coast than elsewhere in the National Park.

Upgang Ravine had long been noted for its assembly of rare plants, including sawwort, bee orchid and bithynian vetch. In 1988 it was severely disturbed by the construction of a new sea wall but, fortunately, remnants of the original vegetation were seen to have survived in 1990 and it is to be hoped they will eventually colonise the adjacent bare earthworks. Another rare plant in this area is the white-flowered hoary pepperwort which fringes Sandsend's car parks in summer.

North of Sandsend, the disused railtrack is colonised with a colourful variety of plants, including narrow-leaved everlasting pea which is not known away from the coast. Wormwood grows on Kettleness cliffs with fern grass and wild carrot.

Wild cabbage grows on exposed cliffs from Boulby to Staithes, where it is accompanied by bristly oxtongue, wild parsnip, parsley, hop, weld and woody nightshade. Other species mainly confined to the coast include wall rocket, ramping fumitory, alexanders, slender thistle, sea mouse-ear and red valerian.

Shore Plants

Extensive disturbance caused by 19th century mineral extraction has created an unusual habitat at Saltwick, where unimproved grassland plants such as burnet saxifrage intermingle with acid heath and wetland communities including the rare water whorl grass.

Saltwick, Ruswarp Batts, Runswick Bay and Sandsend provide the only habitats akin to coastal dunes where marram grass, sand couch grass and lyme grass can grow.

Because most of the shore lies below high water mark and is regularly scoured by fierce wave action, strandline plants can only survive in a few inlets where streams have cut a way through the cliffs. At Ruswarp and Sandsend, small patches of sea sandwort occur with shore, frosted and common orache. Sea hard grass and saltmarsh grass may be found in clumps of sea-washed turf and the mauve flowers of sea rocket are occasionally seen in sandy inlets. Only Hayburn Wyke and Sandsend provide shingle beaches suited to sea beet.

The River Esk is tidal as far as Ruswarp and it is on these estuarine mudflats that the richest saline vegetation occurs. Mud rush and sea aster interspersed with sea club rush, sea spurrey, scurvy grass and sea arrowgrass give way to sea wormwood, sea bindweed, wild celery and hemlock water dropwort on more elevated banks.

Rivers, Ponds and Reservoirs

Flowing Waters

With less than 3% of the National Park covered by open water, aquatic plants tend to be few and far between. The rivers, for the most part, are fast running streams draining the acidic upland plateau and it is not until they reach quieter stretches in more level lower land, that aquatic vegetation gains a roothold. Water milfoil, with its tolerance of acidic waters, is one of the first to appear in a stream bed, soon accompanied by mats of water crowfoot. In the Derwent downstream from Langdale End, the Rye downstream from Hawnby, the River Leven, Pickering Beck and one or two smaller rivers, rafts of water crowfoot, (either *Ranunculus aquatalis* or *Ranunculus peltatus*) gradually give way to flowing streamers of river water crowfoot (*Ranunculus fluitans*) as the waters become shallower. At this stage the vegetation is likely to be enhanced by marsh marigold, pondweed, water plantain, watercress and fool's watercress, accompanied at the water's edge by tall sedges (*Carex riparia* or *Carex acutiformis*), water mint, sweet grass and hemp agrimony.

Bankside vegetation emphasises ecological differences between the various river systems. Nutrient-rich banks of Roxby Beck and the River Esk near Grosmont have the rare greater chickweed. On river banks in Farndale, Bilsdale and Newtondale may be found impressive stands of wood club rush, while Lonsdale supports a fine array of tussock sedge. Large bittercress flourishes alongside a whole range of watercourses away from the limestone fringe. An equally attractive white-flowered waterside plant, wood stitchwort, is virtually restricted to Eskdale and Bilsdale, where it is frequently accompanied by an attractive garden outcast, pink purslane. A strong aniseed aroma alongside many waterways reveals banks of sweet cicely but very local are the mats of yellow-flowered musk in Rosedale and streamside bushes of mountain currant in Raisdale. The locally rare purple loosestrife flourishes along parts of the Esk and yellow flag and monkey flower can be found on several river banks.

Scalby seacut, a manmade waterway which runs for a short way through the National Park, has a unique assembly of aquatics due in part to a manipulated water level. Local rarities to be found here are unbranched bur-reed and lesser water plantain. A few miles westward, in a crystal clear beck running over limestone, stream crowfoot (*Ranunculus penicillatus* var. *calcareus*) grows luxuriantly. Marestail appears infrequently in base-rich streams.

Still Waters

With water supplies now piped to field troughs on most farms, ponds are no longer a necessity for watering stock and many have been filled in, resulting in the disappearance of their specialised vegetation. However, a few ponds have survived, mainly in the south-west. These have been augmented in recent years by new ponds, many created with fishing or duck shooting in mind but often as a means of encouraging wildlife. Recently dug ponds tend to be planted with showy species such as water lilies, reedmace, purple and yellow loosestrife and yellow flag but other native plants quickly establish, presumably transported by birds.

Location, age and management are reflected in wide plant diversity. Ponds at Kildale and Raincliffe are the only known sites for ivy-leaved duckweed; near Suffield grows the rare golden dock; Appleton pond has floating marshwort; and at Cropton, the rare lesser pondweed can be found. West Ayton pond, despite drying out most summers and being open to cattle, has a rich vegetation including fine-leaved water dropwort *(Oenanthe aquatica)*, water whorl grass and marsh yellow-cress, while sea club rush has colonised Evan Howe pond. Below Needle Point in Newtondale, Beulah pond has a rich vegetation with bogbean, marsh cinque-foil and bottle sedge.

Most shallow ponds eventually acquire a covering of water crowfoot and water forgetmenot *(Myosotis scorpioides, M. laxa* or *M. secunda)*, with pondweed spreading across the water. Almost inaccessible ponds on the coast have a rich undisturbed flora with short-leaved water crowfoot *(Ranunculus trichophyllus)*, sea arrowgrass and true bulrush *(Schoenoplectus lacustris)* at Roger Trod, and great spearwort with lesser reedmace at Beast Cliff. Grey bulrush grows in a pond near Lockton.

Ponds in the uplands tend to be more acidic and less species rich, usually fringed with rushes, sweet grass, marsh stitchwort and lesser spearwort. Floating vegetation frequently consists of pondweed *(Potamogeton polygonifolius)* with mats of bulbous rush and, less commonly, floating scirpus. A rare pondweed *(Potamogeton alpinus)* grows in a pond on Blakey Rigg. The beautiful flowers of bogbean occasionally enliven a sombre upland pond and secreted amongst the mass of vegetation may be found the pale mauve flowers of the scarce marsh speedwell. Another flower dispersed on the moorland rivulets is a national rarity – creeping forgetmenot *(Myosotis stolonifera)* and, equally sparse locally, is marsh St John's wort.

Lake Gormire is the only naturally formed large expanse of open water in the National Park. It supports a wealth of aquatic vegetation which includes a national rarity, tufted loosestrife. Throxenby Mere, although an artificial lake, has also acquired a rich flora with marsh cinquefoil, skullcap, amphibious bistort and the locally rare marsh stitchwort.

By contrast, reservoirs on the moors north of Eskdale and on the Hambleton plateau tend to be colonised by few species such as shoreweed, rushes, water plantain and sweet grass, although at Scaling Dam, rarities including hornwort, pondweed *(Potamogeton perfoliatus)* and orange foxtail have been recorded. At Arden Lake a record for awlwort requires confirmation. Grinkle Park and Crosscliff lakes illustrate only too well the deleterious effect of *Rhododendron ponticum* invasion – practically all other vegetation has been eliminated by this aggressive introduction.

Land surmounting underground reservoirs frequently provides valuable habitat for terrestrial, not aquatic, plants. With stock-proof fencing, and covered with introduced hardcore, these small artificial mounds at Thornton-le-Dale, Silton, Farndale, Ampleforth and elsewhere are species rich with plants of grassland and disturbed ground.

Roadside Verges

With a network of 888 km (551 miles) of roads spread across the National Park, most of which are fringed by verges, it is estimated that approximately 2.9% or 4,200 ha (10,378 acres) of the total Park area consists of roadside verge. Diversity exists in verge width, topography, management and function, thus creating an extensive range of plant communities from sheep nibbled species-poor moorland turf to lush herb-rich woodland ground flora.

More than 450 plant species (over half the total number recorded in the National Park) have been recorded on roadside verges, which hold an important reservoir of native plants. Historically, verges have evolved where ancient trackways have gradually been upgraded to meet the demands of successive travellers. Paleolithic hunters, iron-age farmers, Roman soldiers and Norman mercenaries, monastic sheep graziers, cattle drovers and pack-horse panniermen, horse-drawn coaches, pony sleds and now tractors, cars, coaches and ever wider farm machinery have all influenced the character, and consequent vegetation, of roadside verges and tracks.

Verges today have to satisfy safety requirements concerning road traffic and are frequently mown close to road junctions and signposts. Equally they have to be managed with minimum cost, thus the cutting on minor roads is often contracted out to local farmers who interpret the guidelines according to time available and local need. Usually this results in a single swathe

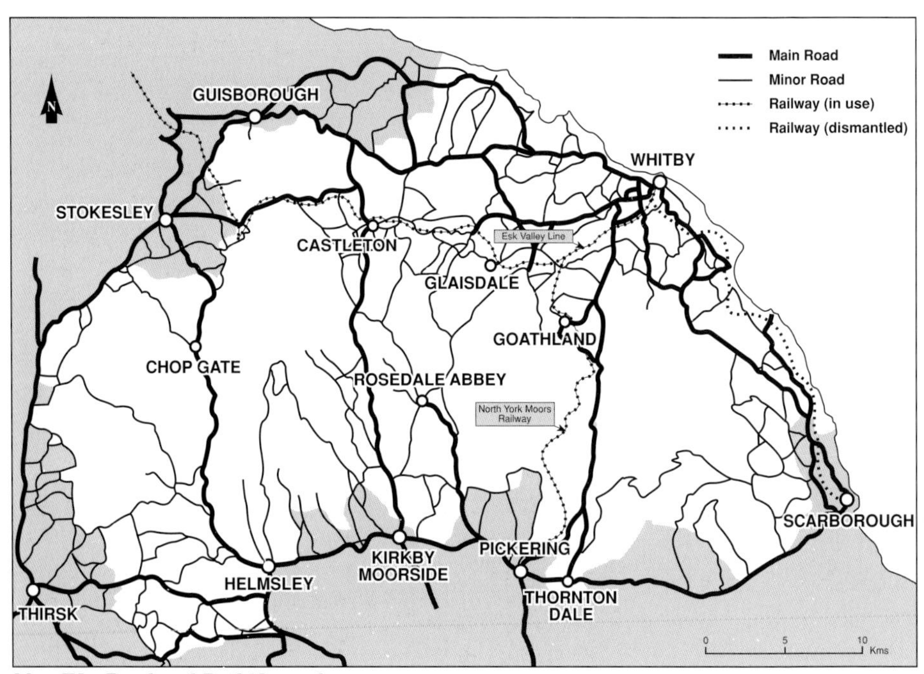

Map IV – Road and Rail Network

adjacent to the road being cut two or three times a year, leaving a tiered habitat in which a range of species can find a niche. On main roads verge cutting is usually more frequent and extensive, favouring the growth of aggressive species. Cutting is invariably done with a flail mower, decaying vegetation being left on the ground to the detriment of more sensitive plants. Some wider verges, such as those around Old Byland are cut to provide hay or silage which encourages a richer sward. Elsewhere, the verge is used for parking vehicles or machinery, a practice which in moderation encourages low growing plants but when the verge is used as storage ground for silage bales, the ground flora is virtually eliminated.

A few ancient tracks, such as Rudland Rigg, remain unsurfaced and are strewn with plants such as felwort, eyebright, sand spurrey and spring whitlow grass. For the most part, roadsides are rarely sprayed with herbicides, but fertilizer run-off from nearby fields or frequent cutting soon encourages a species-poor range of rank grasses, such as false oat grass, cocksfoot and ryegrass, with cow parsley and hogweed. Once established, this type of verge allows little opportunity for incursion by more interesting species. Verges such as this occur widely throughout the National Park, especially alongside major roads, thus highlighting the ecological importance of contrasting herb-rich verges.

Roads Across the Moor

On moorland roads and into some Eskdale villages sheep grazing maintains turf of tightly matted acid-tolerant species but, where fencing or cattlegrids prevent sheep access, a surprising diversity becomes apparent. When sheep deaths caused by fast-moving traffic on the Whitby to Pickering road topped 600 in the mid 1980s, it was decided to erect fencing, with a significant change to the roadside flora becoming apparent as sheep could no longer graze the grassy verges.

Up to 130 species have been recorded on moorland verges, including buckshorn plantain, silvery hairgrass and apple mint. It is not uncommon to find calcareous outcrops where wild thyme, mountain everlasting, carline thistle and field madder grow amongst typical moorland plants such as heather, bilberry and heath rush. Wet moorland roadsides are colonised by sundew, sneezewort, rushes and sedges. Frequently a track or road is bounded by high banks and on these better drained habitats cowberry may be abundant, with bell heather, slender St John's wort and crowberry also occurring. Other moorland verge species include:

Bent grasses
Wavy hairgrass
Dandelion
Selfheal
Tormentil
Procumbent pearlwort
Heath speedwell
Early hairgrass
Sheep's fescue
Sweet gale
Daisy
Musk thistle
Fairy flax
Heath grass
Knotted pearlwort
Cross-leaved heath
Sweet vernal grass
Matgrass

Verges on Limestone

Understandably, the richest verges are to be found on the corallian limestone, with exceptional plant communities on verges at Murton Bank, Caydale, Roxby, Rievaulx, Ampleforth, Keldy, Egton, Dalby, Levisham, Hackness, Thornton-le-Dale, Yedmandale and Hutton Buscel.

Calcareous free-draining soils, combined with a warm aspect or proximity to a woodland edge, especially where mowing or rabbit grazing restricts more aggressive species, often have a range of species rarely seen elsewhere in the National Park. The rare spiked sedge grows near Coxwold; fly orchid at Dalby; petty whin and creeping willow on a verge at Stape; lily of the valley and baneberry thrive near Rievaulx; while four very uncommon ferns – moonwort, adderstongue, beech and oak fern – all occur on roadside verges.

With so much enclosed limestone grassland now converted to species-poor temporary leys or reseeded pasture, the native plant communities on calcareous road verges are especially important. In addition to more common lime-loving species, the following have been found on roadsides:

Wild basil
Crested hairgrass
Rockrose
Hairy oat grass
Basil thyme
Spurge laurel
Long-stalked cranesbill
Stemless thistle
Greater burnet saxifrage
Ploughman's spikenard
Spiny restharrow
Spindle
Burnet saxifrage
Greater knapweed
Upright brome
Dewberry
Golden rod
Weld
Wood melick

Straightening and widening of roads has left several lay-bys where thin soils and a scattering of debris offer suitable habitat for common spotted orchid, pyramidal orchid, dark mullein, yellow rattle, storksbill and black horehound.

Various garden escapes have naturalised on road verges. Both blue sowthistle and winter heliotrope appear to be spreading, the latter especially on roadsides along the coastal fringe. Alkanet, dame's violet, greater celandine and welsh poppy are widespread on verges near villages.

Where verges cut through ancient deciduous woodland, such as on the Mulgrave estate, around Hawnby, Grosmont, Hackness, Roxby and Wass, rich vegetation, typical of woodland ground flora, survives. As most plants in this situation flower in spring, they seed early and are little affected by subsequent verge cutting. Primrose is widespread and often grows with bluebell, wood anemone, dog's mercury, wood violet, dog violet, wood sorrel, early purple orchid and yellow pimpernel. Less common are columbine, twayblade, giant bellflower, wood barley and wild daffodil. Steep wooded banks and shady rocky outcrops such as Hackness windings, Wass hairpins and Broxa bank have wood melick, bitter vetchling and cow-wheat.

A further distinctive wet grassland community on verges occurs in ditches where sneezewort, fleabane, ragged robin and cuckoo flower may be accompanied by hemp agrimony, butterbur, marsh woundwort and reed grass.

RAILWAYS

Within the National Park boundary are some 71 km (45 miles) of railway still in use and 27 km (17 miles) of abandoned railroad where the lines have been removed but the thoroughfare remains. Despite the occasional use of a "weed train" whereby the ballast is sprayed with herbicide, the rail network provides a safe haven for many plants. More than 370 of the 850 species recorded in the Park have been found to occur on rail ballast or railside verges. Particularly important are the enclaves of rare species such as greater butterfly orchid, meadow thistle, small toadflax and kidney vetch which thrive on land subject to minimal interference.

The wealth of plants on railway land reflects both the great diversity of soil, aspect, climate and exposure which the lines traverse and the specialised management historically exercised on tracks and station precincts. This latter feature is especially noticeable on the Esk Valley Line and the North Yorkshire Moors Railway, where stations, platforms, former sidings and coal yards portray some fascinating plant assemblages. As trains continue to operate on these lines, it is both dangerous and illegal to investigate the rail flora without obtaining authorisation.

Esk Valley Line

Thale cress, silvery hair-grass, small toadflax, fern grass and squirrel-tail fescue have their largest local populations in cindery rail ballast in Eskdale. Trailing St John's wort, elsewhere a small and somewhat rare plant, grows in profusion on clinker banks. Just out of reach of the train herbicide sprayer, yellow toadflax and comfrey are interspersed with orange hawkweed and American willowherb. Close by the rails, apparently indifferent to herbicides, are mats of pink-flowered convolvulus, sage green hairy sedge and yellow blooms of creeping cinquefoil. Woodland sections of the line have banks and cuttings rich with woodland flora including primrose, giant bellflower, greater butterfly orchid, bluebell, anemone and cow-wheat.

Drainage channels provide an ideal habitat for bog asphodel and ivy-leaved water crowfoot, while marshes and bogs alongside the track conserve many decreasing wetland plants such as marsh cinquefoil, devilsbit scabious, ragged robin, water mint, meadow thistle and valerian. Sweet cicely and wood horsetail are plentiful, interrupted here and there with spikes of twayblade and common spotted orchid, mats of hop trefoil or apple mint and clumps of tansy, horseradish or wild carrot. Crumbling masonry has been colonised by welted thistle, climbing fumitory and reflexed stonecrop, while damper railsides with overhanging trees occasionally have yellow archangel or woody nightshade.

Brittle bladder fern, hartstongue fern, maidenhair spleenwort and wall rue grow plentifully in the mortar of platforms, retaining walls and a few bridge parapets. Disused coal bunkers at Danby, Glaisdale and elsewhere are ablaze with opportunist flowers such as dark mullein, wild mignonette, broom, common spotted orchid, American willowherb, ox-eye daisy and mallow. Abandoned sidings have been colonised by stonecrop, yellow toadflax, foxglove, burnet rose, St John's wort and many more. One of the most interesting features of stations on the Esk Valley Line is the legacy of garden plants, once the

pride and joy of resident station masters and now naturalised in waste ground close by stations. These include:
Cotoneaster
Purple toadflax
Lilac
Buddleia
Geranium
Mahonia
Aubrietia
Golden rod
Snowberry
Snow in summer
Roses
Dianthus
Cornflower
Snapdragon
Columbine
Box
Globe thistle
Opium poppy
Rose of Sharon
Pelargonium
Alyssum
Lobelia
Candytuft
House leek
Montbretia
Welsh poppy
Aster
Pink oxalis
Honesty

Battersby Junction has a strange admixture of plants introduced with roadstone and naturalised garden outcasts. [See Wasteland]. A mature monkey puzzle tree standing proud at Danby station bears testimony to the time when this railway and its stations were a hub of activity.

North Yorkshire Moors Railway

Originally part of the LNER network and now operated privately, usually with steam locomotives, the North Yorkshire Moors Railway is similar to the Esk Valley Line in that it crosses open moorland and winds its way through a wooded riverside gorge. Yet its north-south axis and the fact that it cuts through a cleft in the corallian limestone as it approaches Pickering, result in a still wider variety of plants on its tracksides.

Extensive sidings at Grosmont station, its northern limit, formerly boasted a display of blue fleabane but it is possible that over-zealous weed spraying may have eliminated this locally rare plant. Not likely to be inadvertently destroyed, however, are the blue sowthistles which stand well back from the line. Also at Grosmont, in the shelter of a railside retaining wall grow wood melick, wall rue and maidenhair spleenwort. Children of Grosmont School have successfully introduced many indigenous wild flowers into a meadow alongside the railtrack.

As the track cuts through the ancient woodland between Grosmont and Goathland, less common species such as pendulous sedge, broad helleborine, tutsan and native golden rod are evident. Bistort and spearmint occur sparsely, but giant bellflower is prominent on railbanks with light shade. The northern end of this railway has numerous stone or brick bridges and embankments, many of which have been liberally colonised by ferns and plants such as wall lettuce, herb robert and stonecrops.

Where the middle section of the railway traverses a wide boggy expanse, sweet gale, water plantain, greater tussock sedge, common reed, pond sedge and yellow flag are among the fringing vegetation. Herb-rich fens alongside the track have extensive stands of tall pond sedges, interspersed with bur-reed, great reedmace and local rarities – wood club rush and meadow rue.

In shallower ditches close by the rails may be found marsh marigold, marsh cinquefoil, northern marsh orchid, skullcap, sundew, marsh pennywort and deergrass. Heath vegetation dominates drier areas with wild thyme, creeping willow, centaury and rest-harrow amongst ericaceous shrubs.

Levisham station presents a riot of midsummer colour, combining a residue of native flowers and ferns with carefully tended beds and hanging baskets reminiscent of the railway's heyday.

The southern section of the railway through Newtondale is lined with a mixture of conifer plantations and remnants of limestone woodland. The trains steam past bushes of purging buckthorn, spindle, dogwood, burnet rose and spurge laurel, while covering wild basil, marjoram and lesser toadflax growing in the ballast.

Disused Railway

Skirting the coast from Scarborough to Whitby runs a cinder track which carried the coastal railway until 1965. Now a permissive path, it retains the original ballast but as it is heavily used, its vegetation is minimal. However, the railside verges retain much of their original plant cover which has now mostly reverted to scrub and woodland. A plant that has successfully colonised this rail route is broad helleborine, which is quite plentiful near Fylingdales. Wood vetch scrambles over several scrubby banks and narrow-leaved everlasting pea occurs in a few places.

North of Sandsend, the cinder track leads through a wonderfully rich area, with the old track and extensive adjacent wasteland colonised by a variety of plants including water purslane, rough hawksbeard, adderstongue fern and northern marsh orchid.

As indicated by this summary of railway plants, the rail companies have many rare and valuable plant communities on their lands but as far as can be ascertained, have not as yet adopted a conservation strategy towards their long-term survival.

Hedgerows

In much of the moorland area and parts of the southern limestone plateau, field boundaries consist of stone walls. On the coastal plain, in lower valleys, on the western farmland and in parts of Eskdale, however, hedges are more usual. Despite the loss of 198 km (124 miles) during the 1970s and 1980s, over 2,000 km (1,250 miles) of hedges still exist in the National Park. Many remaining hedges are in a poor state, although some form valuable wildlife habitats and "corridors" across farmland.

Hedgerow composition varies according to origin, age, situation and recent management, and ranges from single species low-cut hawthorn strips to botanically rich remnants of ancient woodland. Where they border intensively farmed land, hedgerows are usually kept down to about one metre high by flail cutting. This creates a uniform height and often removes saplings which could have matured into hedgerow trees. Infrequently, young ash, oak, holly and cherry trees are marked and left to grow on. In some areas the old practice of hedge-laying has been continued.

Of least interest botanically are enclosure hedgerows, planted of hawthorn on straight boundaries from 1790 onwards. Only occasionally a self-sown elder or holly thrusts its way upward among the hawthorn. More interesting in composition are hedgerows of ancient origin, perhaps once planted but, more likely, originating as narrow strips of wildwood left to form boundaries as woodland clearance opened up new farmland. As this process has been ongoing for more than 3,000 years, it is likely that many of today's hedges have a long history. Some have a remarkable range of species and, structurally, show evidence of repeated hedge laying. Of particular interest are those which contain rarities such as purging buckthorn, wild privet, spindle and dogwood.

The most successful hedgerow shrubs are adapted to rigorous cutting back year after year, and produce a succession of colour in their blossom, leaves and fruit. The delicate white flowers of blackthorn, appearing even before the leaves open, are a familiar herald of spring on many roadsides. Cherry plum is quick to follow, its blossom opening alongside the new leaves. Crab apple, though flowering sparsely when severely pruned, is widespread in hedgerows and blossoms freely as a tree. Gorse and broom, prolific on lighter soils, provide a fragrant and arresting display of gold when in bloom.

Some hedgerows have distinct local characteristics, perhaps reflecting their differing origins. Around Arden, bird cherry is a common hedgerow plant, though elsewhere it is normally seen as a tree. Spurge laurel, usually a plant of limestone woodland, occurs in hedgerows near Lealholm; wych elm dominates hedges north of Hutton Buscel; and Ugglebarnby has a fine display of wild roses on its roadsides. Gean or wild cherry is plentiful in Sleightholmedale hedgerows and holly is almost universal in hedges on stock-rearing farms where it provides useful winter browse and shelter.

Much more local are clumps of aspen whose shimmering leaves give a splash of autumn gold to hedges at Wrench Green, and bushes of barberry, which was almost eradicated earlier this century after discovery of its association with a cereal rust fungus. The white flowers of field rose are prevalent in the Helmsley district and one can only hazard a guess as to the origins of *Eleagnus umbellata* in a Silpho hedge and a cluster of *Rosa multiflora* in a hedge near Westerdale.

Ash, wych elm, field maple, goat willow, rowan, oak and birch are common components of mixed hedgerows and where these exist as wayside trees, they create a valuable landscape feature.

Hedgerow Hangers-on

Climbing plants add an extra dimension to hedgerow composition, with perennials such as ivy and honeysuckle clambering up any available support. Bindweed or bellbine covers many hedges with its large white bells in late summer just as the scarlet fruits of black bryony become entwined with long branches of bramble. Ramping fumitory, wood vetch and hop support themselves mainly on hedges near the coast but cleavers or goosegrass is not fussy as to its whereabouts. Very rarely, white bryony and wild clematis find a sunny hedgerow on which to flourish.

The base of a long-established hedge offering a sheltered microclimate, is a frequent habitat for woodland plants like moschatel, often with herb robert and wood anemone, sweet violet, cuckoo pint and more rarely, in Troutsdale, Murk Esk valley and Oldstead, green hellebore. Other herbaceous plants associated with hedgerows include:

Cow parsley
Greater stitchwort
Primrose
Upright hedge parsley
Bluebell
Rough chervil
Red campion
Hogweed
Bugle
Hedge garlic
Lesser celandine
Ground ivy
Hedge mustard
Cowslip
Sweet cicely

Where a field has been sprayed with herbicide right up to the hedge, this varied ground flora is often replaced by a mass of sterile brome and cleavers.

Bridges and Walls

The dry, almost vertical, stonework of bridges, walls and similar masonry would, at first, seem to be an uncongenial place for plants but a surprising number of species find this very specialised habitat to their liking. Old lime mortar is amply colonised by small ferns and plants such as herb robert, rue-leaved saxifrage, wall lettuce, spring whitlow grass and mouse-ear hawkweed.

Reflexed stonecrop, wallflower and wall rue grow on the walls of Danby Castle. The masonry of Mount Grace Priory supports a colourful assortment of ferns and stonecrops; old railway bridges at Commondale and Moorgates are clothed with ferns on shady brickwork although the sunny side is almost bare. On Rosedale's old ironstone mine structures grow biting stonecrop and the dainty fern grass. Walls at Busby Hall, Whorlton Church, Kirby Knowle and Goathland are a few of the numerous locations where maidenhair spleenwort sprouts from old mortar. Black spleenwort is more frequent on natural rock faces such as the Bridestones, Needlepoint, Mallyan Spout and Beast Cliff, whereas the colourful little ivy-leaved toadflax is often abundant on stone and brick retaining walls by roadsides, railway cuttings and bridges.

Railway station platforms along the Esk Valley Line are valuable places for fern colonies, and on the shady sides of several bridges in the upper dales may be found clusters of common polypody (hereabouts far from common) and hartstongue fern. Pellitory of the wall is abundant on precinct walls of Whitby Abbey, while just across the Esk around Sandsend and Dunsley is the stronghold for another largely coastal wall plant – red valerian.

The crumbling limestone ruins of Helmsley Castle and Rievaulx and Byland Abbeys provide a calcareous dry wall habitat. On Helmsley Castle walls grow a myriad of bright purple fairy foxglove which reseeds itself annually to the delight of visitors. It is often accompanied by harebells and thyme-leaved sandwort. Further up the valley at Rievaulx most vegetation is removed from the old walls, leaving mainly annuals such as hairy rockcress and thale cress amongst a few tussocks of thyme and stonecrop species. In the warm shelter of Wass Bank, the walls of Byland Abbey support the rare eastern rocket, normally a southern European plant.

MOORLAND

NYMNP

Bog pimpernel

Mike Yates

Chickweed Wintergreen

Chris Wilson

Herb Rich Meadow

NYMNP

Butterfly orchid

Nan Sykes

Meadow cranesbill

NYMNP

MARSH II

NYMNP

Globe flower

Nan Sykes

Northern marsh orchid

Chris Wilson

WOODLAND

NYMNP

Giant bellflower

Nan Sykes

Yellow star of Bethlehem

Chris Wilson

Quarries

For centuries, both sandstone and limestone have been quarried extensively throughout the area of the National Park, mostly in small quarries for local houses, farm buildings and field walls. In recent years, with improved transport, extraction has become concentrated in a few areas on the southern fringe, leaving numerous old quarries to revegetate naturally. Those conveniently sited on farms have often been used for rubbish disposal but many have been totally abandoned for a long period. At least 30 can now be regarded as of high conservation value on account of the plant communities which have become established.

Understandably, those on the northern sandstones have a more limited flora than those on the southern limestone but are not without interest. Cliff Rigg quarry at Great Ayton is important for its regenerating shrub and woodland communities, interspersed with bare sandy areas supporting little mouse-ear and cudweed. Aislaby quarries near Sleights, which provided stone for Whitby Abbey and several London buildings, have abundant scrub vegetation with smooth sedge and hedge bedstraw in the ground flora.

However, it is the disused limestone quarries in the south of the National Park which form rich botanical sites. They provide opportunity for colonisation by several lime-loving plants which have all but disappeared elsewhere as their habitat – limestone grassland – has been lost to modern farming or forestry. On these sites grow rarities such as fly orchid, bee orchid, fingered sedge and pyramidal orchid. A quarry near Ruston has beaked hawksbeard and bristly oxtongue, both rare plants in the area. Deadly nightshade grows in species-rich quarries at Hutton-le-Hole and Helmsley, while Sneck Yate quarries have the only recorded site for soft trefoil, along with burnet saxifrage. Gromwell is plentiful in a Forge Valley quarry. In long abandoned quarries at Kepwick, a rich turf includes carline thistle, brittle bladder fern and heath grass. A more scrubby quarry in Gowerdale has clustered bellflower, bloody cranesbill and columbine, while globeflower thrives in an old stone quarry near Murton.

Other plants often to be found in such quarries are:

Viper's bugloss
Quaking grass
Fairy flax
Rough hawkbit
Lady's bedstraw
Wild strawberry
Crested hairgrass
Harebell
Mouse-ear hawkweed
Salad burnet
Small scabious
Marjoram
Ragwort
Rockrose
Felwort
Wild thyme
Kidney vctch
Golden rod

Many quarries hold valuable communities of otherwise scarce plants and deserve protection in order to safeguard a much diminished habitat.

WASTELAND

Plants are naturally adapted to a specific habitat or area and this is usually reflected in distribution patterns. However, man has inadvertently interfered in this distribution by transferring seeds and plants in waste and spoil to new locations which can be colonised rapidly by some species. This has happened at Battersby rail junction, at Grosmont on remains of old iron workings (now a public car park) and at a number of refuse tips.

At Battersby Junction, where trains from Whitby on the Esk Valley Line do a reverse manoeuvre before heading off for Middlesbrough, the station and shunting precincts were created with introduced hardcore containing a variety of rogue seed. A colourful selection of plants which seem to have become naturalised by this means includes clary, evening primrose, scotch thistle, corn chamomile, hemlock, weld, wild mignonette, aster, corn salad, tall melilot, apple mint, welsh poppy, purple toadflax and viper's bugloss.

At Grosmont, old building remains and waste tips abandoned a century ago provide a comparatively rich soil for plants to colonise, resulting in a medley of lowland herbaceous plants, garden escapes and pioneer species. Commoner species such as bush vetch, ox-eye daisy, primrose, hairy tare and meadow vetchling grow side by side with pirri-pirri burr, Oregon grape, crown vetch, broad helleborine, box, spotted medick and dark mullein.

Waste tips tend to offer a transient plant habitat but a number of species are adapted to cope. Amenity tips, such as in Limekiln Lane, Thornton-le-Dale, have a seed resource which enables annual colonisation by such plants as scarlet pimpernel, thyme-leaved sandwort, pearlwort, blue fleabane, corn spurrey, common melilot and various geraniums, St John's worts and mallows.

Much attention has been focused on moorland, woodland and grassland, with man-made habitats like road verges, railtracks, quarries and wasteland regarded as being of less conservation importance than semi-natural habitats. In reality, it is very often these apparently useless areas which provide a refuge for many wild plants. Car parks, verges, refuse tips and old quarries, in particular, frequently support a rich and varied flora.

ADDITIONS TO THE FLORA

Despite the recent marked diminution of the local flora, new plants continue to arrive. Many strange newcomers are attributable to the modern gardener motorist who, apparently, finds it easier to dump a sackful of rubbish on a verge or waste ground than to make compost. How long these garden throw-outs will survive remains to be seen but amongst those apparently now naturalised in the wild are:

Globe thistle
Box
Snow in summer
Yellow loosestrife
Houseleek
Spotted dead nettle
Periwinkle
Opium poppy
Blue sowthistle
Tuberous comfrey
Fairy foxglove
Abraham, Isaac and Jacob
Evening primrose
Soapwort
Borage
Leopardsbane
Oregon grape
Marigold
Pick-a-back plant
Flowering rush
Pirri-pirri burr
Lesser meadow rue
Stinking iris
Ostrich fern
Montbretia
Knotweed
Golden rod
Lungwort
Butcher's broom
Purple toadflax
Shasta daisy
Honesty
London pride
Candytuft
Aconite
Flowering currant
Foam flower
White star of Bethlehem
Stinking hellebore

and various species of campanula, geranium, cotoneaster, allium, sedum, dianthus, anemone, scilla and spurge.

A recent addition to the local flora is an aquatic – *Crassula helmsii* – first noted in the 1980s in a pond at Danby. Hardcore imported for Boulby mine forecourt provided ideal habitat for bristly oxtongue which was scarcely recorded before. New Zealand willowherb now flourishes along forest rides and creeping speedwell is a recent invader of mown grass. The present popularity of rearing pheasants for shooting is responsible for introducing plants such as buckwheat, sunflower and globe artichoke as feedstuffs, while attractive blue-flowered chicory and flax, established on a few roadsides, are organic farm escapes. The cliffs of Khyber Pass, Whitby support two introduced plants, one a garden pink and the other a yellow daisy-like flower known as grindelia. This is the only known site where grindelia is naturalised.

Introductions of alien species, whether deliberate or accidental, can have significant effects on the native flora as a result of aggressive competition. This can be seen in woods where *Rhododendron ponticum* has been introduced for game cover or amenity value and has practically eliminated other ground flora. Japanese knotweed has proved to be so rampant in some parts of the country that it is now illegal to introduce this plant to the wild. Although several exotic species are now naturalised in this area, they are no replacement for lost native plants.

Conservation of Habitats

The North York Moors contain a wide variety of wild flowers but even the National Park status has not fully protected habitats and plants from change since the 1950s. Aside from the extensive heather moorland, many semi-natural habitats are small and fragmented. It is, therefore, often the man-made habitats of road and rail verges, old quarries and wasteland, together with areas that have not been subject to intensive use, where much of the native flora can still be found.

Unfortunately, modern use of the countryside has caused many habitats to become isolated from one another which has greatly reduced the likelihood of dispersal and expansion. This may eventually threaten the survival of some sensitive species. However, a number of recent conservation measures should be of positive benefit. For example, managing field boundaries and hedgerows for conservation can help to link isolated plant communities; changes in the agricultural support system may lead to less intensive use of some farmland and the development of new habitats; and local wildflower plants and seeds are being used in some situations to extend habitats, although they will never replace the complex communities already lost.

Conservation of wildlife is now taking a stronger role in land-use planning countrywide and in the North York Moors National Park a range of policies is being carried out to assist with the protection and enhancement of wildlife habitats. Working with other conservation organisations and landowners, various schemes have been proposed and some are underway. These include protection of limestone grassland and abandoned quarries; tree and hedge planting and management; identification of areas of moorland for less intensive management; re-establishment of moor-edge woodland on bracken slopes; investigation of the potential for arable land to be positively managed for conservation of cornfield weeds; expansion of populations of rare plants; and appropriate management of road and rail verges.

Implementing this work, including greater awareness and liaison, requires public investment and the co-operation of those who own, manage and farm the land. After a drastic reduction of the wild flora in post-war decades, there is now a better prospect for the future of wild plants within the North York Moors National Park and, although there will be some plants that are never likely to return, there should be increasing opportunity for existing populations to expand.

Wild Plants of the North York Moors National Park

Wild Plants of the North York Moors National Park

The sequence of families follows the *Excursion Flora of the British Isles,* by A. R. Clapham, T. G. Tutin and E. F. Warburg, 3rd edition, 1981. Nomenclature from the *New Flora of the British Isles* by C Stace, 1991 is shown by [ ]. English names given are those in common usage.

The number of tetrads in which a species occurs is shown by the number after the English name. No number indicates inadequate data.

The letter **M** refers to the inclusion of a distribution map.

STONEWORTS
CHARACEAE

Stoneworts are plentiful where unpolluted water is held in farm and forest ponds, shallow streams, small reservoirs and lakes on calcareous substrate, such as Arden, Newtondale, Sawdondale and Dalbydale.

CLUBMOSSES
LYCOPODIACEAE

Stagshorn Clubmoss 5
Lycopodium clavatum
Occurs rarely throughout the area on drier moors amongst heather and bilberry, in mossy hollows on forest rides and rocky gill ledges. Dalby Forest, Greenhow, Gurtof Wood and Wykeham Forest.

SELAGINELLACEAE

Lesser Clubmoss 7
Selaginella selaginoides
Occasionally found in base-rich flushes and wet heath on the moors. Hasty Bank, Incline Foot, Daletown Common, Eskerdale, Goathland Moor and Tranmire.

HORSETAIL FAMILY
EQUISETACEAE

Common Horsetail 296 M
Equisetum arvense
Away from the high moors widespread and often extensive on waste land, rail ballast and dry grassland. A tiresome garden weed where established.

Water Horsetail 94 M
Equisetum fluviatile
Frequent in shallow water, marshes, alder carr and lakeside.

Dutch Rush 1
Equisetum hyemale
Only known site is in a shady woodland edge near Mallyan Spout where several plants are scattered amongst bracken and leaf litter.

Marsh Horsetail 224 M
Equisetum palustre
Widespread and may be abundant in damp grassland, marshes and streamsides.

Wood Horsetail 175 M
Equisetum sylvaticum
Grows in wet shady places on acid soils or on moist humus. Its delicate fern-like

Common Horsetail

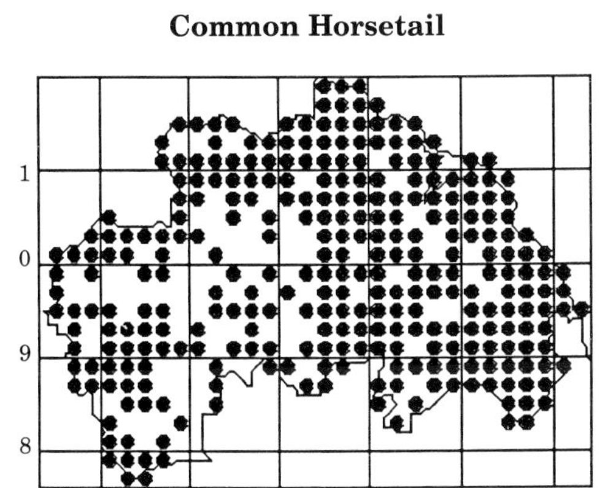

Water Horsetail

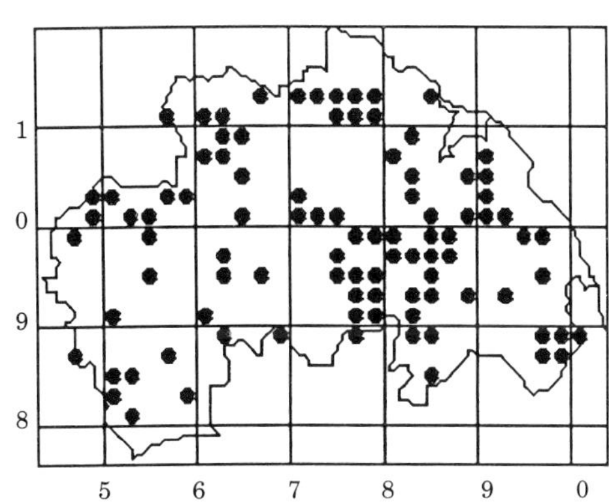

Marsh Horsetail

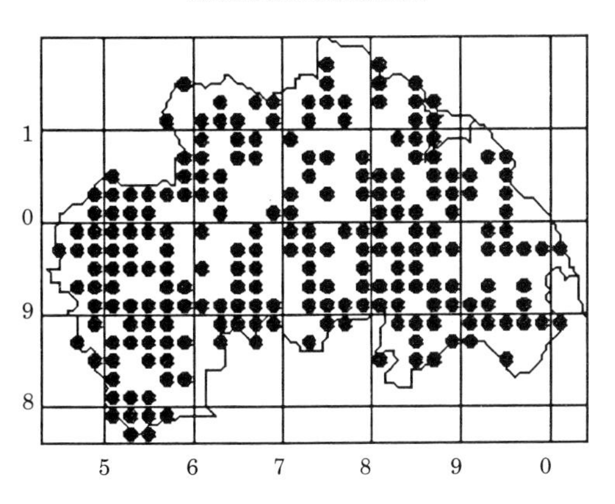

Wood Horsetail

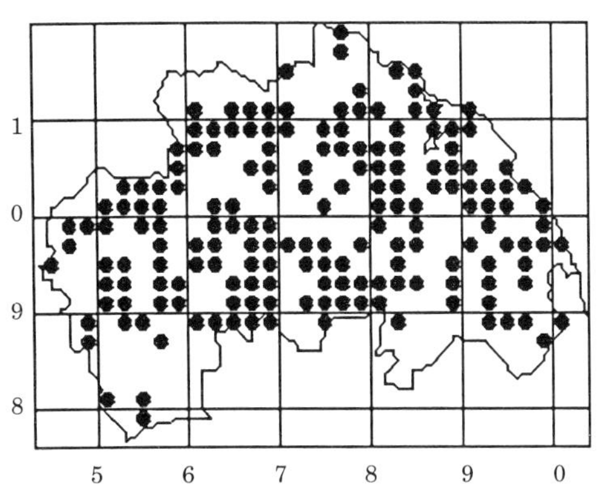

shoots may be the dominant vegetation in large patches, eg Bransdale.

Great Horsetail 122 M
Equisetum telmateia
Grows to profusion in seepage areas on boulder clay cliffs and covers large patches both around calcareous springs in rank grassland and in wet clay runnels in forest and roadside.

FERN FAMILIES

OPHIOGLOSSACEAE

Moonwort 14 M
Botrychium lunaria
A rare plant of rough unimproved dry grassland and moorland turf, often lurking beneath bracken on tracksides. Possibly much under-recorded as its frond is rapidly nibbled off by sheep. Farndale, Glaisdale, Fryupdale, Bransdale, Ampleforth and Saltergate.

Adderstongue 41 M
Ophioglossum vulgatum
Small colonies occur on grassy pathsides, on coastal cliff ledges and in damp hollows in old undisturbed base-rich pastures often with cowslip. Rare forked-spike plants grow in Harwood Dale. Seems to survive moderate grazing but is lost if land is ploughed. A large colony flourishes under the protection of bracken fronds on a scrubby bank at Cloughton Newlands; also plentiful in undisturbed ground at RAF Fylingdales.

OSMUNDACEAE

Royal Fern 1
Osmunda regalis
Believed extinct in this area prior to the survey until an old established colony was refound in 1989 near Harwood Dale. So far as is known, this is the sole survivor of numerous sites which have disappeared through depredation by fern collectors or loss of habitat through land drainage. Inaccessible on private land, it is now protected under a management agreement with the National Park.

HYMENOPHYLLACEAE

Tunbridge Filmy Fern
Hymenophyllum tunbrigense
This moss-like fern has been known for more than a century at Hayburn Wyke. Although recent searches failed to locate the plant, there is every reason to assume that it continues to grow amongst the extensive and partly inaccessible dripping rocks.

HYPOLEPIDACEAE [DENNSTAEDTIACEAE]

Bracken 393 M
Pteridium aquilinum
The "problem" plant of the moors, bracken is spreading both uphill into the heather moorland and down into daleheads and intake grazing. Absent only from very wet areas, and from exposed moor tops, bracken dominates most dalesides thus reducing sheep grazing and providing a breeding ground for sheep ticks which perpetuate both sheep and grouse diseases. Bracken encroachment in the North York Moors is regarded as a serious threat to moorland vegetation and economic viability. Various research projects are underway to find a solution. At the present time (1992) a moth caterpillar from South Africa which is known to feed on bracken is undergoing laboratory testing as a potential biological control agent. In the meantime, about

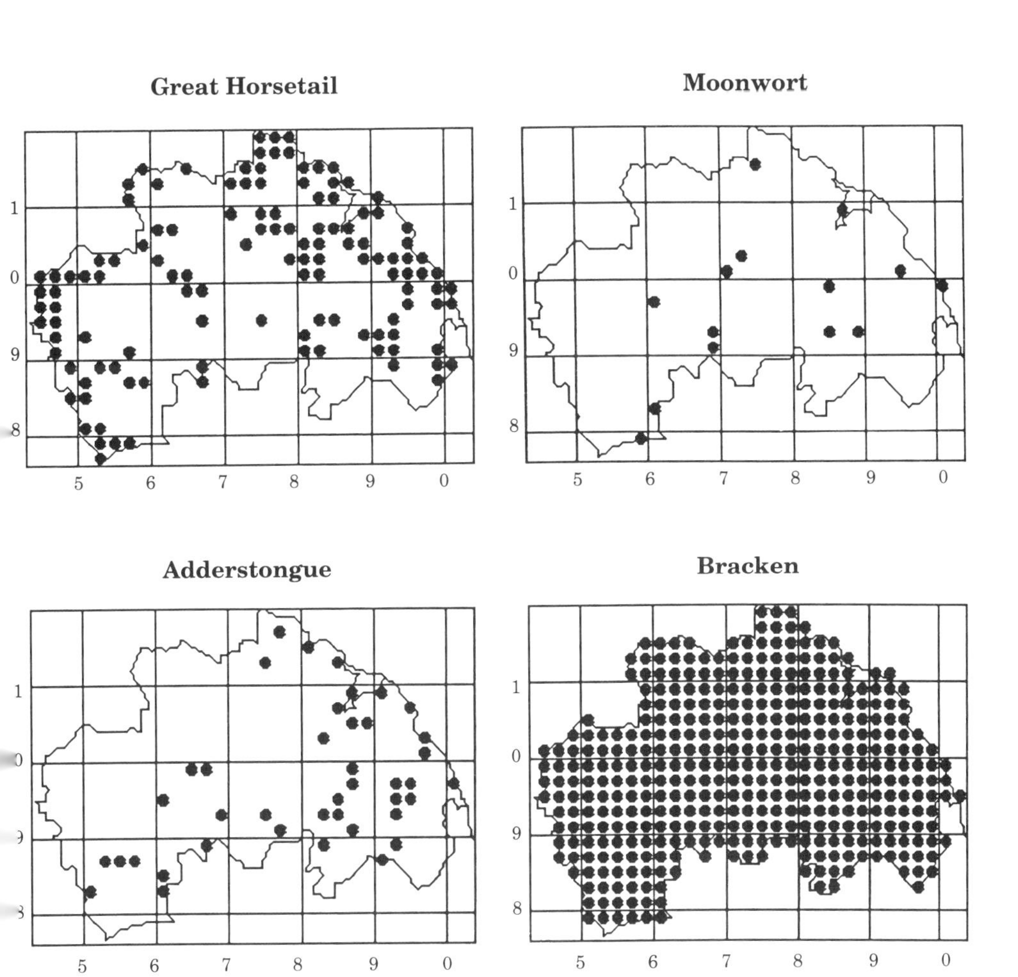
Great Horsetail
Moonwort
Adderstongue
Bracken
1
0
9
8
5
6
7
8
9
0

1000 hectares (2500 acres) a year are treated with selective herbicide. A long-term sustainable strategy needs to be developed which will ensure that bracken encroachment is halted in a cost-effective manner with minimum risk to other moorland vegetation. A number of reasons suggested for the spread of bracken include atmospheric pollution, drying-out of the moors, decline of cattle rearing and removal of upland tree cover.

THELYPTERIDACEAE

Mountain Fern 189 M
Oreopteris limbosperma
The distinctive yellow-green lemon-scented fronds of this fern form an almost continuous fringe alongside most upland streams and may be plentiful in wet acid heath with moving water.

Beech Fern 15 M
Phegopteris connectilis
Small patches occur on humus-rich rocky or shale outcrops in shady gills and damp undisturbed ancient woodland. This fern clothes an extensive rockface in upper Bransdale and may be found partly concealed in gills of the Upper Rye also in Northdale, Raindale and Wheeldale and along the streamside at Hartoft.

ASPLENIACEAE

Black Spleenwort 16 M
Asplenium adiantum-nigrum
Growing in moist shade, it can be found on stonework of Helmsley Castle and Byland Abbey; in old quarries at Kepwick; on rocky ledges of Beast Cliff; by waterfalls at Goathland and Hackness; on Bridestones, Whitestone Cliffs and Needlepoint; and sparsely, on perimeter walls of the old school at Kirby Knowle as well as a variety of stony habitats including railway masonry.

Sea Spleenwort 1
Asplenium marinum
Its only known site on local cliffs is on sea-sprayed rocks at Hundale Point.

Maidenhair Spleenwort 36 M
Asplenium trichomanes
Often prolific in suitable locations, especially on platforms, bridges and retaining walls of the Esk Valley railway. Also on old walls of Mount Grace Priory, Busby Hall, Byland Abbey, Helmsley Castle and on calcareous rock faces in Nettledale, Newtondale, Havern Beck Valley, Rosekirkdale and Falling Foss.

Wall Rue 30 M
Asplenium ruta-muraria
Usually growing on the shady side of walls and rocks. Found at Danby Castle, Lythe and Danby churchyards and Esk Valley station platforms.

Rusty-back Fern 1
Ceterach officinarum
Long-established on a wall in Hartoft. Not known elsewhere.

Hartstongue Fern 103 M
Phyllitis scolopendrium
Widespread in shady base-rich soil; in stone and brickwork of bridges and retaining walls on Esk Valley and North Yorkshire Moors railway lines; in old rabbit "types" (traps) on Dalby Warren; church precincts, river bridges and in coastal ravine woodlands on boulder clay where it grows enormous fronds. By contrast it has survived recent long dry summers in miniature form.

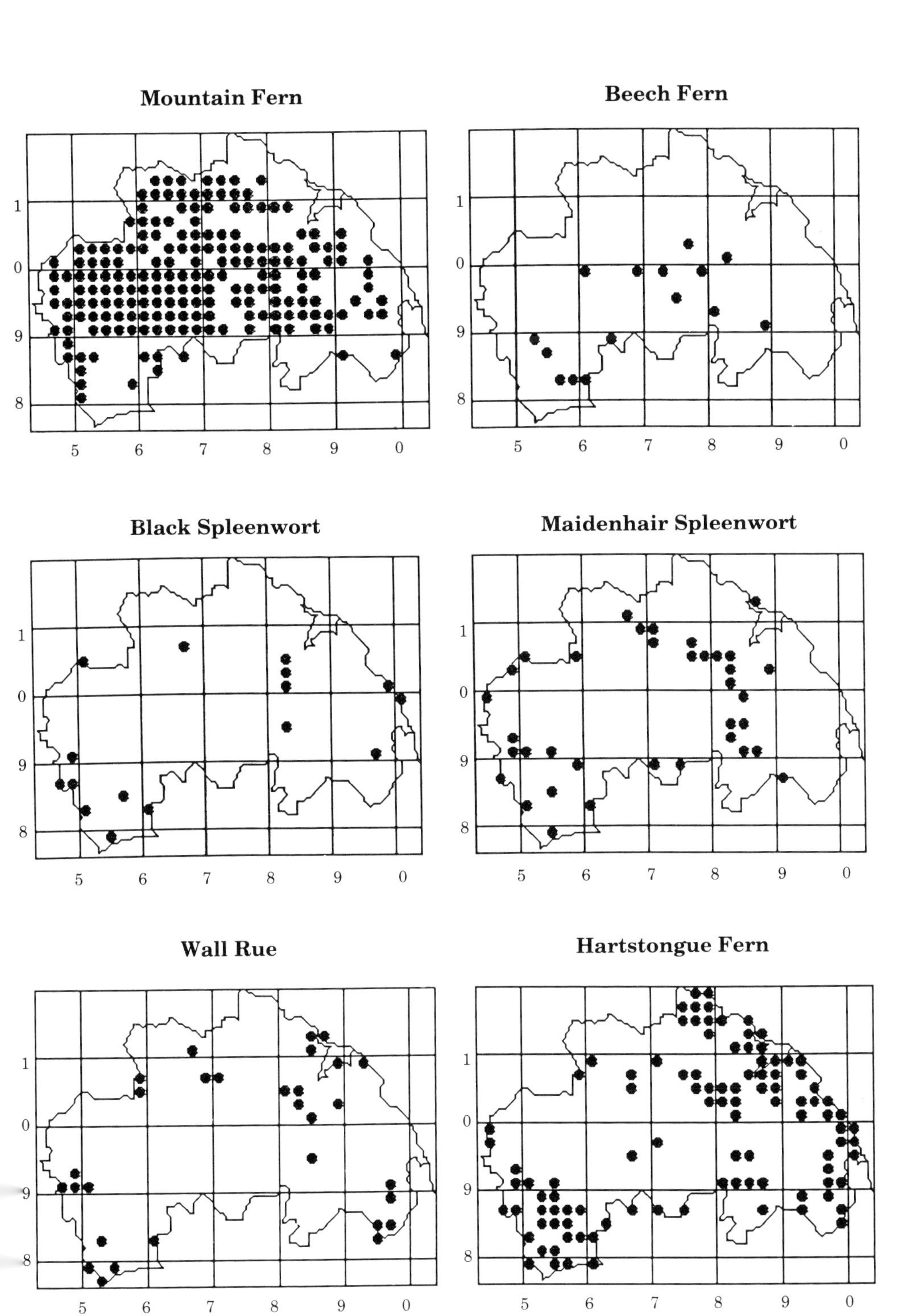
Mountain Fern
Beech Fern
Black Spleenwort
Maidenhair Spleenwort
Wall Rue
Hartstongue Fern
1
0
9
8
5
6
7
8
9
0

ATHYRIACEAE [WOODSIACEAE]

Lady Fern 323
Athyrium filix-femina
This graceful fern is abundant in moist acid woodland, on seepage lines in upland gills and fringes of most moorland streams, often growing alongside mountain fern.

Brittle Bladder Fern 36 M
Cystopteris fragilis
On rocky outcrops of Lockton Bank, Levisham Brow, Havern Beck and several Ryedale gills. Also on disused limekilns and on old walls of Danby Castle and Mount Grace Priory.

ASPIDIACEAE [DRYOPTERIDACEAE]

Male Fern 358
Dryopteris filix-mas
Abundant in hedgerows, scrub, open woods and forest margins, often with other ferns. Large fronds create impressive "shuttlecocks" in woodland glades.

Golden Scale Fern 118 M
Dryopteris affinis
The thick covering of ginger-coloured scales on this fern make it prominent in many upland woods, on forest edges, rough hillsides and verges on acid soils.

Broad Buckler Fern 376
Dryopteris dilatata
Very common in wet woodland especially in daleside forest plantations where it frequently dominates the ground flora. Flourishes in deep shade as well as open glades and rides.

Narrow Buckler Fern 20 M
Dryopteris carthusiana
Thinly dispersed with only a few plants in each location, this fern occurs in two distinct habitats – on wet peat on open moorland and in shady, damp woodland.

Hay-scented Buckler Fern 1
Dryopteris aemula
This beautiful but elusive (and nationally rare) fern of damp deciduous woodland has been found only at New Wath, near Goathland. Attempts to locate historical records in Hayburn Wyke, Cockmill and Cockrah woods have been unsuccessful – but these are large woods and further searching is needed.

Soft Shield Fern 85 M
Polystichum setiferum
Mainly found in lower Eskdale and coastal valley woods where it grows on base-rich moist ground with yellow archangel and smooth sedge. Essentially a plant of ancient woodland, fine specimens occur in Rigg Mill and Littlebeck woods. Also occurs in long-established damp hedgerows.

Hard Shield Fern 86 M
Polystichum aculeatum
The dark wintergreen fronds of this fern are often found hanging down a shale exposure in gills; frequent in non-acid seepage beneath overhanging rocks; and on shady wooded slopes.

Oak Fern 16 M
Gymnocarpium dryopteris
A rare fern in this locality. Small colonies occur on damp acid soils in steep rocky gills and dalehead streamsides, often secreted beneath overhanging rock and vegetation. Danbydale, Snip Gill, Worry Gill, Northdale, Borrowbydale.

Brittle Bladder Fern

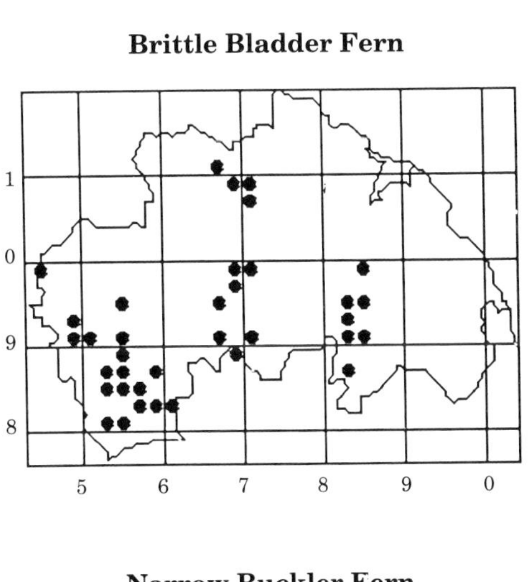

Golden Scale Fern

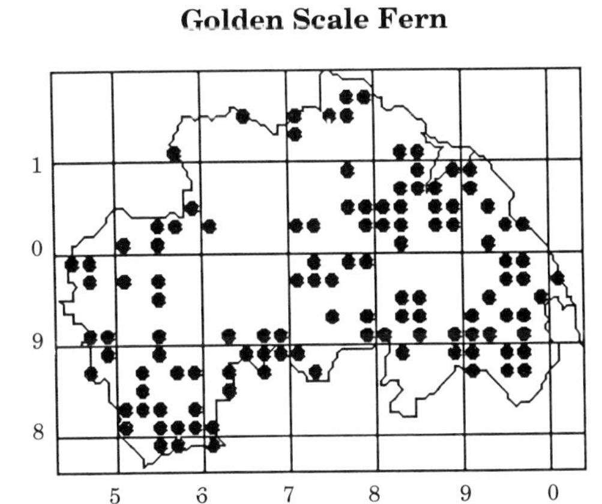

Narrow Buckler Fern

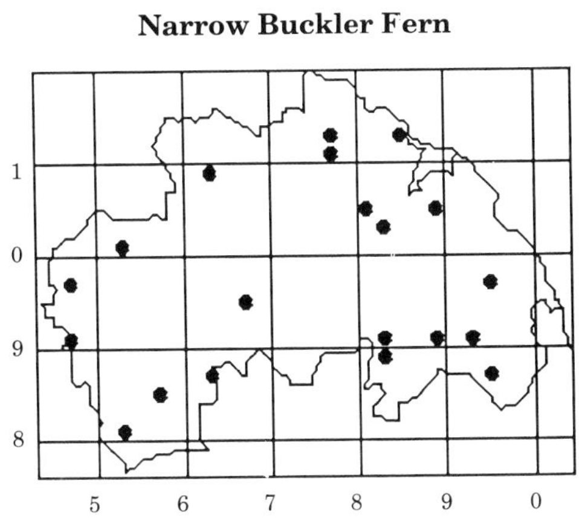

Soft Shield Fern

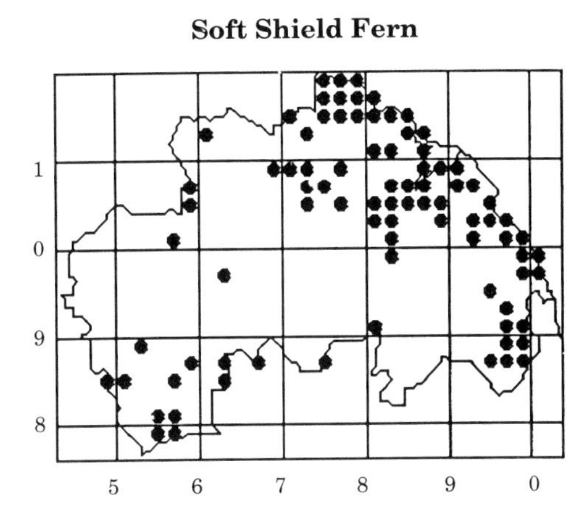

Hard Shield Fern

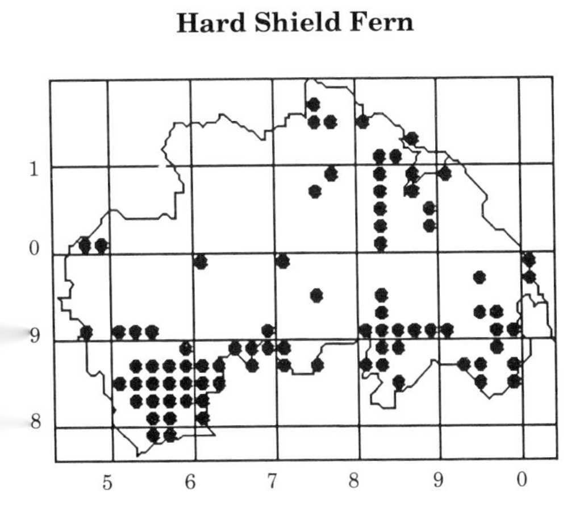

Oak Fern

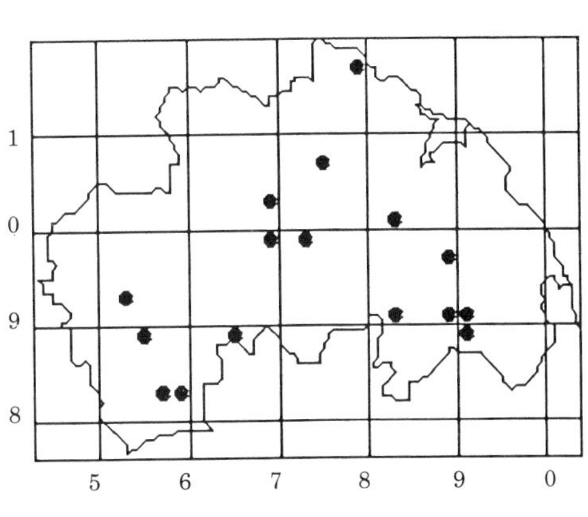

BLECHNACEAE

Hard Fern 319 M
Blechnum spicant
The "fishbone" fertile fronds of this widespread fern are common on acid and peaty soils in shady hedgebanks, dalehead gills, forest rides and damp moor edge.

POLYPODIACEAE

Polypody 114 M
Polypodium vulgare
Not a common fern in this area although colonies may be large where they occur, for example, on tumbledown field walls, rocky hedgebanks, stone bridges and woody gills. Often epiphytic on mature trees, polypody covers a leaning ash near Beckhole up to 12 metres high on the trunk's mossy north-facing side.

MARSILEACEAE

Pillwort 0
Pilularia globulifera
Formerly established on the water's edge at Lake Gormire but not seen in recent years. This may be due to a change in water level or eutrophication of the water resulting from a growing duck population which is encouraged for shooting.

PINE FAMILY
PINACEAE

Larch 281 M
Larix kaempferi, L. decidua, L. x *eurolepis [L. marschlinsii]*
The sparkling green of new spring foliage and its autumnal gold give variety to forestry plantations where Japanese and European Larch and the hybrid have been planted extensively, both for amenity purposes and as a nurse crop for broadleaved trees. Although not a native tree, larch regenerates freely, often in recently felled compartments. Mature larches are important landscape features as on the top of Whitestone Cliff. A form known as "Hangman's larch", in which a secondary trunk forms an elbow before resuming upright growth, has been noted at Danby and Great Ayton.

Scots Pine 326 M
Pinus sylvestris
Not native in this area but widely planted as a forest crop and for shelter belt or amenity use. Natural regeneration occurs and a few young pines soon become established on unburnt and ungrazed moorland such as at Bridestones, Westonby, Troutsdale and Lowna.

Sitka spruce *(Picea sitchensis)* and Norway spruce *(Picea abies)* are grown extensively in forest plantations.

CYPRESS FAMILY
CUPRESSACEAE

Juniper 9 M
Juniperis communis
A relic of post-glacial colonisation and believed to have been much more widely distributed on the moorland escarpments and valleys. It cannot withstand burning and now occurs only in a few remote gills and moor edges. Single or small clusters of shrubs grow in Baysdale, Keysbeck, Fryupdale and Danbydale. A sizeable colony survives on north-facing scree at Greenhow Botton. No natural regeneration of these ageing shrubs has been found.

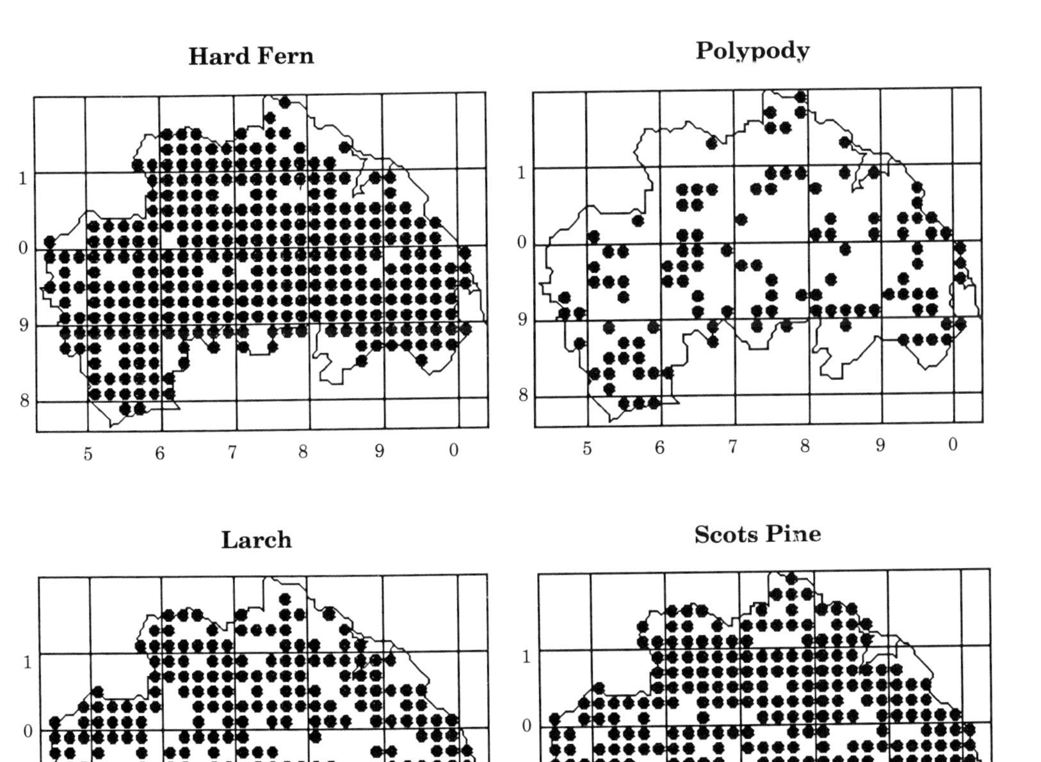
Hard Fern
Polypody
Larch
Scots Pine
1
0
9
8
5
6
7
8
9
0

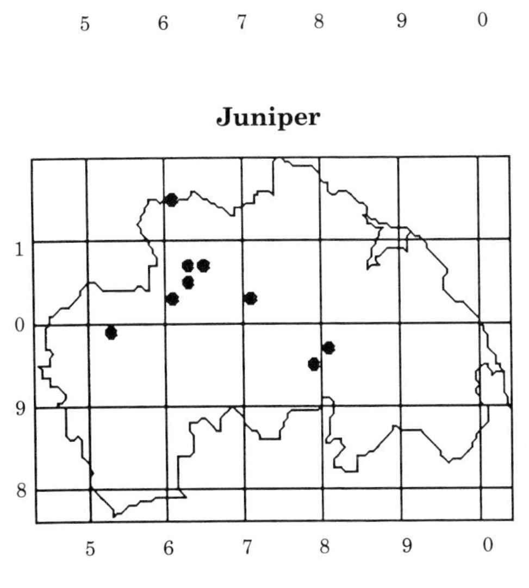
Juniper
1
0
9
8
5
6
7
8
9
0

YEW FAMILY
TAXACEAE

Yew 65
Taxus baccata
Formerly planted in practically every churchyard where many very old yews survive. It is believed that in church environs it provided a source of timber for mediaeval bowmen without exposing its poisonous foliage to village livestock. Only known to occur naturally at Yew Tree Scar in Newtondale and in Guisborough woods. Although young seedlings are occasionally found in open woodland and plantations, presumably bird-sown, it seems they rarely grow to maturity under a close tree canopy.

BUTTERCUP FAMILY
RANUNCULACEAE

Marsh Marigold 227 M
Caltha palustris
The familiar "Kingcup" creates an early flowering golden splash to most upland riversides; common in marshy fields, wet woodland and fens.

Globeflower 9 M
Trollius europaeus
Approaching its southern limit in Britain, colonies occur infrequently in undisturbed woodland and marshes in Newtondale, Gowerdale, upper Ryedale, Hartoft Dale and Goathland. In a contrasting habitat, globeflowers grow sparsely on the north-facing slope of a revegetated disused limestone quarry at Murton.

Green Hellebore 14 M
Helleborus viridis
Small colonies flourish in ancient deciduous woods and hedgerows in Forge Valley, Ellerburn, Rievaulx, Troutsdale and Goathland.

Stinking Hellebore 1
Helleborus foetidus
A garden escape, it has naturalised on a laneside at Oldstead.

Baneberry 13 M
Actaea spicata
Restricted in Britain to a narrow east-west zone which includes limestone ashwoods at the southern edge of the Park. Forge Valley, Yedmandale, Helmsley and intervening valley woods have scattered small populations, usually in light shade.

Wood Anemone 285 M
Anemone nemorosa
In damp hedgerows and old deciduous woodland its white, pink or mauve flowers often carpet the ground, especially on acid or waterlogged soil. Essentially a woodland plant, it seems able to survive in undisturbed grassland and hedgerow after removal of tree cover but rarely occurs in recent plantations.

Traveller's Joy 4
Clematis vitalba
A southern species rarely found here, it has been planted in Marnardale, but the origins of plants entwined in hedgerows at Wydale, Wrench Green and Ruswarp are unknown.

Meadow Buttercup 357 M
Ranunculus acris
Very common in rough grassland on verges and wayside, also in pasture where its unpalatable leaves are avoided by grazing stock.

Creeping Buttercup 392
Ranunculus repens
Tolerant of a wide range of habitats, it is found in almost every grassy field, hedgebank, verge and garden except on the high heather moorland. It survives

Marsh Marigold

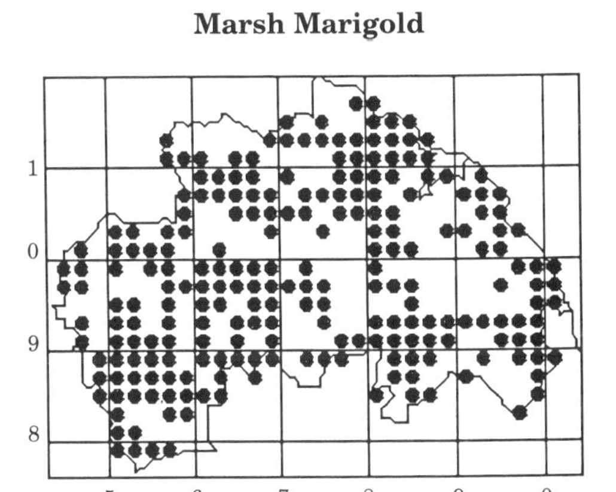

Globeflower

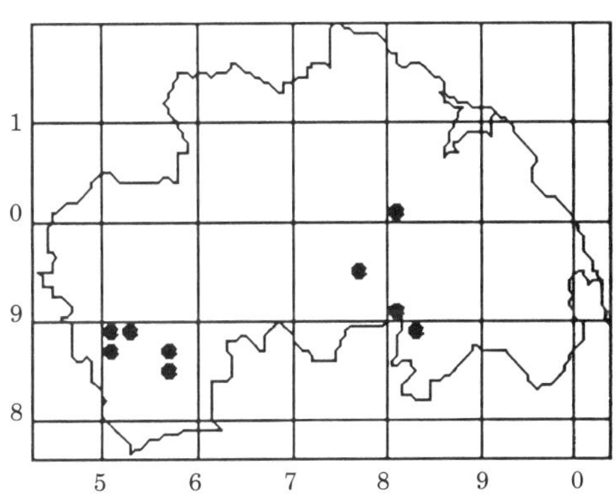

Green Hellebore

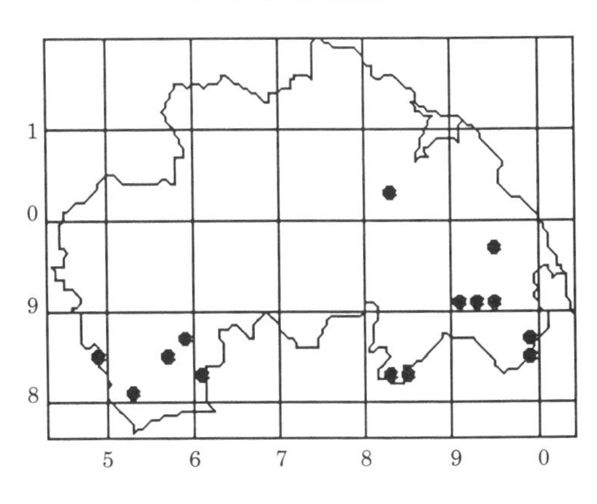

Baneberry

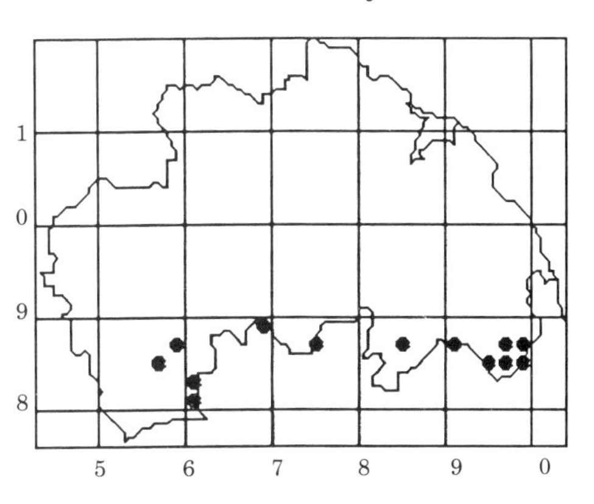

Wood Anemone

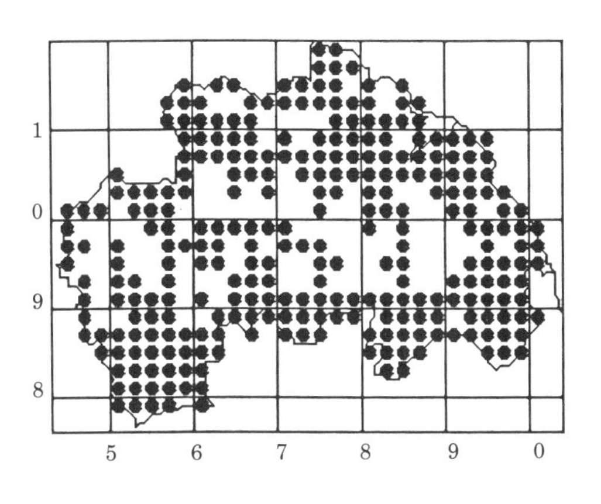

Meadow Buttercup

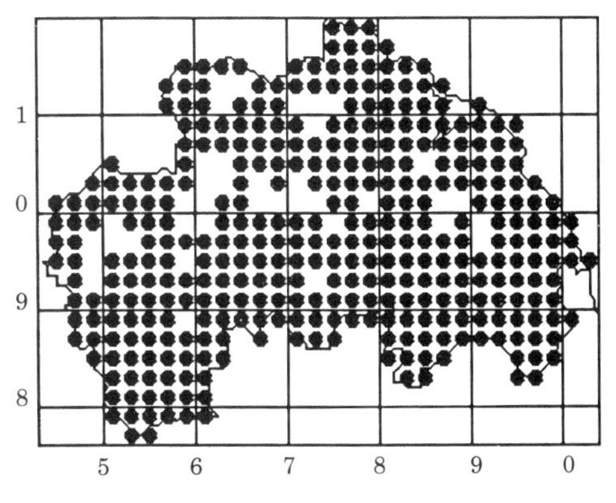

disturbance, trampling and grazing, and turns unimproved meadows golden in the early summer.

Bulbous Buttercup 119 M
Ranunculus bulbosus
One of the first spring flowers on long established grassland, verges and old pasture on less acidic soils.

Corn Crowfoot or
Corn Buttercup 2
Ranunculus arvensis
A few plants were discovered in a wheat field at Faceby in 1991 where an acute corner had been inaccessible to a herbicide sprayer. It has since been found in a garden at Dalby. No other records exist in this area and nationally it is listed as a cornfield plant in serious decline.

Hairy Buttercup 2
Ranunculus sardous
Only known on a farm near Howldale but may be under-recorded.

Goldilocks 86 M
Ranunculus auricomus
The uneven petals of this flower are a familiar spring sight in ancient woodland on enriched soils where it grows in moist glades, on hedgebanks and shrubby margins. More rarely occurs in old hay meadows.

Great Spearwort 7
Ranunculus lingua
Likely to be native in pools on Beast Cliff but quite often planted in new ponds and has been introduced to lakes at Arden and Elleron.

Lesser Spearwort 285 M
Ranunculus flammula
Its yellow flowers and spear-shaped leaves are a common sight in pools, shallow streams, marshes and wet grassland, except in fast flowing or very acid water.

Celery-leaved Crowfoot 10 M
Ranunculus sceleratus
Only a few known sites – on the fringes of standing water at Mount Grace Priory, Saltwick and Throxenby, and on streamsides in Beedale, Caydale and Yedmandale.

Lesser Celandine 328
Ranunculus ficaria
This familiar plant seems able to flourish almost anywhere except on the high moors. Abundant on grassy banks, in open woodland, pasture, path sides and churchyards. More frequent in damp shade but occurs on sunny hillsides and cliffs.

Ivy Water Crowfoot 52 M
Ranunculus hederaceus
Mainly in the higher dales and moorland fringe, small patches sprawl over wheel ruts, muddy pathways, shallow grassy puddles and stream outlets where water stands most of the year. Often grows with starwort and bulbous rush.

Moorland Water Crowfoot 49 M
Ranunculus omiophyllus
Grows in similar habitats to *Ranunculus hederaceus*, but with a tendency to higher ground on Snilesworth and Arden Moors.

Long-leaved Water Crowfoot 8
Ranunculus fluitans
Forms a mass of vegetation in a few fast flowing waterways – Thornton and Pickering Becks, River Derwent below Langdale End, River Rye downstream from Rievaulx and River Esk downstream from Danby.

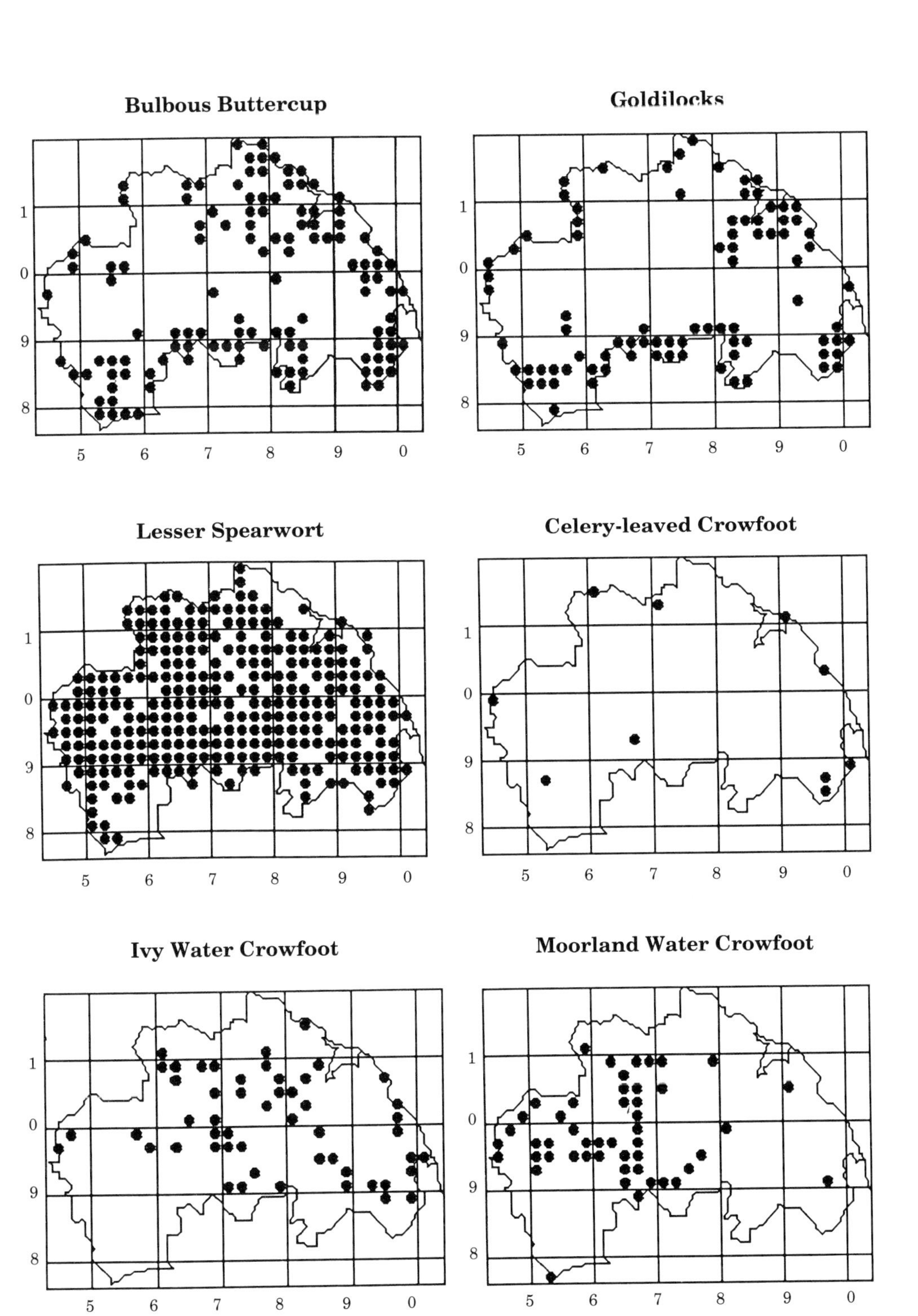
Bulbous Buttercup
1
0
9
8
5
6
7
8
9
0
Goldilocks
1
0
9
8
5
6
7
8
9
0
Lesser Spearwort
1
0
9
8
5
6
7
8
9
0
Celery-leaved Crowfoot
1
0
9
8
5
6
7
8
9
0
Ivy Water Crowfoot
1
0
9
8
5
6
7
8
9
0
Moorland Water Crowfoot
1
0
9
8
5
6
7
8
9
0

Short-leaved Water Crowfoot 1
Ranunculus trichophyllus
Found only in a pond at Roger Trod.

Common Water Crowfoot 10
Ranunculus aquatilis
Has been found occasionally at the edge of reservoirs and ponds.

Pond Water Crowfoot 9
Ranunculus peltatus
Grows in Lake Gormire, River Derwent and ponds at Blandsby, Cropton, Suffield, Raincliffe and West Ayton.

Stream Water Crowfoot
Ranunculus penicillatus
Var. *calcareus* grows in fast-flowing calcareous waters of Beedale beck.
Var. *penicillatus (R. pseudofluitans)* often occurs with *R. fluitans.*

Winter Aconite 7 M
Eranthis hyemalis
Introduced in the 16th century, it is still widely planted in gardens and occasionally spills over into churchyards and grassy areas which are carpeted with its golden flowers in late winter. Hackness, Hutton Buscel and Battersby are among its haunts.

Monkshood 14 M
Aconitum napellus
Possibly native in ancient woods at Lowna, Sleights, Rievaulx, Ellerburn and Mulgrave. Although highly poisonous, it is still a popular garden plant and occasionally naturalises where rubbish has been tipped.

Columbine 19 M
Aquilegia vulgaris
Native dark purple-flowered plants grow singly or in small clusters in older woodland on limestone and on scrubby hillsides. Paler forms originating from garden throwouts have naturalised elsewhere.

Meadow Rue 2
Thalictrum flavum
Survives in marshes in Newtondale and near Byland.

Lesser Meadow Rue 1
Thalictrum minus
Established in a Hutton Buscel hedgerow possibly from a garden outcast.

BERBERIS FAMILY
BERBERIDACEAE

Barberry 12 M
Berberis vulgaris
An early introduction as a medicinal herb, it later became associated with a cereal rust and was widely eradicated. Occasional shrubs survive in old hedgerows and quarries in Forge Valley, Sawdondale, Dalbydale, Seave Green, Thirlby, Coxwold and Fylingthorpe.

WATER LILY FAMILY
NYMPHAEACEAE

White Water Lily 9 M
Nymphaea alba
Possibly native on Beast Cliff but introduced and thriving in man-made ponds at Fryup, Chopgate, Harwood Dale Forest and Rigg Mill.

Yellow Water Lily 3
Nuphar lutea
A native plant amongst lush vegetation of River Derwent below West Ayton Bridge. Planted in pools at Sutherland and Whorlton.

Winter Aconite

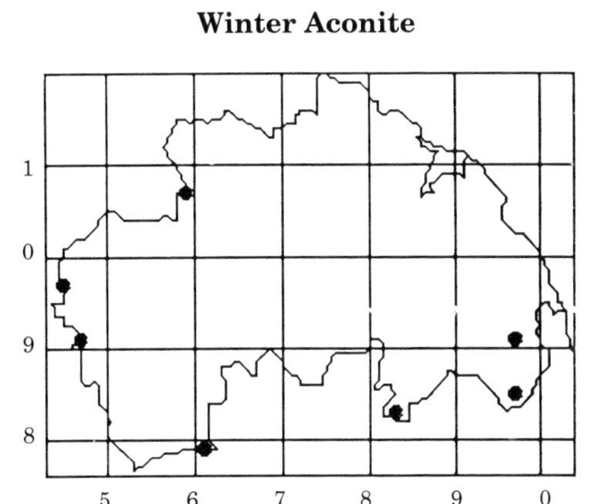

Monkshood

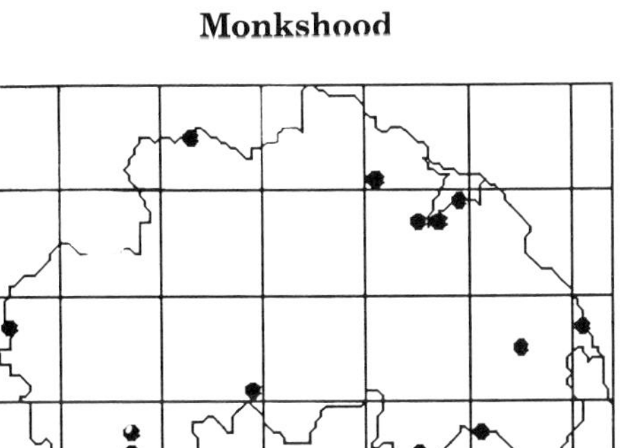

Columbine

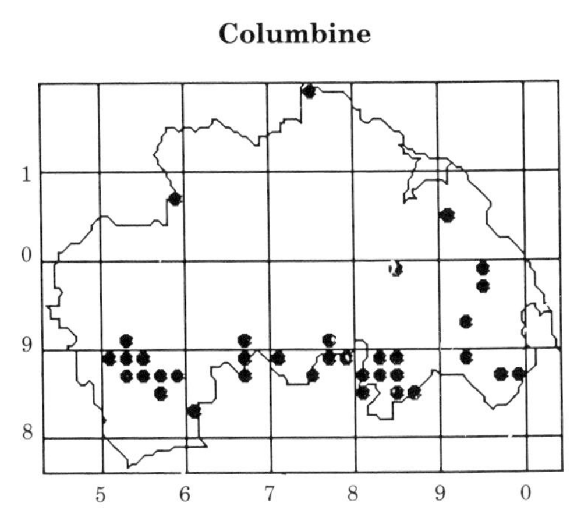

Barberry

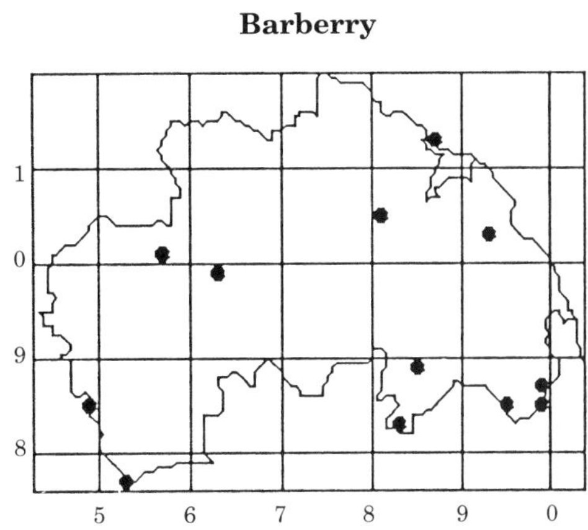

White Water Lily

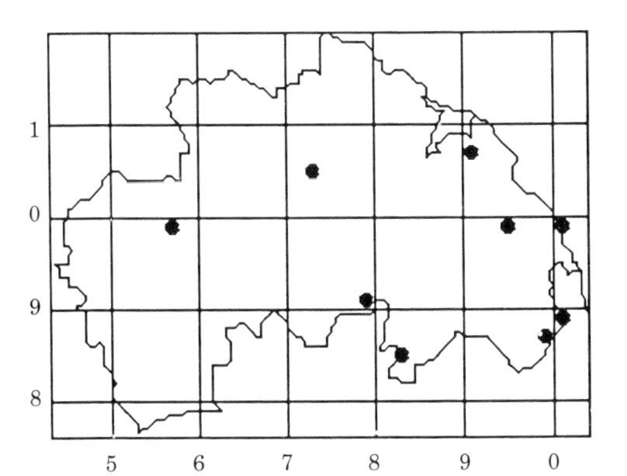

HORNWORT FAMILY
CERATOPHYLLACEAE

Hornwort 2
Ceratophyllum demersum
Grows in Pickering Beck in the lower part of Newtondale and in Scaling Dam reservoir. Has been planted in a new pond in Harwood Dale.

POPPY FAMILY
PAPAVERACEAE

Field Poppy 93 M
Papaver rhoeas
Widespread on light arable and nearby wasteland, though usually few in number. Once in a while a cereal field turns scarlet with the flowering of poppies germinated from a long dormant seed bank released by a change in cultivation.

Long-headed Poppy 32 M
Papaver dubium
Grows in similar situations to field poppy, on light well-drained but usually more acid soils.

Opium Poppy 2
Papaver somniferum
A garden escape which has naturalised on verges at Barnby and Staithes.

Welsh Poppy 36
Meconopsis cambrica
Another garden escape which is quite widespread. It often grows on walls, banks and waste ground near houses and farms.

Greater Celandine 23 M
Chelidonium majus
An old medicinal herb often grown in cottage gardens and naturalised on hedgebanks and walls near villages.

FUMITORY FAMILY
FUMARIACEAE

White Climbing Fumitory 92 M
Corydalis claviculata [Ceratocapnos claviculata]
Frequent in dry acid heath in oak/birch woodland and forest plantations. It scrambles over bramble thickets on woodland margins, amongst woodland edge vegetation and is often the only ground flora in deep shade beneath trees or bracken.

Yellow Fumitory 33
Corydalis lutea [Pseudofumaria lutea]
Quite often naturalised on walls near villages.

Ramping Fumitory 15 M
Fumaria capreolata
Its localities are few but plants may be numerous, clambering over hedgerows in coastal areas, especially around Hinderwell and Raw.

Wall Fumitory 20
Fumaria muralis
No previous reference to this plant has been found for this area but the recent survey located several plants both along the coast and inland. Is it a plant which has moved in lately, or had it been overlooked? It was found on arable fields, on grassy roadside verges and hedge bottoms.

Common Fumitory 71 M
Fumaria officinalis
Quick to colonise new roadside verges and disturbed ground with alkaline soils, it also survives in small numbers on many well drained arable fields.

Small White Fumitory 2
Fumaria parviflora
Usually associated with arable fields on southern chalk, it grows rarely in the Forge Valley and Suffield areas.

Field Poppy

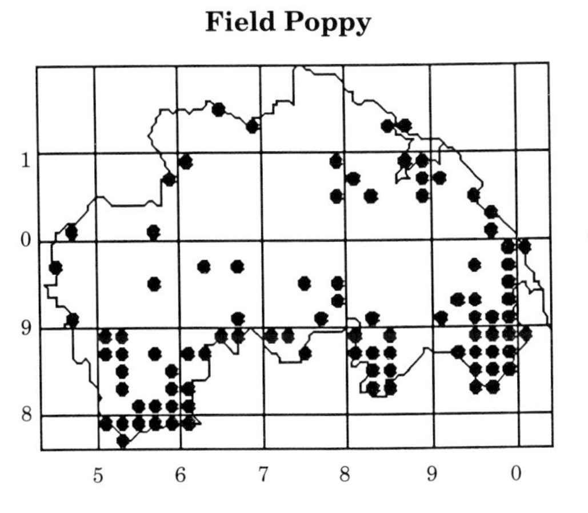

Long-headed Poppy

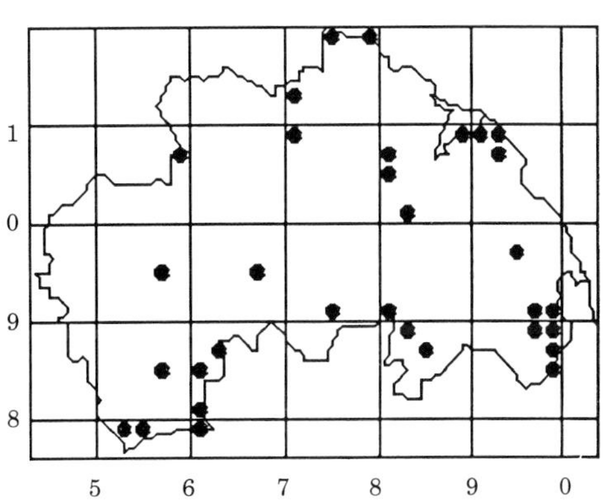

Greater Celandine

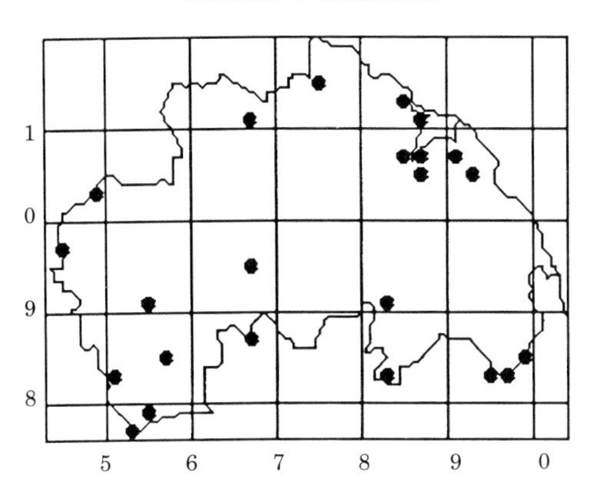

White Climbing Fumitory

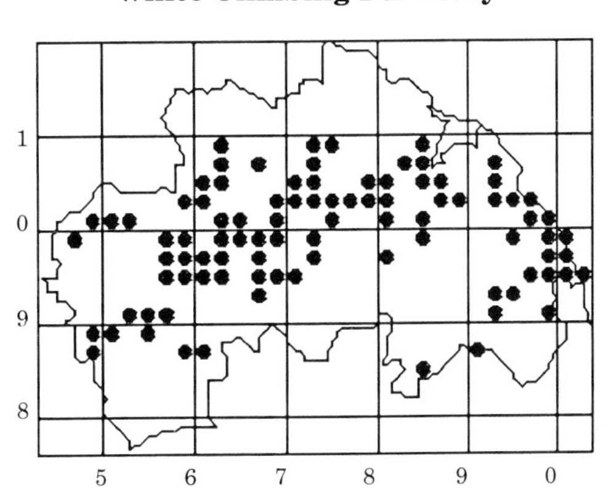

Ramping Fumitory

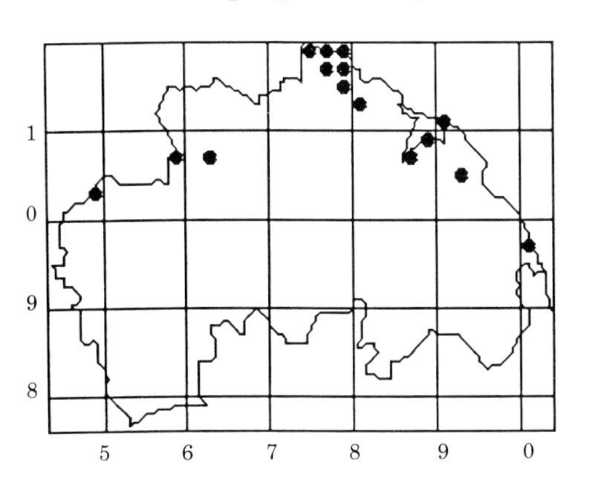

Common Fumitory

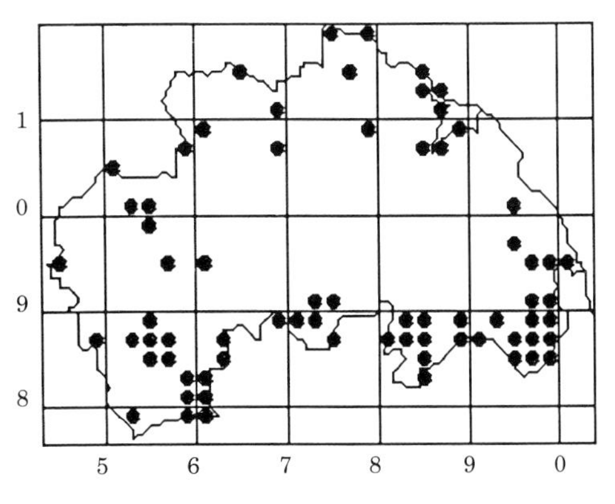

CABBAGE FAMILY
CRUCIFERAE [BRASSICACEAE]

Rape 19
Brassica napus
In recent decades, oil producing varieties of rape have provided a startling yellow springtime mosaic in arable areas and useful early blossom for hive bees. Also grown as a fodder crop, rape plants frequently persist on fieldside or verge.

Turnip 15 M
Brassica rapa
Two subspecies – ssp. *rapa* (turnip) and ssp. *oleifera* (turnip rape) – are grown as winter fodder for stock. Stray plants may establish in nearby ground.

Black Mustard 4
Brassica nigra
Not native in this area and no longer grown as a source of mustard from its seeds but plants occasionally naturalise on verges and ditchsides from rogue seed in other crops.

Wild Cabbage 7 M
Brassica oleracea
Introduced by the Romans and the ancestor of today's vegetable, wild cabbage from the North Yorkshire coast is used by plant breeders to retain natural strains. Grows on cliffs at Khyber Pass, Whitby and at Robin Hood's Bay, Staithes and Boulby.

Charlock 168 M
Sinapis arvensis
Formerly a menace on arable land, especially on calcareous or heavy soils, it is still widespread but largely controlled by herbicides. Usually only a few plants survive in field corners and adjacent disturbed ground.

White Mustard 2
Sinapis alba
Occasionally grown after a corn harvest to provide late sheep feed or mulch. Odd plants survive on nearby verges.

Annual Wall Rocket or **Stinkweed** 3
Diplotaxis muralis
A south European plant believed to have been introduced to Britain from a shipwreck on the Kentish coast about 1770. It has gradually spread north and now appears erratically on waste ground, railside and in gardens around Whitby.

Wild Radish 78 M
Raphanus raphanistrum
A frequent arable weed on neutral to acid soils, usually growing on lighter land. A few plants may establish on verges adjacent to infested fields. The white-flowered form is most frequent, though both yellow and lilac flowers occur. After cultivation, ground at Esklets became white-over with this plant.

Sea Rocket 5 M
Cakile maritima
A driftline plant of sandy and shingle shores, it grows sparingly at Saltwick, Sandsend and Port Mulgrave.

Lesser Swinecress
Coronopus didymus
Found in its typical habitat – a cracked pavement – at Ingleby Greenhow.

Swinecress 16 M
Coronopus squamatus
A flattened insignificant plant characteristic of trampled ground in gateways, stackyards and road edges. It maybe more widespread than records show.

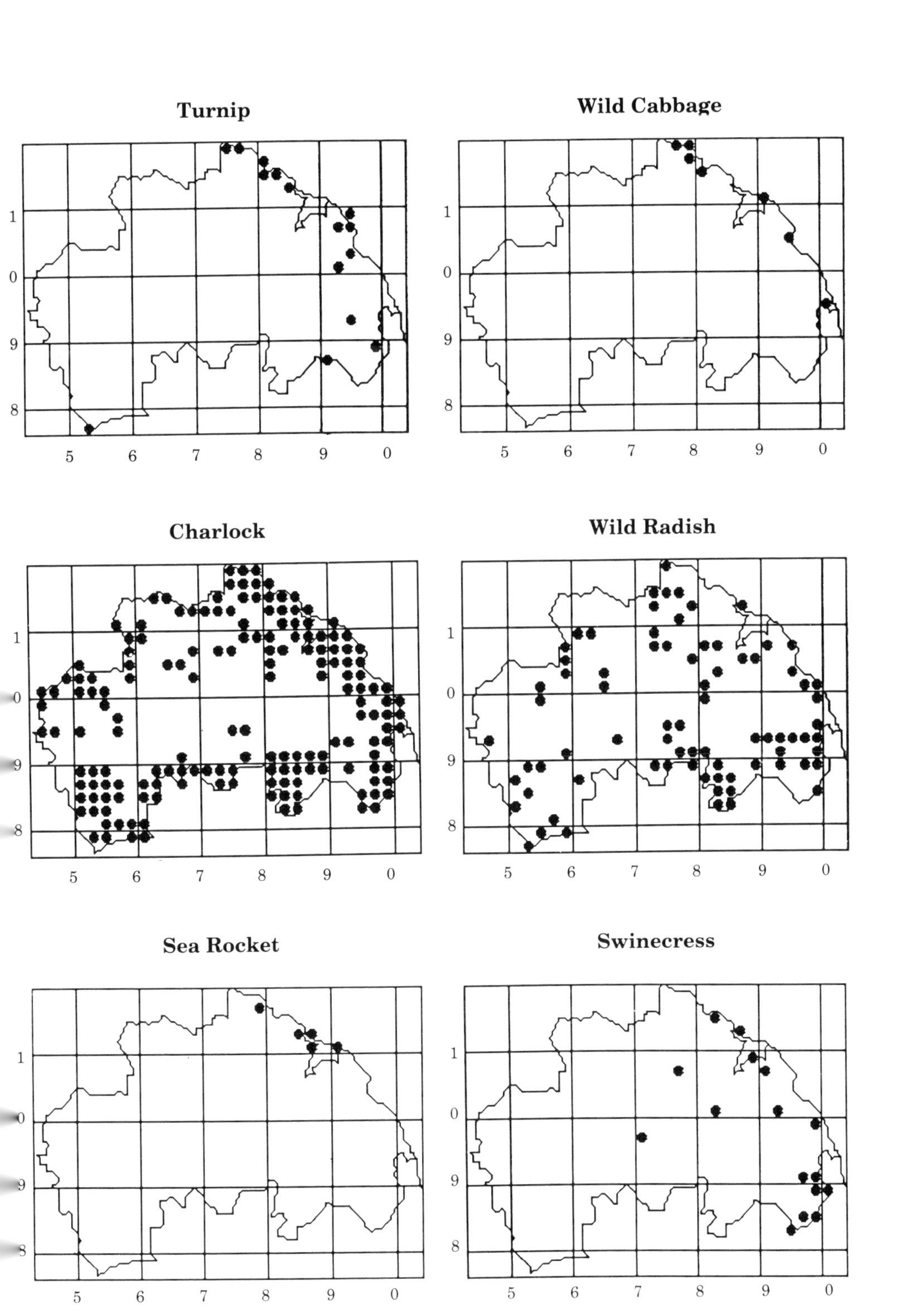
Turnip
Wild Cabbage
Charlock
Wild Radish
Sea Rocket
Swinecress
1
0
9
8
5
6
7
8
9
0

Hoary Pepperwort 4
Cardaria draba [Lepidium draba]
A European plant not known in this country until 1809, it is reputed to have been accidentally introduced to Kent in hay-stuffed mattresses. It has spread north slowly, reaching Yorkshire early this century, and is still rare hereabouts, being recorded only at Ruswarp, Sleights and Sandsend where it is abundant around seafront car parks.

Candytuft
Iberis umbellata
A garden annual which naturalises infrequently from garden throwouts.

Field Pennycress 43 M
Thlaspi arvense
An annual weed of arable land with local distribution, its seed can remain dormant in the ground for decades. It occasionally germinates in quantity but mostly only a few scattered plants appear on field edges or disturbed ground.

Shepherd's Purse 299
Capsella bursa-pastoris
A universal survivor which appears in a range of habitats where ground is subject to disturbance. Its growth forms are equally wide ranging. Absent from the high moors.

Common Scurvy Grass 17 M
Cochlearia officinalis
Abundant in grassland on the boulder clay coastal cliffs where its small white flowers fringe the Cleveland Way. Large clumps thrive on precipitous ledges overhanging the sea.

Danish Scurvy Grass 1
Cochlearia danica
Naturally a seashore species, this dainty pink-flowered plant was found bordering the tarmac of the A19 near Osmotherley – presumably sustained by salt-laden splash from this busy road.

Honesty 21
Lunaria annua
Introduced from southern Europe as a garden plant, it frequently escapes to naturalise on verges and wallsides near habitation.

Spring Whitlow Grass 60 M
Erophila verna
A diminutive winter annual which compensates lack of size by a profusion of plants, its miniature white flowers covering expanses of bare sandy ground, especially on ungrassed verges of the A169. It grows in smaller numbers on walls and rocks but withers away early in the year, leaving no trace of its presence until the following year.

Horse Radish 13 M
Armoracia rusticana
An introduced pot herb once grown in cottage gardens, it is naturalised on roadsides and wasteland. Its prevalence in the Whitby area may indicate a connection with monks of Whitby Abbey.

Cuckoo Flower 333 M
Cardamine pratensis
Common in damp meadows, poorly drained hollows on grazing land, streamsides and ditches. A double-flowered variety grows at Thornton-le-Dale.

Large Bittercress 116 M
Cardamine amara
Frequent along river banks, streamsides with iron deposits and willow/alder carr. It covers large patches of wet peaty bogs in the dales and tolerates quite deep shade.

Field Pennycress

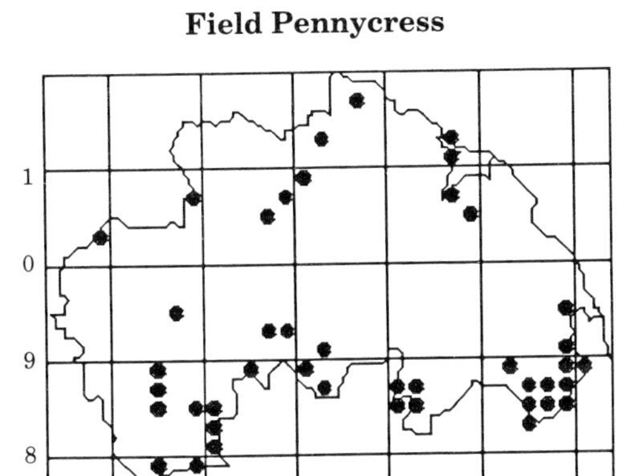

Common Scurvy Grass

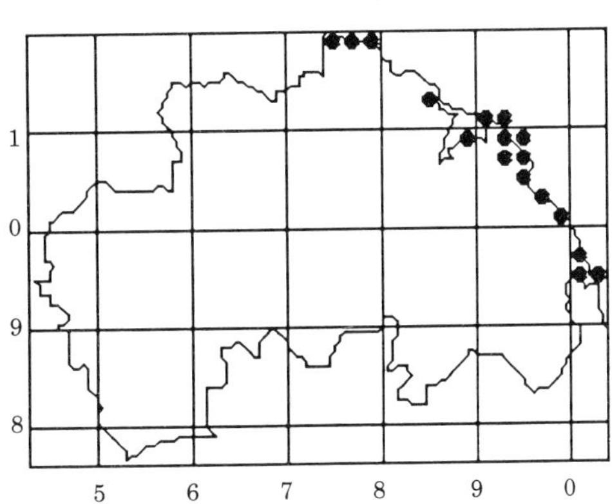

Spring Whitlow Grass

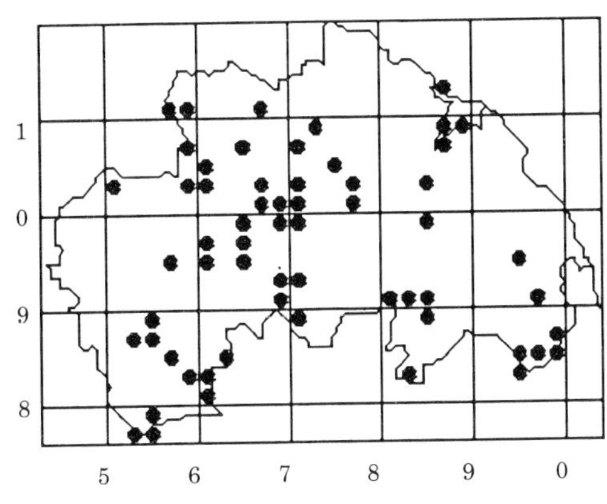

Horse Radish

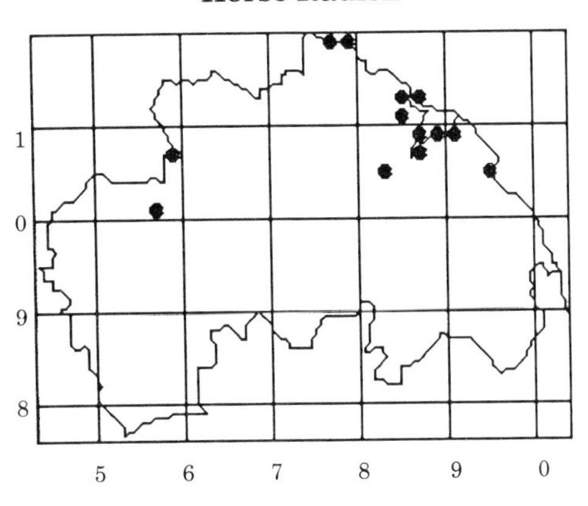

Cuckoo Flower

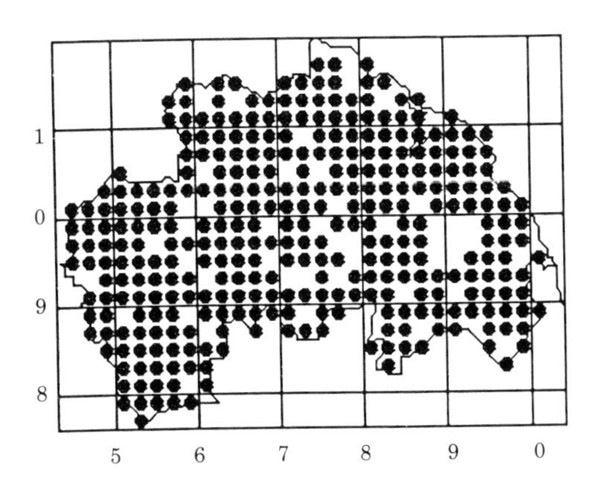

Large Bittercress

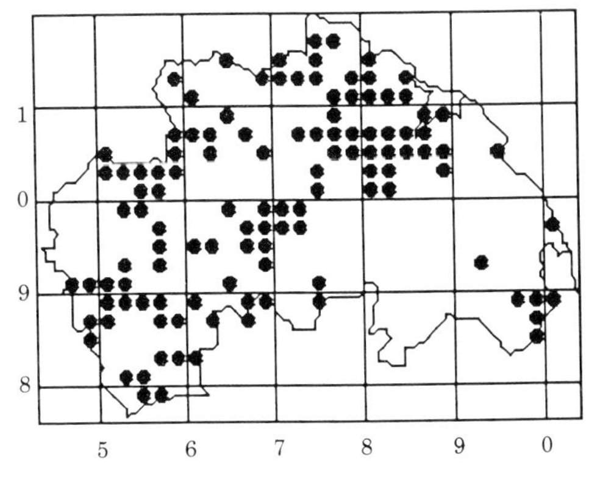

Wood Bittercress 312 M
Cardamine flexuosa
Common in damp ditches, streamsides, wet shady pathways and damp short grass.

Hairy Bittercress 217 M
Cardamine hirsuta
A troublesome garden weed, this plant is difficult to eradicate owing to its prolific seed production. It is also plentiful on wall tops and disturbed ground except where the soil is very acidic.

Greater Cuckoo Flower 1
Cardamine latifolia
[Cardamine raphanifolia]
A Pyrenean plant grown in gardens. It has naturalised close to the Esk between Limber Hill and Lealholm.

Intermediate Yellow Rocket 1
Barbarea intermedia
Found only once, on the riverside at Glaisdale.

Wintercress 50 M
Barbarea vulgaris
Usually only a handful of plants grow in any one location. It appears amongst rank vegetation on damp fertile verges and ditchsides.

Hairy Rockcress 21 M
Arabis hirsuta
Disused limestone quarries, dry walls and sandy paths provide the few habitats where this has been found. Abundant in Kepwick churchyard.

Green Watercress 93 M
Nasturtium officinale
[Rorippa nasturtium-aquaticum]
Common and prolific in clean moving water but too easily confused with the rather similar poisonous water parsnip to pick for a salad.

One-rowed Watercress 2
Nasturtium microphyllum
[Rorippa microphylla]
Known to occur in Forge Valley and Staindale, it is likely to be much under-recorded due to identification problems and hybridisation with green watercress.

Great Yellowcress 2
Rorippa amphibia
Almost confined to the southern half of Britain, this marsh plant has been found in wetland only in Forge Valley and Oldstead.

Marsh Yellowcress 3
Rorippa palustris
Another lowland marsh plant rare in this area and found only at East Ayton and in Eskdale.

Dame's Violet 71 M
Hesperis matronalis
A fragrant garden plant which readily takes to the wild, it has naturalised on sheltered banks in lower Eskdale and Derwent valley, with random populations on roadsides near habitation.

Treacle Mustard 2
Erysimum cheiranthoides
This continental alien is becoming more frequent in southern Britain and made its first known local appearance in a Harwood Dale field in 1989. It may have been introduced with a grass/clover seed mix. It has since been recorded at Dock End, Whitby.

Wallflower 3
Cheiranthus cheiri [Erysimum cheiri]
Plants have been found clinging to rock-faces at Lythe bank and Staithes and on crumbling walls of Danby Castle.

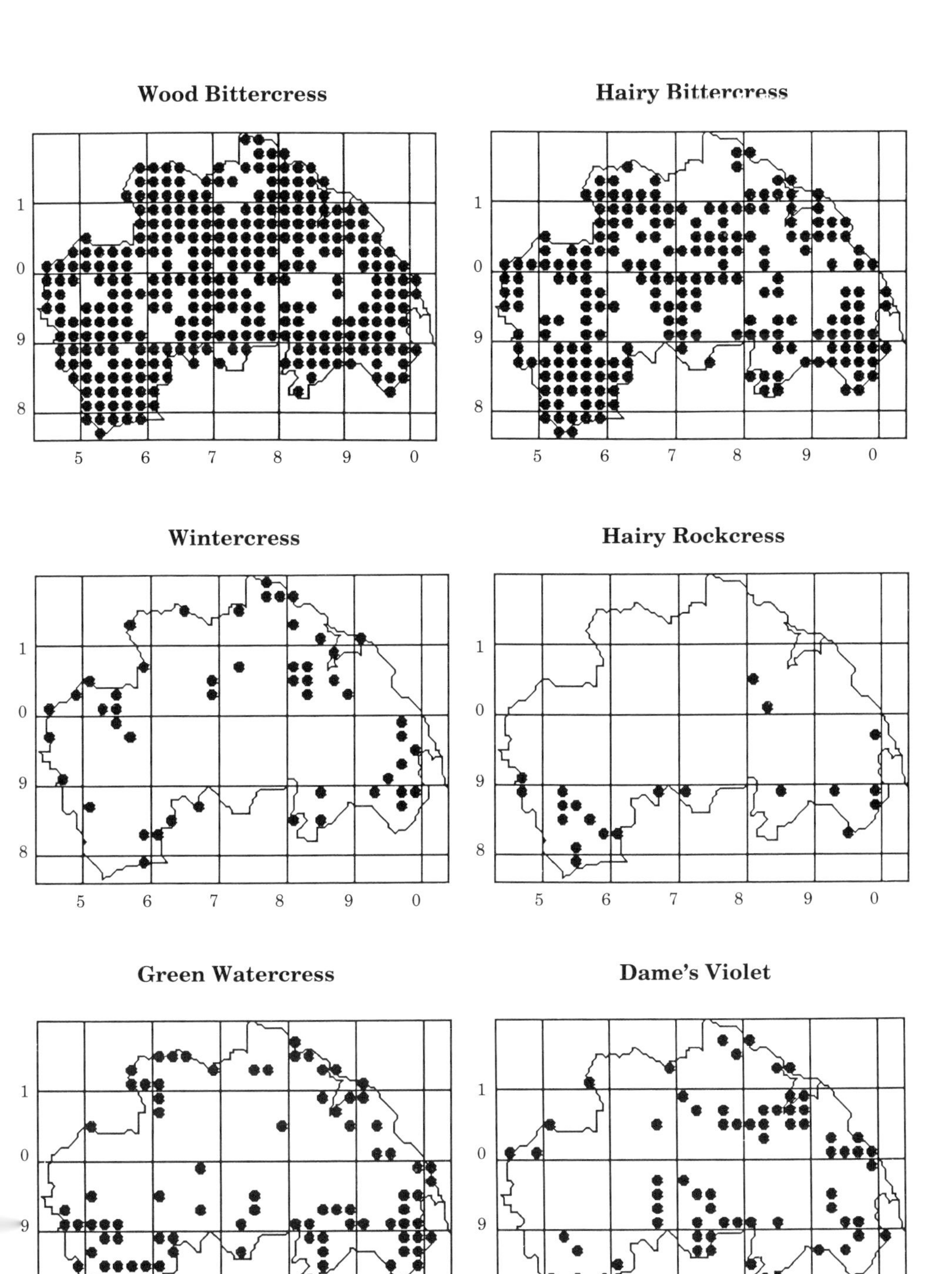

Wood Bittercress
Hairy Bittercress
Wintercress
Hairy Rockcress
Green Watercress
Dame's Violet
1
0
9
8
5
6
7
8
9
0

Hedge Garlic or
Jack by the Hedge 185 M
Alliaria petiolata
Once used as a culinary herb, it grows frequently near habitation on grassy roadside banks, at the base of walls and fences and along scrubby woodland edges. Usually on nutrient rich soils on lower land.

Hedge Mustard 75 M
Sisymbrium officinale
Grows quite commonly on lowland or coastal verges and wasteland.

Eastern Rocket 3
Sisymbrium orientale
An alien plant found growing on the walls of Byland Abbey, scattered on a farm track at Stainsacre and on the cliffs between Whitby and Saltwick.

Thale Cress 19 M
Arabidopsis thaliana
Found in quantity on dry gravelly ballast alongside the Esk Valley railway. Small populations also occur infrequently on drystone walls, gritty paths and in sandy fields.

Gold of Pleasure 1
Camelina sativa
A transient weed of corn and flax fields, it has been recorded once from rogue seed.

Flixweed 1
Descurainia sophia
Formerly a common arable weed on light land but effectively eliminated by herbicides. Recorded once in Harwood Dale.

Awlwort
Subularia aquatica
A submerged plant twice recorded in Arden Lake during the 1980s but recent searches failed to locate it. These searches coincided with long hot summers and were carried out from the bankside. It could be that the plant had retreated to cooler deeper waters in the centre of the lake. It is a plant of the wetter western highlands of Britain and unknown elsewhere in this area.

MIGNONETTE FAMILY
RESEDACEAE

Weld 31 M
Reseda luteola
Nowhere plentiful but scattered plants are widespread in calcareous soils on waste land, quarries, track edges and scrub in sheltered pockets.

Wild Mignonette 19 M
Reseda lutea
Uncommon on disturbed ground, old quarries, rough grazing and wasteland. Found on Cliff rigg, at Battersby Junction, in Grosmont car park and on the disused Scarborough to Whitby rail track.

White Mignonette 1
Reseda alba
An alien on the cliffs at Upgang, this plant may have been brought in by a ship entering Whitby Harbour.

VIOLET FAMILY
VIOLACEAE

Sweet Violet 80 M
Viola odorata
Grows in shady hedgebanks and woodland glades where both white and mauve-flowered plants create colourful and fragrant patches on alkaline soils. It is likely that some originated from garden throw-outs.

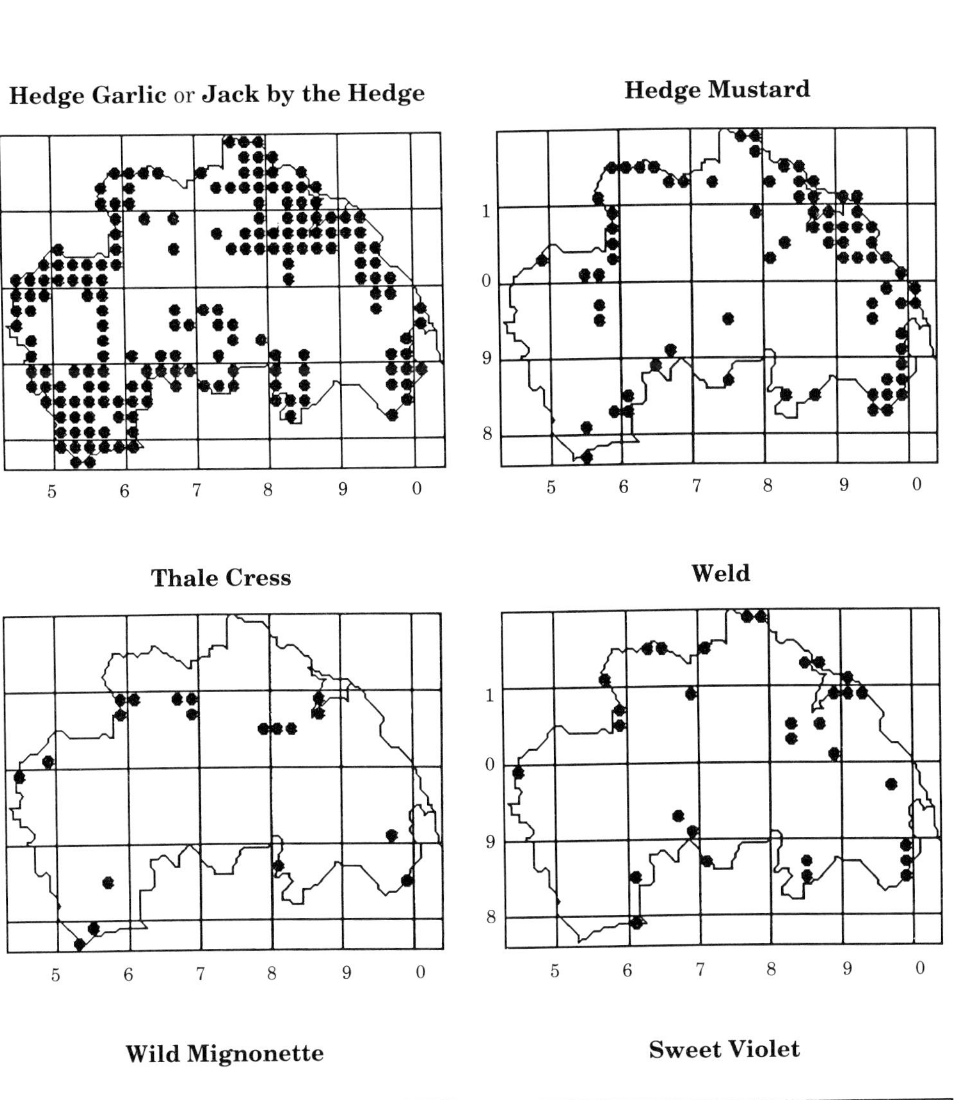
Hedge Garlic or Jack by the Hedge
Hedge Mustard
Thale Cress
Weld
1
0
9
8
5
6
7
8
9
0

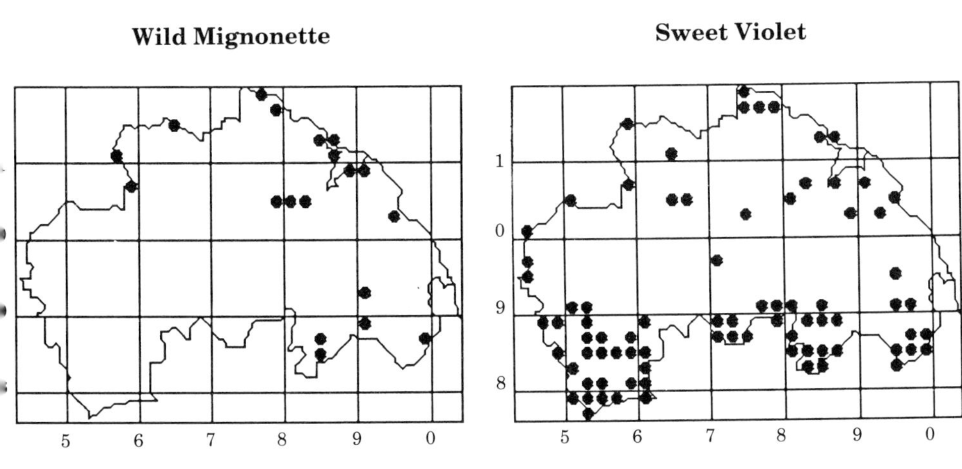
Wild Mignonette
Sweet Violet
1
0
9
8
5
6
7
8
9
0

Hairy Violet 40 M
Viola hirta
An infrequent plant in this area, it grows in short calcareous grassland, especially in Yedmandale and southern valleys.

Common or **Dog Violet** 356
Viola riviniana
The commonest violet of this area, it occurs in a wide range of habitats – forest rides, deciduous woodland, cliffs, churchyards and gardens. In sheep grazed turf it survives vegetatively in miniature form.

Pale Wood Violet 88 M
Viola riechenbachiana
Grows in light shade of long established woods and hedgerows, usually on alkaline soils. In flower before common violet, with which it often grows, though usually in smaller numbers. Hybrids between the two above species are frequent.

Marsh Violet 215 M
Viola palustris
These shy pale mauve flowers are frequent in alder carr undergrowth, acid bogs and moorland flushes but they are often hidden by taller vegetation.

Wild Pansy 19
Viola tricolor
This once common violet has been seen infrequently during the recent survey. It has usually been found in corn stubble and is plentiful only around Raisdale and Ugthorpe. Apparently unable to survive modern farming methods, it has become rare nationally as well as locally.

Field Pansy or **Heartsease** 155 M
Viola arvensis
More resistant to herbicides than wild pansy, this species is still common in arable fields and gardens, especially on lighter soils. Flower colour varies from yellow to purple and two-tone gradations.

MILKWORT FAMILY
POLYGALACEAE

Common Milkwort 153 M
Polygala vulgaris
A plant of less acid pasture and grassy banksides. Flower colours range from white through pink and mauve to deep purple.

Heath Milkwort 203 M
Polygala serpyllifolia
More widespread than the above species, it is a common component of bent/fescue grassland in the dales.

ST JOHN'S WORT FAMILY
HYPERICACEAE [CLUSIACEAE]

Tutsan 10
Hypericum androsaemum
Possibly native in some older woods such as Roxby, Cropton, Easington and Cockmill but most likely to have been planted in Hackness and Duncombe Park.

Common St John's Wort 111
Hypericum perforatum
Grows in abundance in gravelly rail ballast and is widespread on non-acid grassland, roadside verges, woodland edges and field banks. It is most prolific on lower land.

Hairy Violet

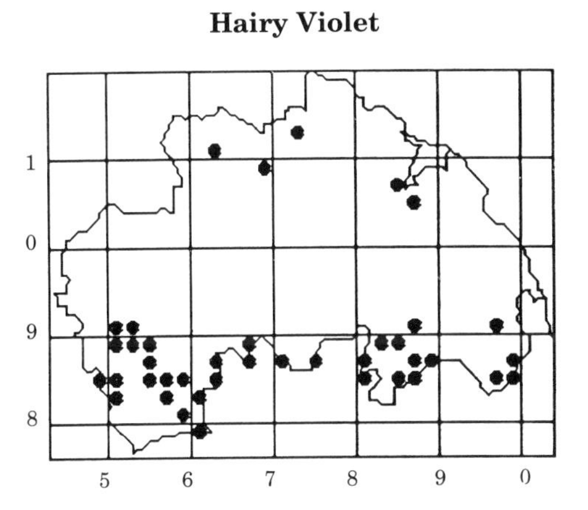

Pale Wood Violet

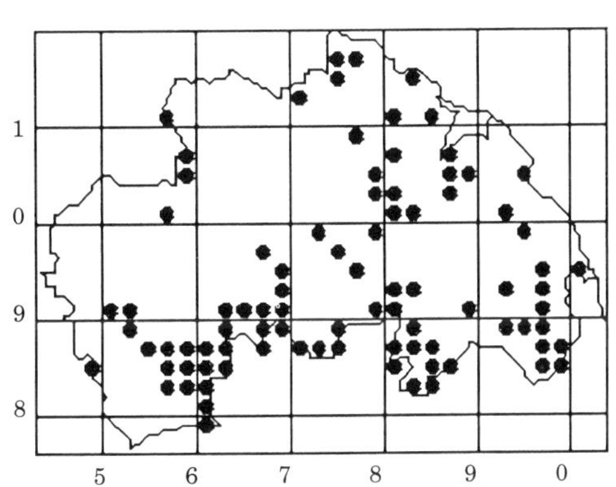

Marsh Violet

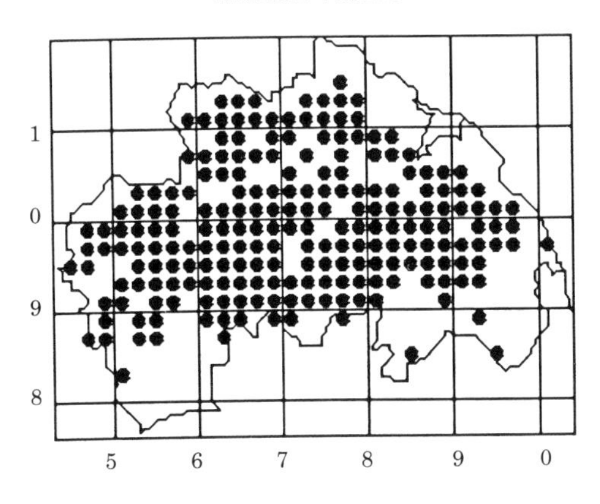

Field Pansy or Heartsease

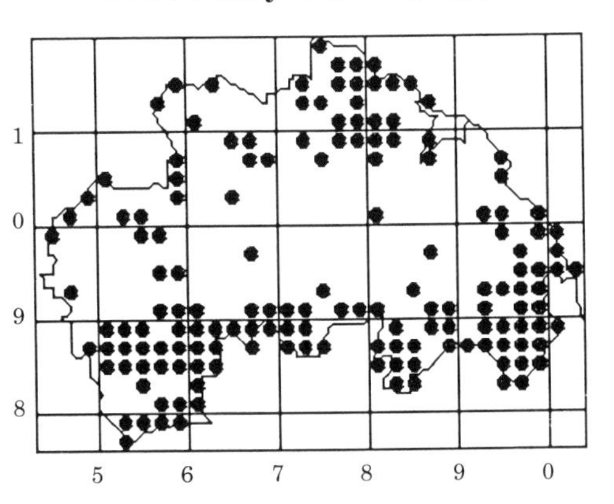

Common Milkwort

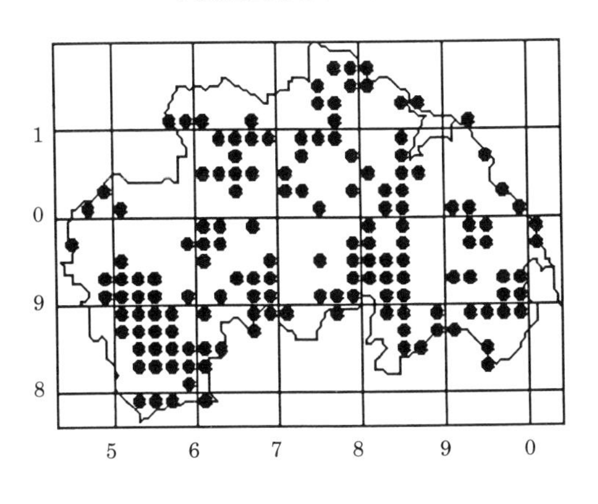

Heath Milkwort

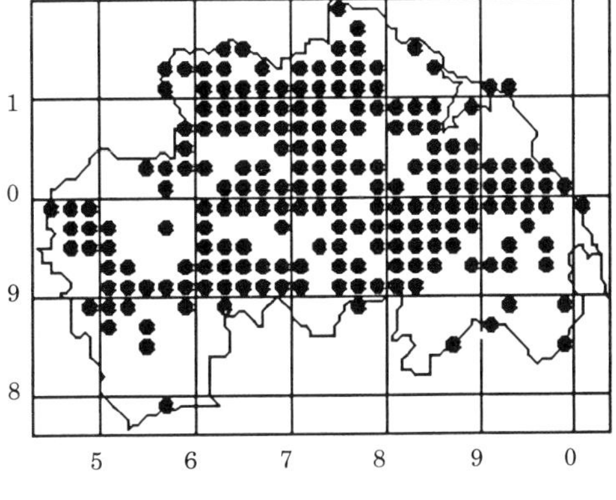

Imperforate St John's Wort
Hypericum maculatum
Quite an unusual plant in this area. It prefers wet heavy soils and has been recorded at Yoadwath, on woodland fringes in Newtondale and on a roadside verge near Faceby Lane.

Square-stemmed St John's Wort 162 M
Hypericum tetrapterum
The clear yellow flowers of this species brighten many a dark ditch in midsummer. Grows widely in most wet grassy situations.

Trailing St John's Wort 50 M
Hypericum humifusum
This often shy plant flourishes on sunny banks of the Esk Valley railway where large showy clusters have little competition on desiccated cindery ground. Its other main habitat is on the warmer slopes of forest rides.

Slender St John's Wort 219 M
Hypericum pulchrum
Its alternative name "Beautiful St John's Wort" is amply justified where it enlivens much of the acid grassland on moorland edge, forest rides and waysides.

Hairy St John's Wort 116 M
Hypericum hirsutum
Frequent in moist rough grassland, woodland glades and scrub on base-rich soils. Forge Valley, lower Ryedale and lower Eskdale.

Mountain St John's Wort 7
Hypericum montanum
An uncommon plant throughout Britain, this pale-flowered St John's Wort has been found infrequently in sandy or calcareous soil on hedgebanks, tracks and rocky outcrops. Wass quarry, Newbridge and Tranmire.

Marsh St John's Wort 6
Hypericum elodes
Forms a floating mat in shallow slow-moving acid water on the moors. Drainage and afforestation have reduced its remaining habitats to six known locations at Scarth Wood Moor, Waupley Moor, Hob Hole, Redman Plain, Troutsdale and Commondale.

ROCKROSE FAMILY
CISTACEAE

Common Rockrose 60 M
Helianthemum nummularium
Frequent on short-grazed calcareous turf, scrub, scree and old quarries, especially on south-facing slopes of the steep upper Rye valleys.

PINK FAMILY
CARYOPHYLLACEAE

Red Campion 279
Silene dioica
Widespread throughout except on very acid soils, the cheerful red flowers of this species brighten many road, rail and forest verges, woodland clearings, hedgebanks and coastal cliffs, from spring until autumnal frosts.

White Campion 41 M
Silene alba [Silene latifolia]
Infrequent on calcareous soils in arable fields, road verges and gateways.

Silene alba x *dioica*
This usually pink-flowered hybrid frequently occurs in the proximity of both parents.

Bladder Campion 40
Silene vulgaris
Small clumps may be found on calcareous soils on sheltered field edges and disturbed wasteland and road verges.

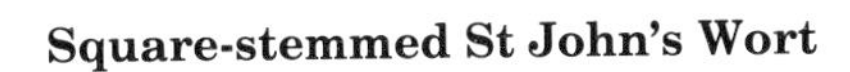

Square-stemmed St John's Wort

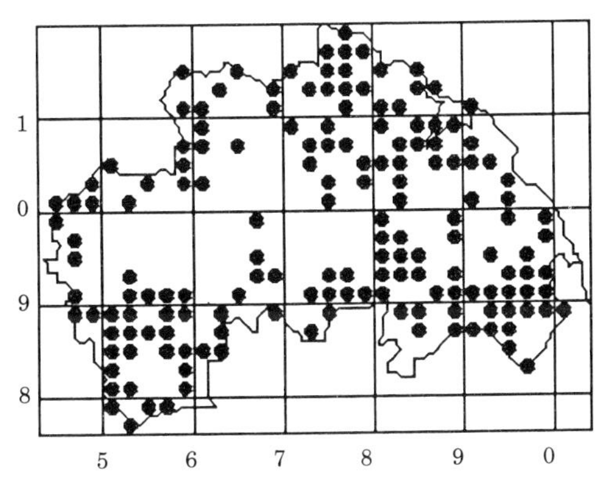

Trailing St John's Wort

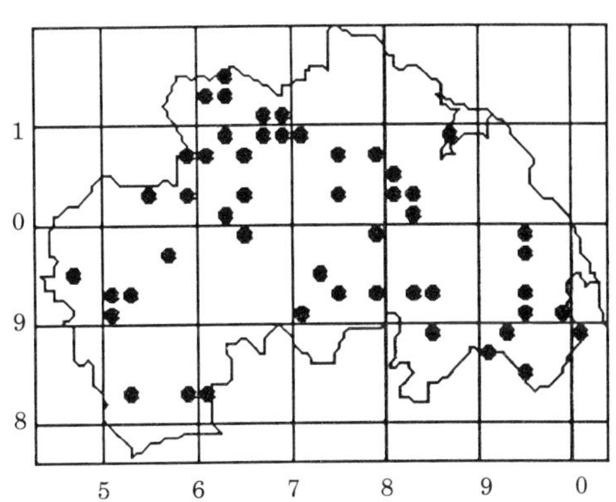

Slender St John's Wort

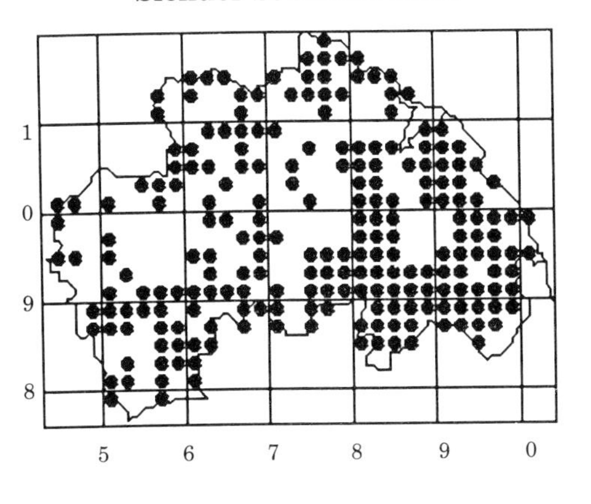

Hairy St John's Wort

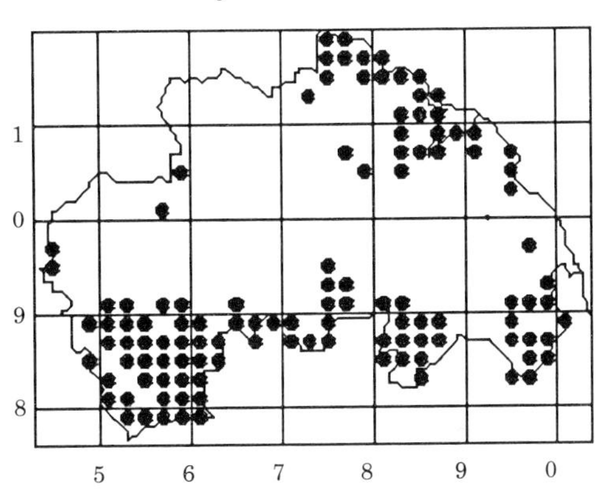

Common Rockrose

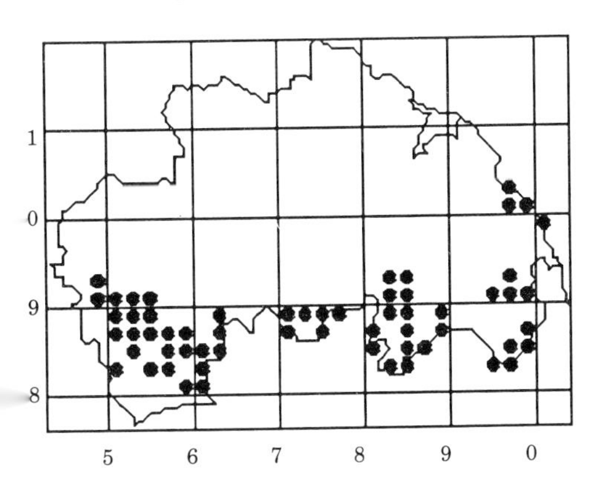

White Campion

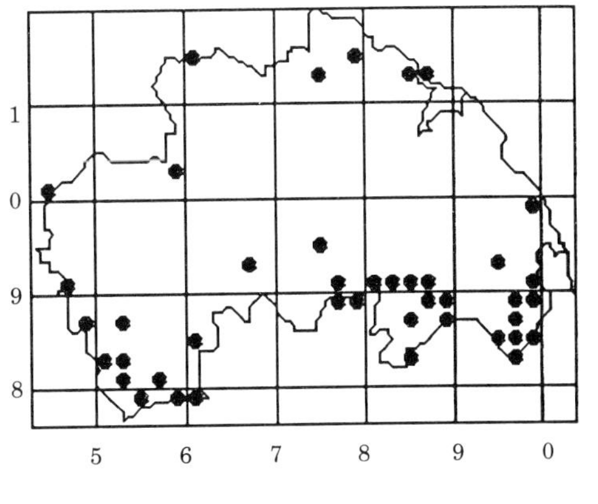

Night-flowering Catchfly 8
Silene noctiflora
A weed of arable land, this species occurs on light, sandy, calcareous soils. Formerly widespread, it is now known in only a few locations in less intensively farmed fields near Thornton-le-Dale, Raincliffe, Sawdon, Suffield and Murton. It is now listed as a nationally scarce plant of cultivated ground.

Ragged Robin 208 M
Lychnis flos-cuculi
This bright pink-flowered inhabitant of wet nutrient-poor grassland provides a splash of colour in many a wayside ditch and marsh on mineral or peaty soils.

Field Mouse-ear 18 M
Cerastium arvense
Occurs rarely in this area on calcareous hedgebanks and field edges. It has also been found in Allerston Forest alongside a track made from limestone quarry waste.

Common Mouse-ear 393
Cerastium fontanum
It is doubtful if any permanent grassland could be found without this plant entwined in the sward. A real survivor, it adopts a rosette growth form in mown lawns and sheep grazed moorland turf.

Sticky Mouse-ear 219 M
Cerastium glomeratum
Its yellow-green leaves are prominent in grass and arable fields on drier, lighter soils. Quite persistent where established, it reappears in reseeded pastures.

Sea Mouse-ear 3
Cerastium diffusum
A tiny winter annual, possibly much overlooked. It has been found in sandy grassland along the coast from Upgang to Saltwick.

Little Mouse-ear 8 M
Cerastium semidecandrum
Another inconspicuous ground-hugging plant, it flowers and seeds in winter. Found on light sandy soils at Sandsend, Ruswarp Batts, Newholm Beck and Cliff Rigg quarry.

Snow in Summer
Cerastium tomentosum
A common garden plant occasionally naturalised on road verges such as Levisham Bank.

Wood Stitchwort 45 M
Stellaria nemorum
A northern plant in Britain, its local distribution is concentrated along the Rivers Seph and Esk. It grows in plenty on the banks of these two rivers and some of their feeder streams and appears less frequently alongside the Hodge Beck, River Seven and other streams.

Chickweed 368
Stellaria media
One of the few plants which may have benefited from modern farming techniques, it flourishes where fertiliser run-off occurs. Very common on moist grassland, pathsides, muddy areas, farm tracks and in gardens.

Greater Stitchwort 353 M
Stellaria holostea
One of the commonest roadside plants, it has a long flowering season and an ability to thrive on all but very acidic soils. Also plentiful in wood and forest clearings, field borders and plantation rides.

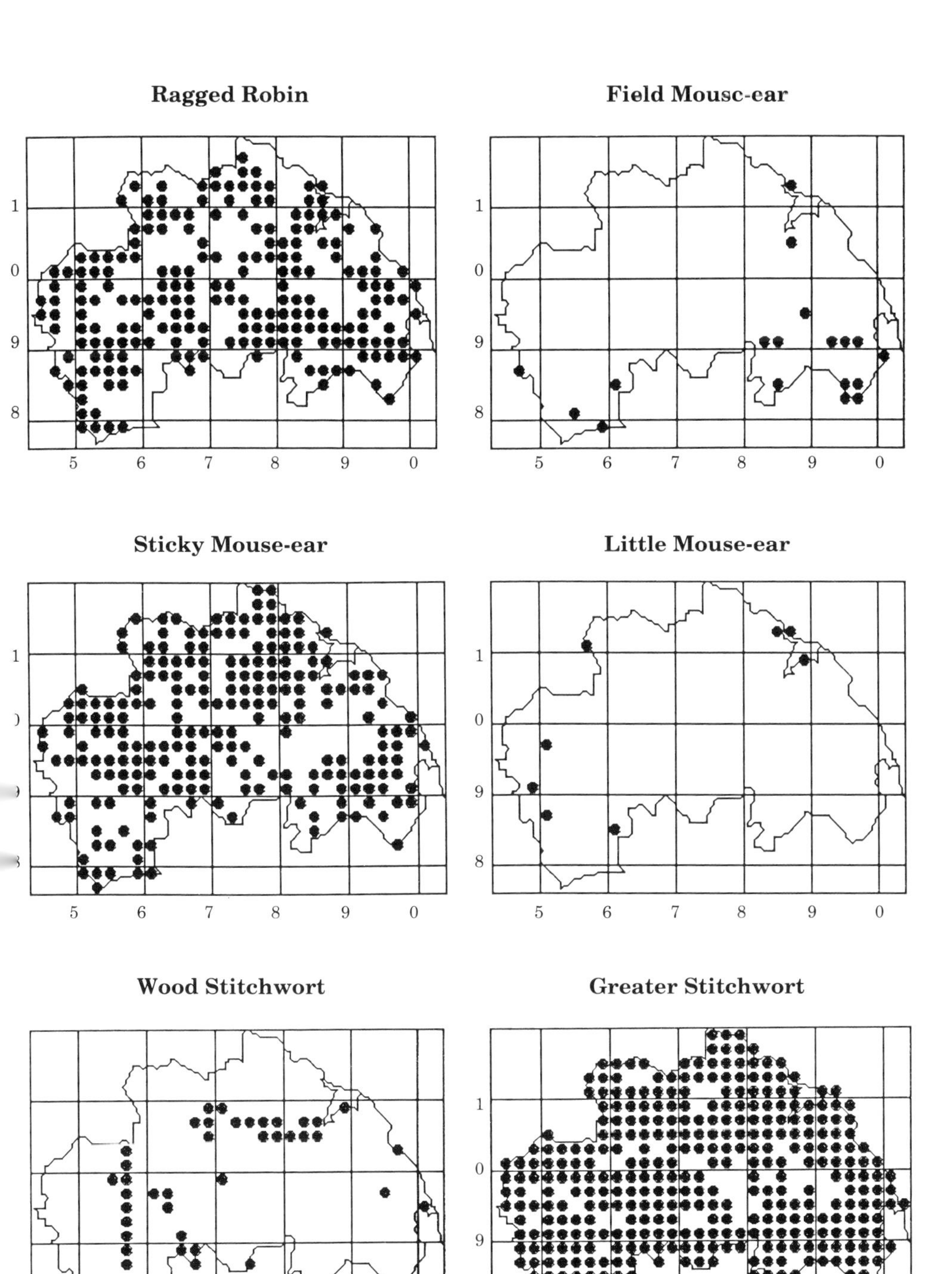

Ragged Robin
Field Mousc-ear
Sticky Mouse-ear
Little Mouse-ear
Wood Stitchwort
Greater Stitchwort

Marsh Stitchwort 5
Stellaria palustris
A rare plant of marsh and fen, it was recorded only at Throxenby Mere, Scaling Dam, Kepwick Lake, Great Fryupdale and Newtondale. It is difficult to find owing to its preference for growing in standing water or sinking mud. The Throxenby plants, like those at Hornsea Mere, are not glaucous, contrary to normal colouration.

Lesser Stitchwort 311
Stellaria graminea
In mid-summer and onwards these starry white flowers are sprinkled over most undisturbed old grassy areas such as churchyards, fringes of playing fields, hedgebanks and verges.

Bog Stitchwort 310 M
Stellaria alsine [Stellaria uliginosa]
Plentiful in upland flushes and bogs, streamsides, marshy grassland and carr woodlands, this plant grows on acid soils where it hides amongst rushes and sedges.

Greater Chickweed 9 M
Stellaria neglecta
Mainly a plant of southern Britain, this delicate chickweed grows infrequently in undisturbed wooded riverbanks at Dalehouse, Osmotherley and Oakdale, and is scattered along the Esk riverside from Castleton to Ruswarp.

Lesser Chickweed 1
Stellaria pallida
A rare member of the chickweed group, it has been recorded once, near Kepwick.

Fringed Pearlwort 24
Sagina apetala
Common on bare sandy ground, in pathways and on walls.

Procumbent Pearlwort 303
Sagina procumbens
Very common in cracks and joints of paving and pathways. Also on trampled turf, lawns and walls.

Knotted Pearlwort 62 M
Sagina nodosa
Very much a plant of forest rides and moor road edge, its single white flowers appear unexpectedly in late summer.

Sea Sandwort 3
Honkenya peploides
Occasionally found on sandy mud at the mouths of Sandsend and East Row Becks and at Runswick Bay.

Three-nerved Sandwort 106 M
Moehringia trinervia
A delicate small-flowered annual often to be found in the leaf litter of conifer plantations and ancient woodland, especially after felling and where filtered light penetrates.

Thyme-leaved Sandwort 94 M
Arenaria serpyllifolia
Grows on bare sand in car parks and fieldside, also on walls and paths. Avoids high exposed ground.

Slender Thyme-leaved Sandwort 3
Arenaria leptoclados
A rare plant in this locality, it was found on disturbed sandy ground at Battersby Junction, by Westworth reservoir and in fine railway ballast.

Corn Spurrey 140 M
Spergula arvensis
An annual weed, it is still widespread on sandy or lighter soils in arable fields and reseeded grassland, sometimes present in large populations.

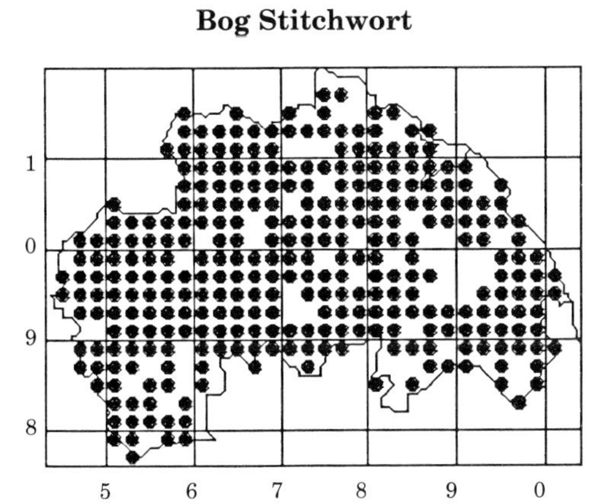

Bog Stitchwort

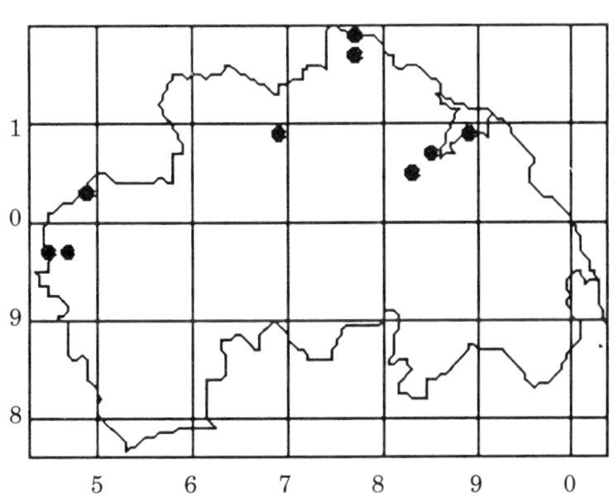

Greater Chickweed

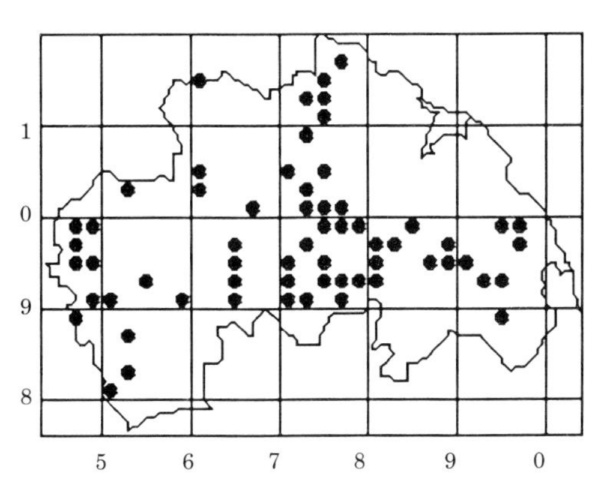

Knotted Pearlwort

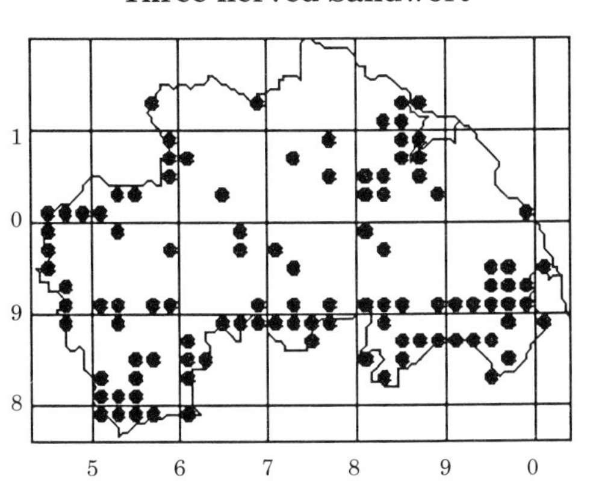

Three-nerved Sandwort

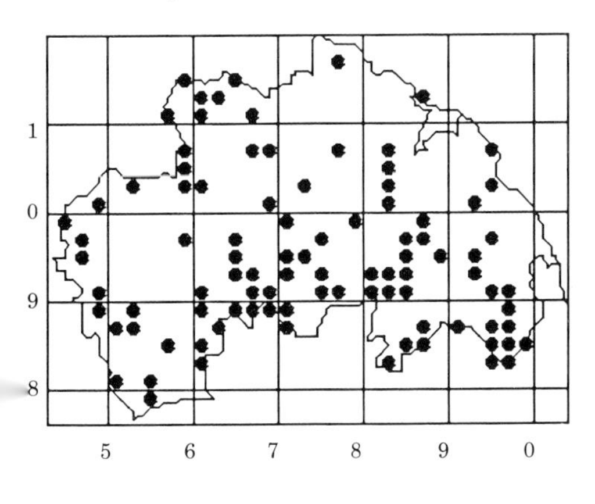

Thyme-leaved Sandwort

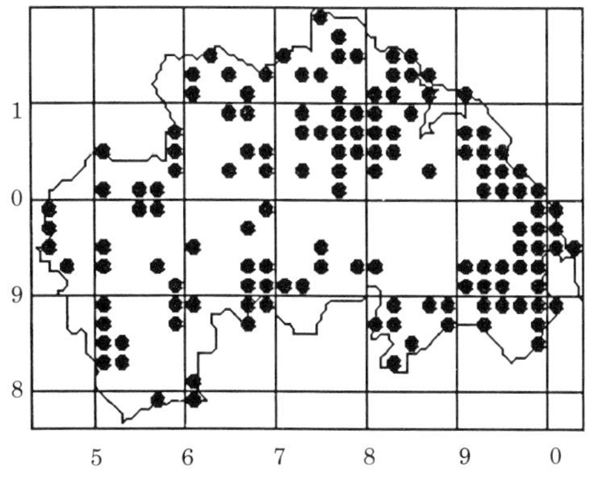

Corn Spurrey

Sand Spurrey 8 M
Spergularia rubra
Appears from time to time on sandy rides in Langdale and Dalby Forests. It was possibly introduced with road-making material but is now naturalised in several locations.

Lesser Sea Spurrey 18 M
Spergularia marina
A saltmarsh plant, it is found on tidal mudbanks between Ruswarp and Whitby. It has spread inland to the splash zone of frequently salted roads, on the A171 near Moorsholm, on the A169 from Goathland to Sleights and on grazed verges of Blakey Rigg. It also occurs on the shores of Scaling Dam.

Greater Sea Spurrey 1
Spergularia media
Occurs in tidal mud at Ruswarp.

PURSLANE FAMILY
PORTULACACEAE

Blinks 132 M
Montia fontana
Its lush green prostrate vegetation sprawls over shallow pools, muddy tracks, damp grassland and spring seepage on upland acid soils, although its minuscule flowers are rarely seen.

Pink Purslane 39 M
Montia sibirica [Claytonia sibirica]
Introduced as a garden plant from North America in the 18th century, it escaped to the wild and is naturalised in many locations in damp woodland, riverside and shady verges. Turkey Carpet, Bransdale Church vicinity, banks of the Rivers Esk and Seven, and Lastingham, Danby and Hodge Becks.

AMARANTH FAMILY
AMARANTHACEAE

Pigweed 2
Amaranthus retroflexus
An alien from tropical America, it occurred recently in fields at Mowthorpe and Harwood Dale. Likely to have been introduced with seed.

GOOSEFOOT FAMILY
CHENOPODIACEAE

Good King Henry 9 M
Chenopodium bonus-henricus
Originally introduced as a culinary herb, it survives on a few roadsides near villages, usually on nitrogen-rich soil. Modern verge management is thought to have reduced its distribution.

Fat Hen 264
Chenopodium album
Common on arable fields and almost any disturbed land in the vicinity of farms. Grit heaps and roadside splash zones carry large populations.

Red Goosefoot 31 M
Chenopodium rubrum
Occurs in plenty wherever farmyard manure is left standing in fields and stackyards but has declined where this practice has diminished.

Sea Beet 3
Beta vulgaris
Single plants have been found scattered along the strandline on Hayburn Wyke and Sandsend shores.

Shore Orache 3
Atriplex littoralis
Normally restricted to saltmarsh, it occurs inland beside the A174 at Boulby

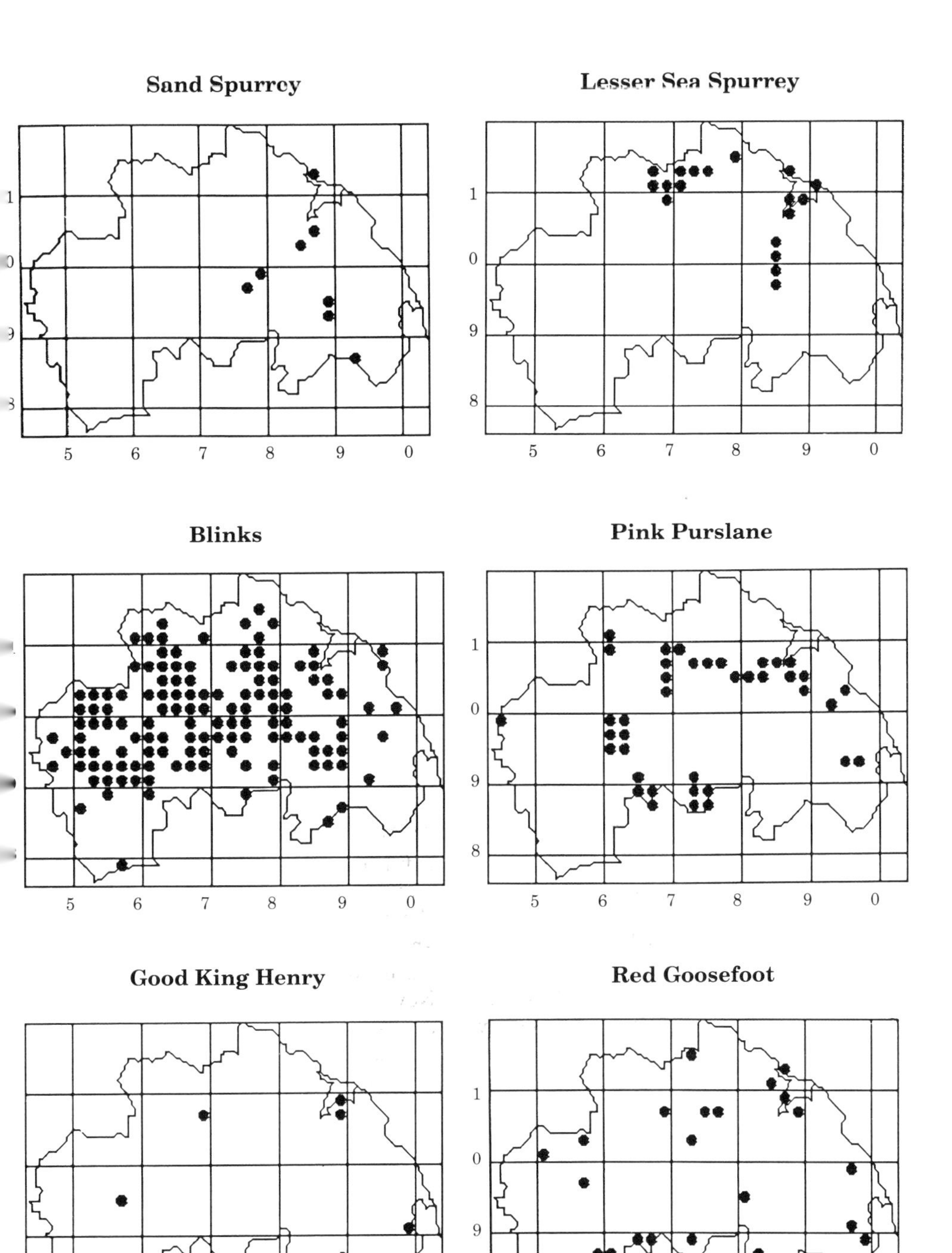
Sand Spurrey
Lesser Sea Spurrey
Blinks
Pink Purslane
Good King Henry
Red Goosefoot
1
0
9
8
5
6
7
8
9
0

and the A171 at Waupley Moor, alongside roads subject to heavy winter salt/sand gritting. It also occurs in its more usual coastal habitat such as at Runswick Bay.

Common Orache 150 M
Atriplex patula
Widespread on disturbed soils at roadsides and rubbish heaps and a common weed of gardens and arable fields on lower land.

Hastate Orache 35 M
Atriplex prostrata
Usually a plant of upper saltmarsh, it occurs within the sea spray zone on coastal cliffs and has been found inland on salty roadside grit heaps.

Frosted Orache 3
Atriplex laciniata
Found infrequently amongst decaying strandline vegetation in Runswick Bay and Stoupe Beck.

LIME FAMILY
TILIACEAE

Large-leaved Lime 15
Tilia platyphyllos
Isolated trees, often large, old and apparently coppiced specimens, grow in ancient woodland in Ryedale gills, Hayburn Wyke, Skiplam, Forge Valley and a few other undisturbed woods. There is need for further study of mature trees recorded as *T. platyphyllos* – their origin (planted or natural) is uncertain.

Small-leaved Lime 39 M
Tilia cordata
Small groups or single trees inhabit most ancient woodland in the southern valleys. Further north, they may be found in the extensive woods of Glaisdale, Mulgrave, Hayburn Wyke, Ramsdale and Boggle Hole. Whilst all the trees examined display most characteristics of *Tilia cordata*, they also indicate varying degrees of hybridisation with *T. platyphyllos*. Those on Castle Hill, Rievaulx, are regarded as native small-leaved lime.

Common Lime 73 M
Tilia x *vulgaris*
(T. cordata x *platyphyllos)*
This is the tree now widely planted on roadsides and in mixed plantations. The imposing avenue along Eastgate in Pickering has to be kept in check by pruning but a fine mature specimen may be seen at Wass. Much loved by bee-keepers, lime trees are viewed with less enthusiasm by those who park cars nearby when in flower.

MALLOW FAMILY
MALVACEAE

Musk Mallow 12 M
Malva moschata
A fine colony, with flowers ranging from white to deep mauve, is established on the old rail cutting at Wykeham. Other smaller populations are found in Ampleforth, Greenhow, Scugdale, Newtondale and Harwood Dale. Some of these may have originated as garden outcasts, but the plants which adorn the old moat of Helmsley Castle are likely to be of natural origin.

Common Mallow 50 M
Malva sylvestris
Grows quite prolifically near the coast where it flourishes on most uncultivated corners. Inland it is confined to a few rough grassy banks and verges.

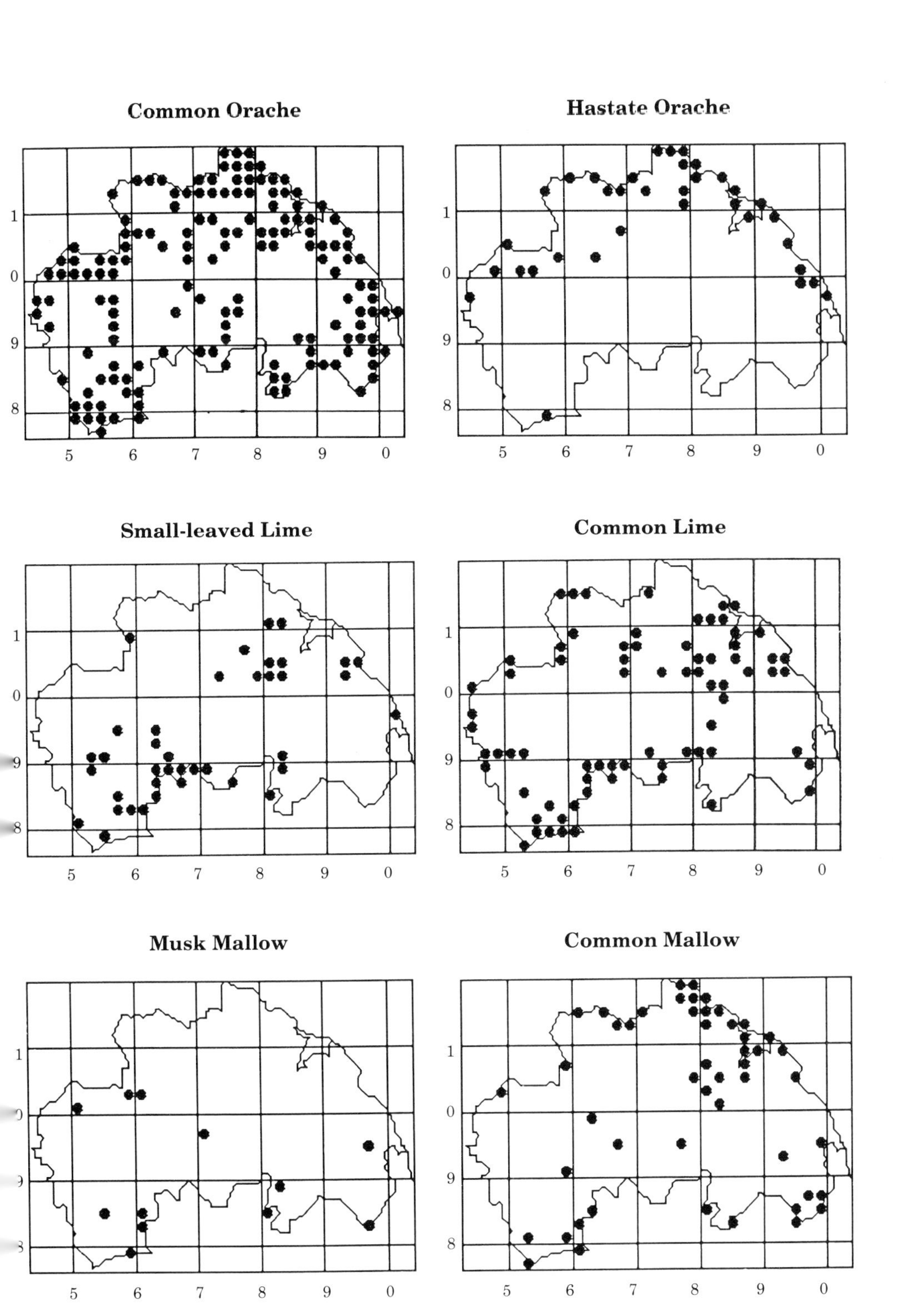
Common Orache
Hastate Orache
Small-leaved Lime
Common Lime
Musk Mallow
Common Mallow
1
0
9
8
5
6
7
8
9
0

Dwarf Mallow 1
Malva neglecta
Found only once, on a stony bank at Newbridge.

FLAX FAMILY
LINACEAE

Fairy Flax 285 M
Linum catharticum
Widespread on grazed turf, both on limestone and upland heath, avoiding only the most acid soil. It frequents permanent pasture, disused quarries and free-draining tracksides.

Cultivated Flax
Linum usitatissimum
Fields of attractive blue-flowered linseed crops have become more frequent locally in recent years and increasingly stray plants are becoming established on adjacent verges, field edges and gateways.

GERANIUM FAMILY
GERANIACEAE

Meadow Cranesbill 141 M
Geranium pratense
A colourful roadside verge plant which is widespread on lower land and in valleys where it flourishes on damp, base-rich or calcareous soils. It is abundant from Helmsley to Sutton Bank.

Wood Cranesbill 1
Geranium sylvaticum
A northern species, recorded only on a roadside adjacent to woodland near Easby.

Bloody Cranesbill 8 M
Geranium sanguineum
A rare plant in this area, this colourful geranium survives only on unimproved rough grassy scrub and rocky outcrops with basic soils. Hawnby, Sutton Bank and Caydale.

Hedgerow Cranesbill 11 M
Geranium pyrenaicum
An introduced garden plant seen occasionally on roadside verges on light or sandy soils such as at Ruston.

Long-stalked Cranesbill 4
Geranium columbinum
A southern plant, rare in the National Park where it grows in limestone fields at Thornton-le-Dale and near Rievaulx.

Cut-leaved Cranesbill 111 M
Geranium dissectum
Grows plentifully on fertile short grass, heaths and waysides.

Dovesfoot Cranesbill 137 M
Geranium molle
Common in dry short grassland, garden lawns, gravelly car parks and cultivated ground. Colonises grit heaps on moorland roadsides.

Small-flowered Cranesbill 13
Geranium pusillum
An unobtrusive tiny-flowered geranium recorded rarely on sandy or well-drained soils.

Shining Cranesbill 13
Geranium lucidum
Not a common plant in the district but occurs occasionally on sheltered limestone walls and rocks, usually near gardens.

Herb Robert 332 M
Geranium robertianum
The bright red leaves and flowers of this plant are often the only splash of colour in dark, shady gills, where it adorns ledges and crevices. It seems to

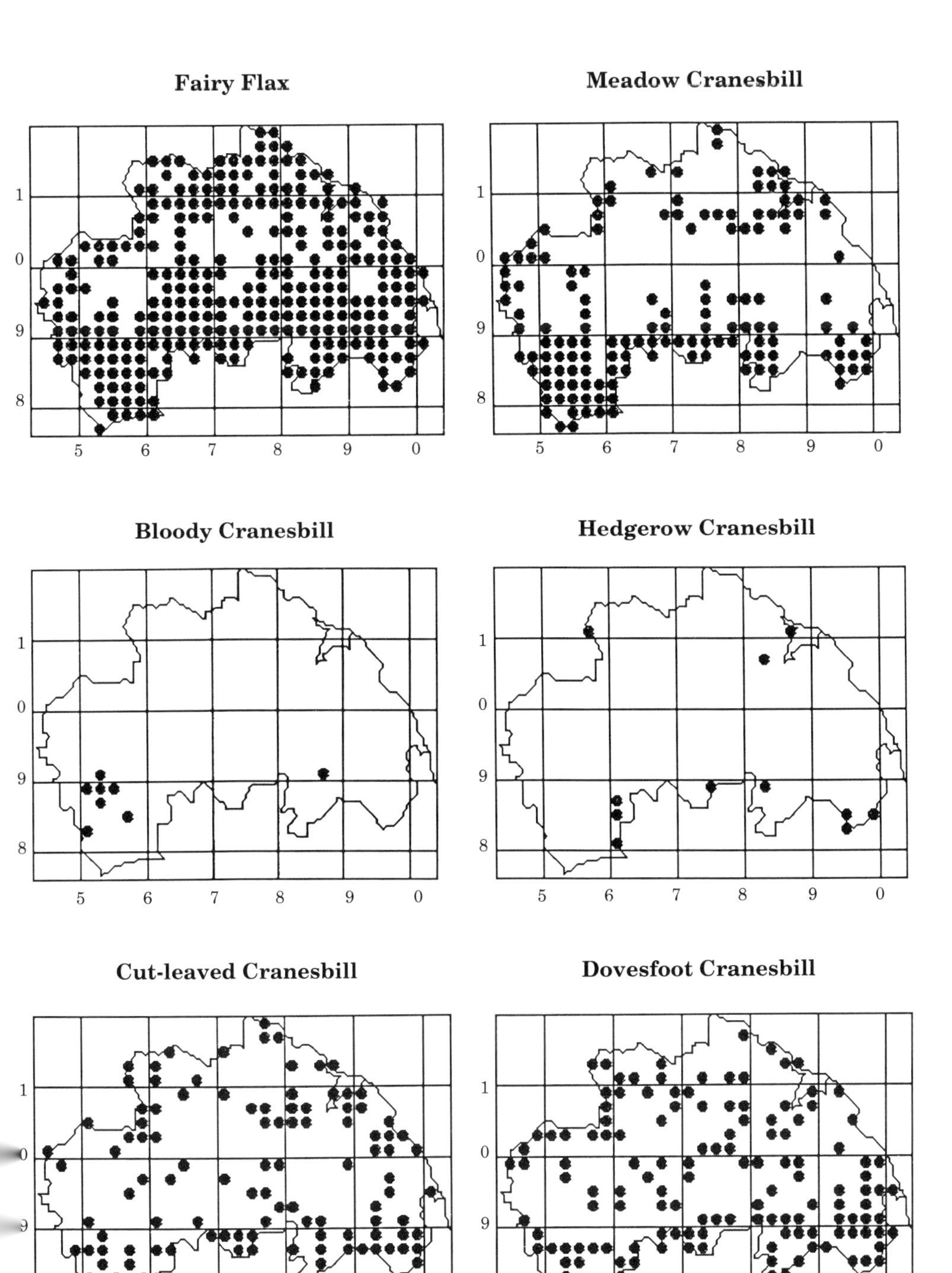
Fairy Flax
1
0
9
8
5
6
7
8
9
0
Meadow Cranesbill
1
0
9
8
5
6
7
8
9
0
Bloody Cranesbill
1
0
9
8
5
6
7
8
9
0
Hedgerow Cranesbill
1
0
9
8
5
6
7
8
9
0
Cut-leaved Cranesbill
1
5
6
7
8
9
0
Dovesfoot Cranesbill
1
0
9
8
5
6
7
8
9
0

flower spasmodically throughout the year on walls, stream banks, woodland edges and waysides.

French Cranesbill 5
Geranium endressii
A garden plant found occasionally on roadside verges.

Dusky Cranesbill 5
Geranium phaeum
Another garden fugitive, it is well established at Hawnby, Old Byland, Oldstead, Newby and Cowesby.

Pencilled Cranesbill 1
Geranium versicolor
A fourth garden geranium which has taken to the wild – this one at Levisham station.

Storksbill 15 M
Erodium cicutarium
Unusual in this area, it grows in small populations on sandy waysides, roadside grit heaps, friable stone walls, quarries and in free-draining set-aside fields. Plentiful on a roadside embankment in Hutton-le-Hole.

WOOD SORREL FAMILY
OXALIDACEAE

Wood Sorrel 367 M
Oxalis acetosella
Very common in well-drained rich humus, especially in ancient deciduous woods; also grows on path edges and clearings where conifer replanting has taken place. Shade tolerant, it tends to replace bluebell on more acid soils, and frequently survives beneath bracken long after woodland clearance.

Upright Yellow Sorrel 1
Oxalis europaea [Oxalis stricta]
A garden plant naturalised amongst old paving slabs at Helmsley Castle.

Procumbent Yellow Sorrel
Oxalis corniculata
Another garden plant found naturalised on a few verges.

BALSAM FAMILY
BALSAMINACEAE

Himalayan Balsam 39 M
Impatiens glandulifera
An alien from the Himalayas, it was brought to gardens in 1839, and is now achieving near pest proportions in the wild. Its efficient seed dispersal ensures rapid colonisation of riverbanks. In this area it fringes much of the Seph, the lower Esk and Rye and numerous smaller streams.

MAPLE FAMILY
ACERACEAE

Sycamore 352 M
Acer pseudoplatanus
Brought to this country in the 15th century, the sycamore is now a familiar and common tree, succeeding particularly well along the windswept coast where it is often planted in shelter belts. It regenerates freely – perhaps too aggressively in some ancient woodlands – and has been recorded almost everywhere apart from the moorland ridge.

Herb Robert

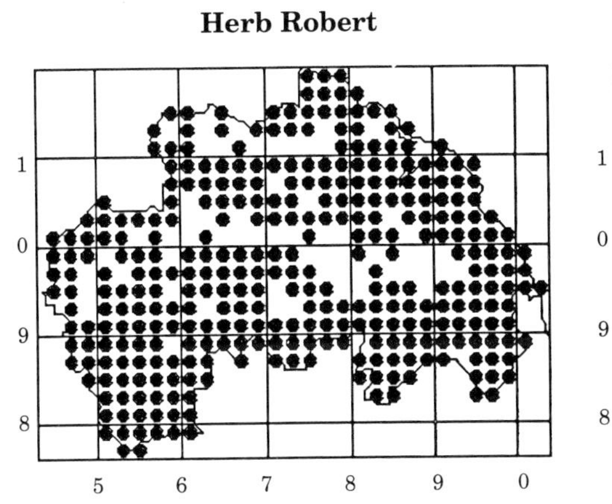

Storksbill

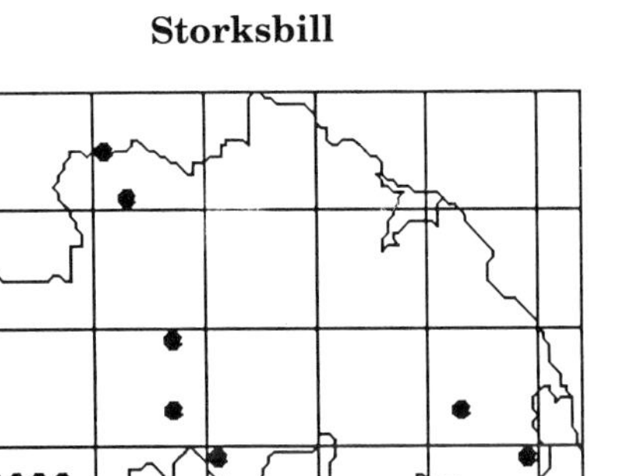

Wood Sorrel

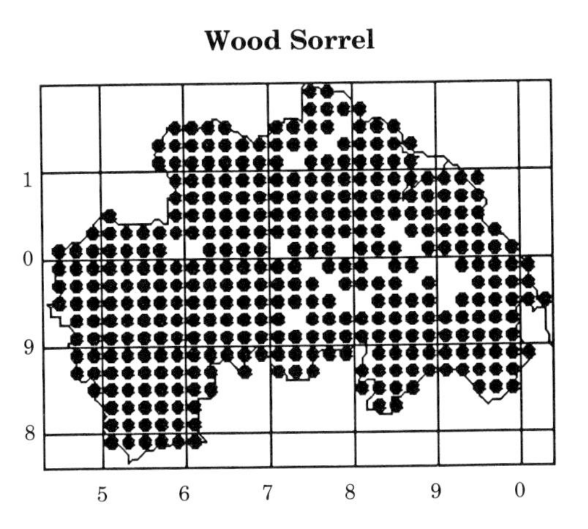

Himalayan Balsam

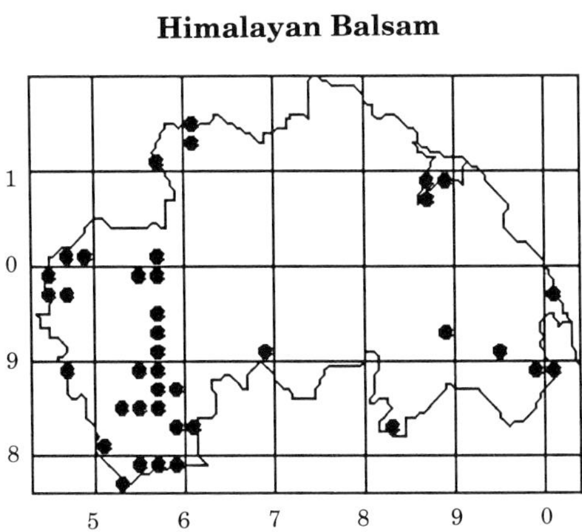

Sycamore

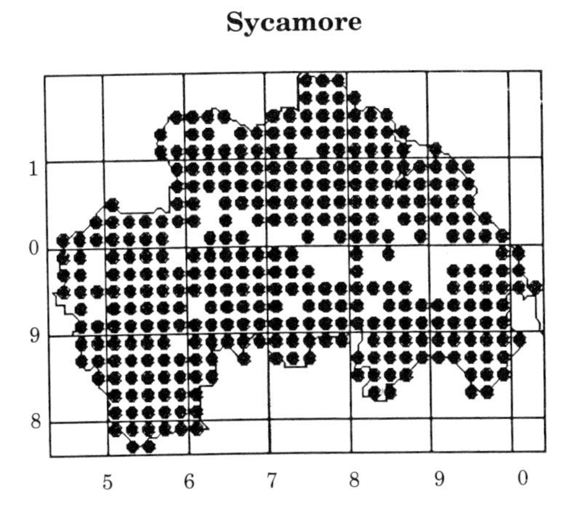

Field Maple 178 M
Acer campestre
Nearing its northern limit as a native tree, it occurs in sheltered hedges and open deciduous woods, especially on fertile lime-rich soils. It avoids exposed high ground. Much planted in new copses, woods and hedgerows, where it adds diversity and autumn colour. Although it is most often seen cut back as a hedgerow component, it makes a fine specimen tree when space permits.

Norway Maple 23 M
Acer platanoides
Another introduced maple, occasionally planted for its early blossom and autumn leaf colour but not an adventurous species and no natural regeneration has been recorded.

HORSE CHESTNUT FAMILY
HIPPOCASTANACEAE

Horse Chestnut 119 M
Aesculus hippocastanum
Introduced from the Balkans in the 15th century, single trees are planted for amenity in villages, parkland and drives. Seen at its best as a village green tree at Cropton.

HOLLY FAMILY
AQUIFOLIACEAE

Holly 361 M
Ilex aquifolium
A frequent plant in pre-enclosure hedgerows. Although nowadays it is often flail-cut with the rest of the hedge, it is not uncommon to see fine mature trees surviving. This may reflect once widespread superstitions associated with holly – or its former value in providing foliage feed and shelter for wintering stock. In older woodland, holly regenerates freely but rarely becomes a well-shaped tree under a closed canopy. Exceptional is Crag Wood, Danby, which is noted for its holly trees.

SPINDLE FAMILY
CELASTRACEAE

Spindle 29 M
Euonymus europaeus
An infrequent plant found in ancient wooodland and long-established hedgerows, mainly in valleys on the southern limestone belt; also on alkaline boulder clay in Roxby and Mulgrave woods. Usually only a few shrubs in each location, growing in glades with minimum shade and competition.

BOX FAMILY
BUXACEAE

Box 3
Buxus sempervirens
A plant of Britain's southern beechwoods, it does not occur naturally in this area, but is frequently grown in gardens. The naturalised plants in Grosmont car park, on Runswick cliffs and around Arden are likely to have originated from garden rubbish.

BUCKTHORN FAMILY
RHAMNACEAE

Buckthorn 4 M
Rhamnus catharticus
[Rhamnus cathartica]
Almost at its northern limit, occasional shrubs survive in uncut older hedgerows and scrub on calcareous soils. Thornton-le-Dale, Saintoft and Forge Valley.

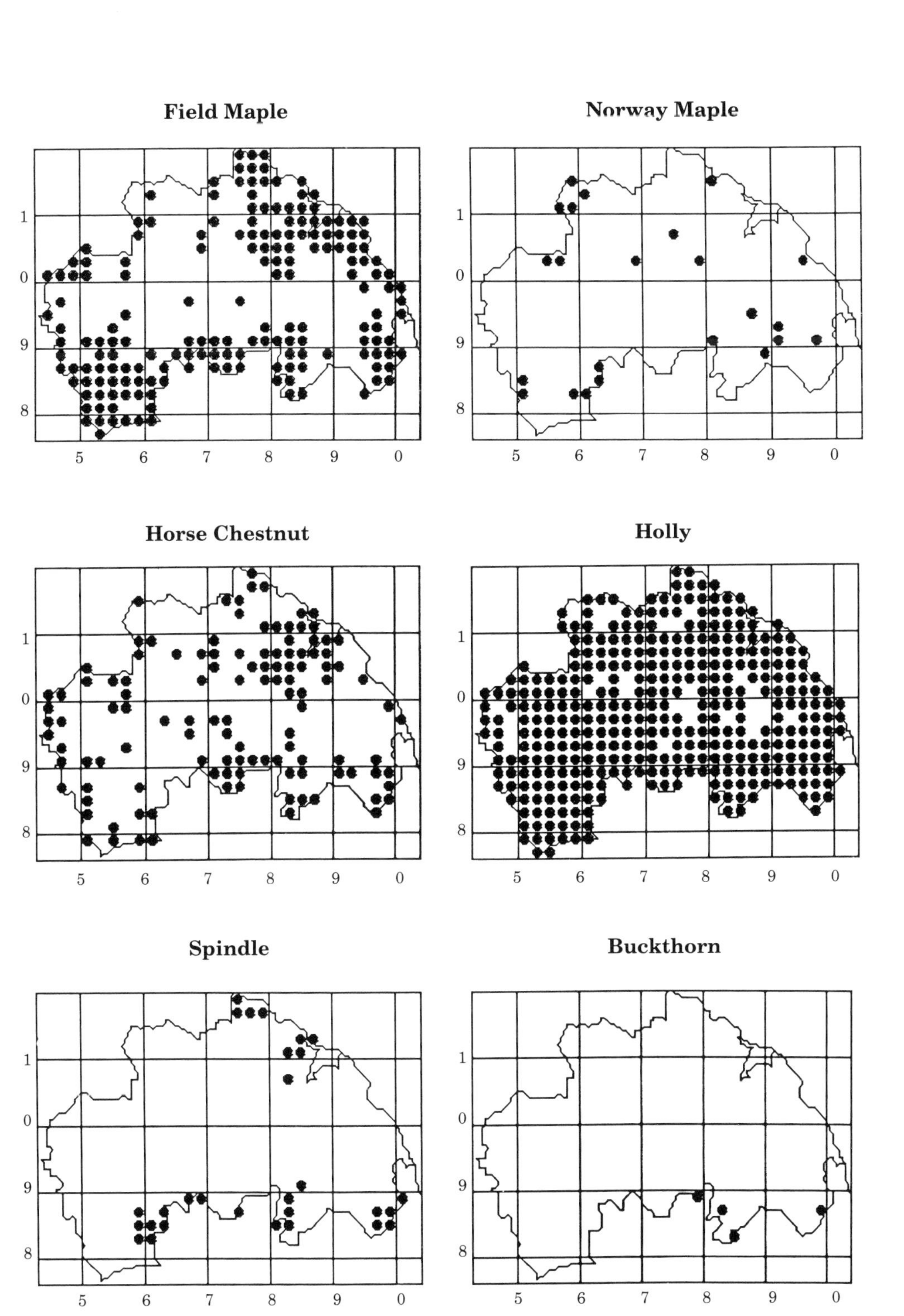
Field Maple
Norway Maple
Horse Chestnut
Holly
Spindle
Buckthorn
1
0
9
8
5
6
7
8
9
0

PEA FAMILY
LEGUMINOSAE [FABACEAE]

Dyer's Greenweed 8
Genista tinctoria
Once described as "one of the worst weeds of pasture", this yellow-flowered shrub is now a rarity almost confined to rough grassland on coastal boulder clay. Only a few plants were found.

Petty Whin 12 M
Genista anglica
A rare elusive shrub of the heather moors, it is almost impossible to detect when not flowering. It has been recorded only on less elevated moors in the south east of the Park. In keeping with some other non-ericaceous shrubs, it is believed to be destroyed by rotational burning of the moorland.

Gorse 338
Ulex europaeus
Widespread on unimproved hill pasture, especially on lighter soils in sunny locations. Often growing with broom, it forms dense thickets on free-draining road, rail and forest verges. A vigorous coloniser on unstable spoil such as in Cliff Rigg quarry.

Dwarf furze 1
Ulex gallii
Rare in the east of Britain, a small cluster of plants has established beside a forest track at Helwath, possibly introduced during conifer planting.

Broom 238 M
Cytisus scoparius
Although individual plants are short-lived, their abundant seed production ensures continuity of the species on sandy road verges, sunny woodland fringes and old pastures on dry acid soils.

Restharrow 37 M
Ononis repens
This low-growing, pink-flowered shrub covers a substantial area when established but its occurrence is sparse. More common in the south of the country, it becomes increasingly a coastal plant as it moves north, and in this area inhabits rocky outcrops, road verges and old quarries along the sea cliffs. It is less common inland on rail ballast, forest ride margins and dry banks with shallow calcareous soils.

Spiny Restharrow 10 M
Ononis spinosa
Much less frequent than the above species but it grows in similar habitats.

Lucerne
Medicago sativa
Occasionally sown as a forage crop, from where it sometimes migrates to adjacent waste land. It has become established in a few scattered locations.

Black Medick 225 M
Medicago lupulina
A common plant on sandy, grazed or trampled turf, avoiding very acid ground. Quite persistent on reseeded grassland and garden lawns.

Spotted Medick 2
Medicago arabica
Appears from time to time in gardens and on waste ground in the Whitby and Grosmont areas.

Tall Melilot 7 M
Melilotus altissima
[Melilotus altissimus]
Introduced to this country by 16th century herbalists, this plant is still uncommon in this area. It has been found occasionally on the cliffs from Hayburn Wyke to Ruswarp, and inland at Battersby, Charltons and West Ayton.

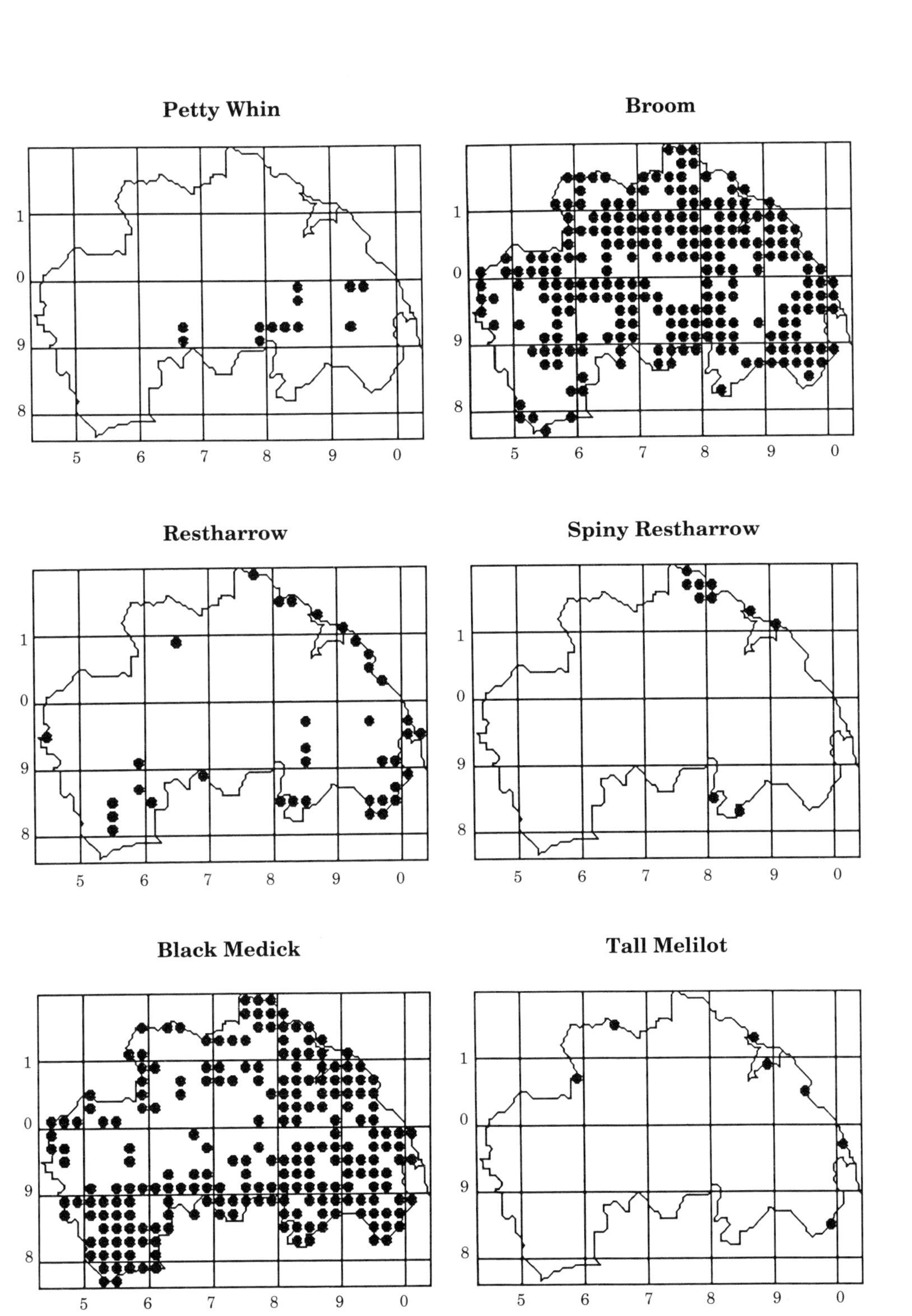

Petty Whin
Broom
Restharrow
Spiny Restharrow
Black Medick
Tall Melilot
1
0
9
8
5
6
7
8
9
0

White Melilot
Melilotus alba [Melilotus albus]
Comes and goes on disturbed ground, mostly after roadworks, and has been noted recently at Pry Rigg and Brompton.

Common Melilot 5
Melilotus officinalis
Despite its name, this melilot is by no means common in northern Britain. Only a few plants have been found in rough grassy places.

Lesser Yellow Trefoil 300 M
Trifolium dubium
Abundant on sheep grazed turf on the moors and short dry grassland in the dales. It survives constant nibbling by growing tight to the ground, where its miniature flowers create pools of yellow on moorland verges. Survives mowing and trampling in gardens, pathways and car parks.

Hop Trefoil 44 M
Trifolium campestre
Short dry grassy banks, gravelly waysides and old limestone quarries provide the habitats where this plant occurs. It is quite uncommon in this area.

Alsike Clover 34 M
Trifolium hybridum
Formerly sown in grass mixtures. Stray plants have naturalised on field edges and tracksides.

White Clover 391 M
Trifolium repens
A very common component of short grassland, it grows especially on less acid soils. It is still widely sown in forage and grazing mixtures.

Strawberry Clover 1
Trifolium fragiferum
Near its northern limit in Britain, this plant has been found only on grassy parts of Ruswarp Batts.

Zigzag Clover 125 M
Trifolium medium
The sharp red flowers of this clover enliven many a roadside verge and grassy hedgebank on fertile soils throughout the summer months.

Haresfoot Clover
Trifolium arvense
A lowland species which occasionally appears on a patch of dry sandy ground, a rocky outcrop or gravelly forest ride.

Soft Trefoil 1
Trifolium striatum
Its only known location is on a bare sandy rock exposure on Sneck Yate.

Crimson Clover
Trifolium incarnatum
Occurred briefly in a kale field at Mowthorpe in 1989, possibly introduced with the crop seeds.

Red Clover 346
Trifolium pratense
Very common on grassy verges, hedgebanks, rough grassland and field edge, except on very acid soils. Often planted in forage mixtures, from where it frequently naturalises nearby.

Kidney Vetch 37 M
Anthyllis vulneraria
Preferring the more equable temperatures of the coast, large and numerous plants thrive on boulder clay in sheltered pockets along the sea cliffs. Inland plants, which tend to be smaller, occur in old limestone quarries and on south-facing slopes on free-draining calcareous soils.

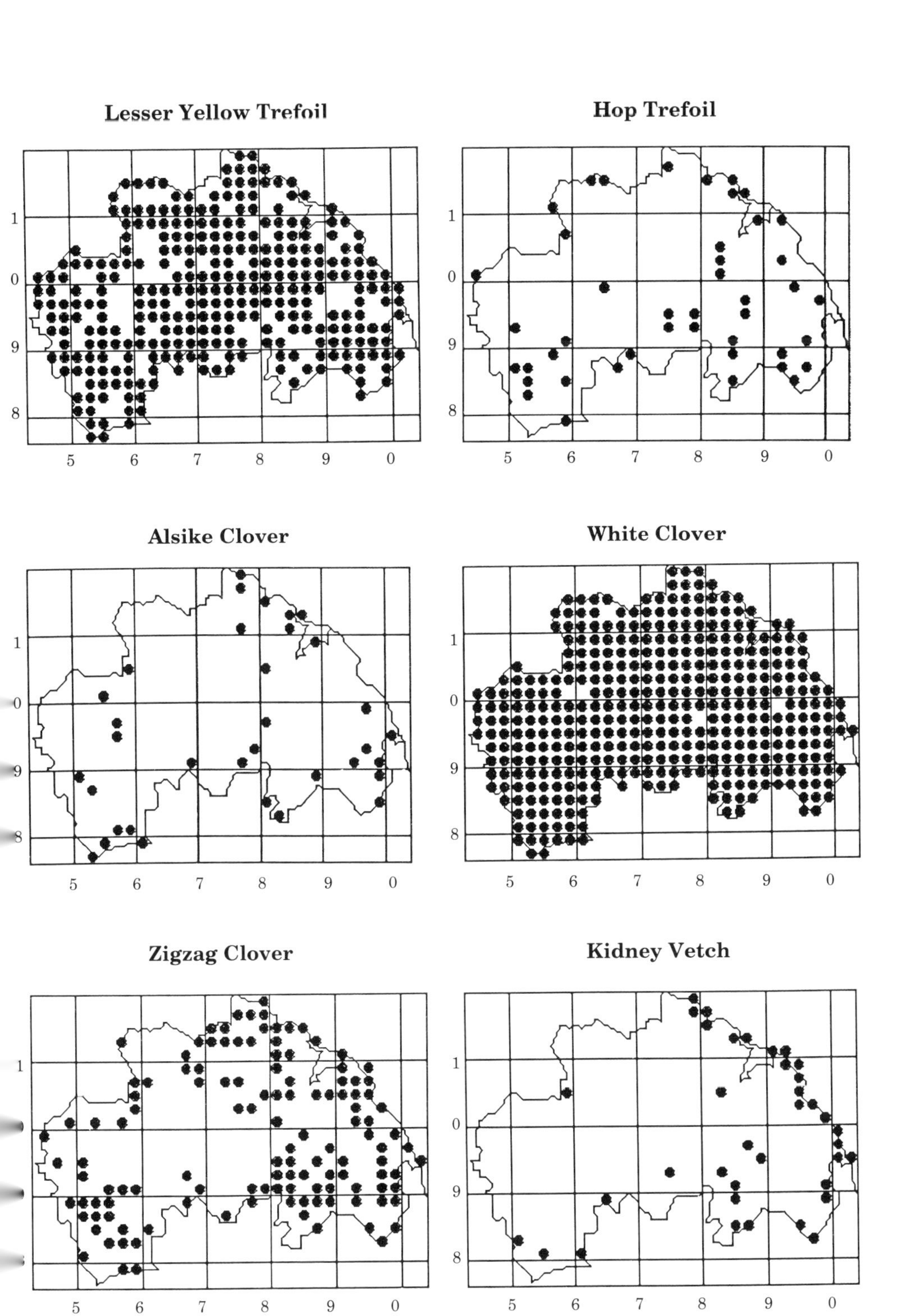
Lesser Yellow Trefoil
1
0
9
8
5
6
7
8
9
0
Hop Trefoil
1
0
9
8
5
6
7
8
9
0
Alsike Clover
1
0
9
8
5
6
7
8
9
0
White Clover
1
0
9
8
5
6
7
8
9
0
Zigzag Clover
1
5
6
7
8
9
0
Kidney Vetch
1
0
9
8
5
6
7
8
9
0

Birdsfoot Trefoil 372
Lotus corniculatus
Abundant in short turf and rough grassland everywhere except on the high moors and waterlogged soils. Sunny road and railside banks are a favoured habitat.

Large Birdsfoot Trefoil 296 M
Lotus uliginosus [Lotus pedunculatus]
In ditches, wet pastures and marshes it replaces birdsfoot trefoil but the two species often grow together in intermediate habitats.

Purple Milk Vetch 2
Astragalus danicus
A rare plant of short calcareous grassland, it has been recorded only on pastures at Ellerburn and Ruston. Apparently it was more widespread when swards were controlled by rabbit grazing.

Hairy Tare 54 M
Vicia hirsuta
Railway ballast along the Esk Valley line carries large populations of this erstwhile troublesome weed. Nowadays it is rarely seen in cornfields but appears occasionally in short vegetation on dry roadside banks.

Tufted Vetch 288
Vicia cracca
Abundant and colourful, it scrambles over hedgebanks, grassy verges and fieldside vegetation.

Wood Vetch 42 M
Vicia sylvatica
Most frequent in coastal ravine woods and on sea cliffs; unusual inland on old established hedges and scrub woodland. It has been found in woods at Grosmont, Egton Bridge, Roxby, Lockton, Tidkinhow, Gerrick, Sutherland, Kildale and Baysdale.

Bush Vetch 307 M
Vicia sepium
Common on rail and roadside verges, in hedgerows, field and wood margins and rough grassland.

Common Vetch 127 M
Vicia sativa
Despite its name, it is by no means the commonest vetch in this area. Formerly grown for fodder, it has naturalised on field edges and waysides in farmed areas.

Bithynian Vetch
Vicia bithynica
A rare plant throughout Britain, it has long been established on the south-facing species-rich slope of Upgang Ravine. Regrettably, this site was ravaged by coastal defence works in the late 1980s. Amazingly, a few plants survived and hopefully will spread as the excavated lower ravine revegetates. It is said to grow on inaccessible cliffs at Lythe but this awaits confirmation.

Spring Vetch 2
Vicia lathyroides
An annual plant seen rarely in this locality. It has been recorded on sheltered heathy banks in Bickley forest.

Meadow Vetchling 323
Lathyrus pratensis
A very common roadside plant, it clambers over grass, herbs and hedges throughout the lowland. Its cheerful yellow flowers adorn field edges, pathsides, forest margins and scrubland.

Bitter Vetchling 231 M
Lathyrus montanus
[Lathyrus linifolius]
The commonest vetch in dry acid upland areas, where it inhabits thickets, verges, cliff tops and moorland banks.

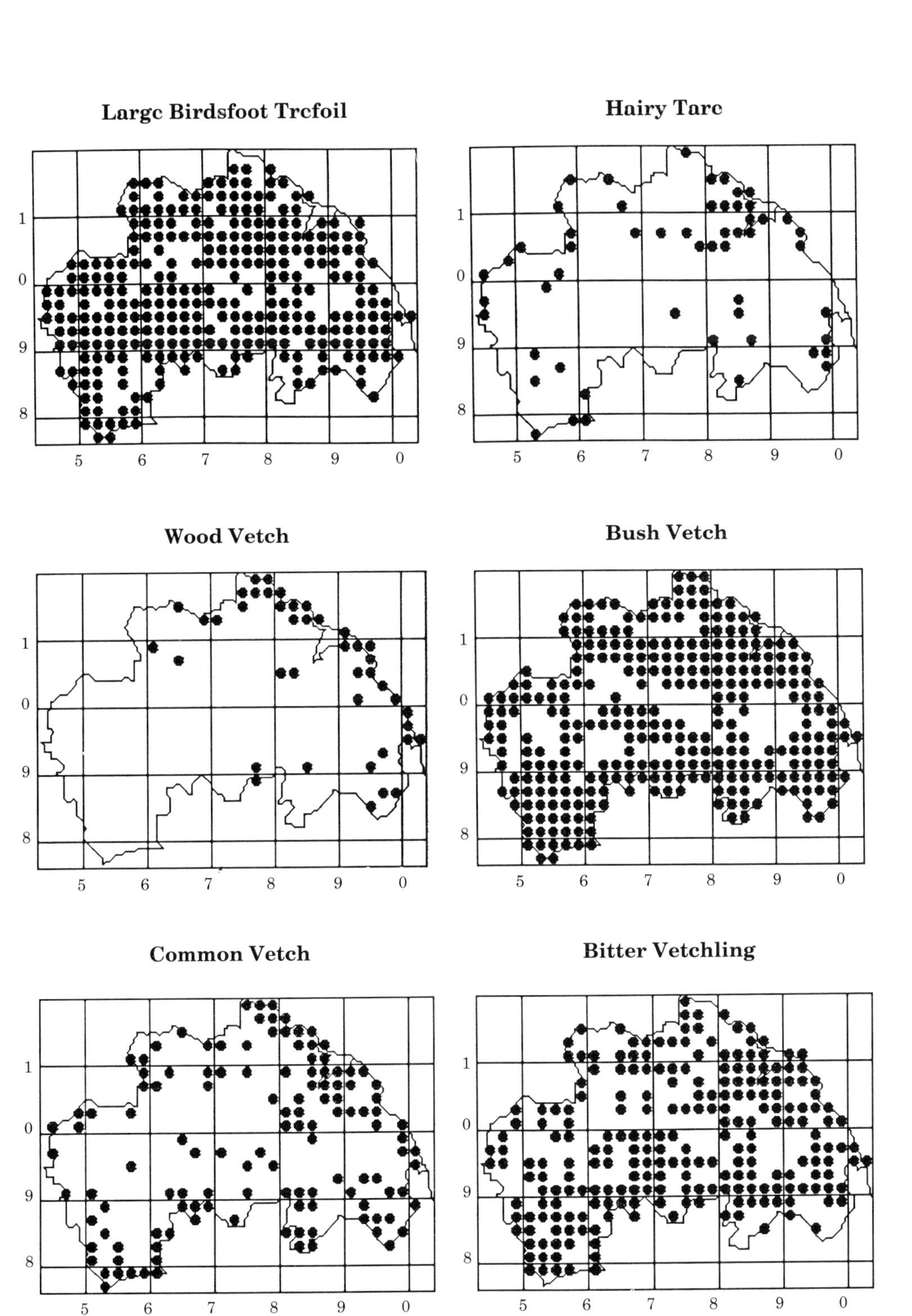
Large Birdsfoot Trefoil
1
0
9
8
5 6 7 8 9 0
Hairy Tare
1
0
9
8
5 6 7 8 9 0
Wood Vetch
1
0
9
8
5 6 7 8 9 0
Bush Vetch
1
0
9
8
5 6 7 8 9 0
Common Vetch
1
0
9
8
5 6 7 8 9 0
Bitter Vetchling
1
0
9
8
5 6 7 8 9 0

Narrow-leaved Everlasting Pea 6
Lathyrus sylvestris
A mid-European plant rarely seen this far north, it survives mainly in the less rigorous climate of the coast. It grows in rough grassland and woodland edge at Port Mulgrave and Overdale and along the old railtrack at Sandsend and Fylingthorpe.

Crown Vetch 1
Coronilla varia [Securigera varia]
A 17th century introduction from southern Europe, this unusual pink-flowered vetch has its only known site in the north of Britain at Grosmont car park, which is sited on slag heaps formed during the ironstone working era.

ROSE FAMILY
ROSACEAE

Dropwort 24 M
Filipendula vulgaris
The pink-tinted white flowers of this delightful plant are seen infrequently on sunny road verges, pathsides and woodland edges on limestone. Usually only a few plants in each location. Survives on one or two calcareous forest rides.

Meadowsweet 344 M
Filipendula ulmaria
A strewing herb used by Elizabethans to create indoor fragrance, this familiar and prolific marsh plant grows abundantly in low-nutrient wetland situations – ditches, riversides, wet woods and marshy grassland – throughout the Park except on acid peat.

Cloudberry 1
Rubus chamaemorus
A Scottish Highland plant which is rare this far south. Known only at May Moss where it grows on a raised bog with marsh rosemary.

Stone Bramble 12 M
Rubus saxatilis
Rare on rocky outcrops and damp stony waysides in undisturbed ancient woodland on limestone.

Raspberry 244 M
Rubus idaeus
By eating its fruit and dispersing undigested seeds far and wide, birds ensure a widespread distribution of wild raspberry. It grows in scrubby areas, open woods and on wasteland and verges particularly on light land.

Dewberry 27 M
Rubus caesius
Only found on the fringes of long-established deciduous woods and undisturbed grassy rides on calcareous soils.

Bramble 355
Rubus fruticosus agg.
No attempt has been made to differentiate the approximately 250 subspecies of this plant. Suffice it to say that bramble in one form or another has been recorded in practically every tetrad, except on the moorland ridge. It is a rapid coloniser of felled forest and abandoned hill pasture. Abundant on coastal cliffs, it also forms an impenetrable understorey in dappled shade of open woodland, where it provides winter browsing for roe deer. Bramble thickets on roadside and unmanaged grassland offer a safe haven for many birds and an eagerly picked fruit harvest in the autumn.

Marsh Cinquefoil 42 M
Potentilla palustris
The reddish-purple flowers of this uncommon marsh plant can be found amongst taller sedges – usually *Carex acutiformis* – in fens, streams and marshes in Commondale, Newtondale, Sutherland and in several nutrient-rich moorland flushes.

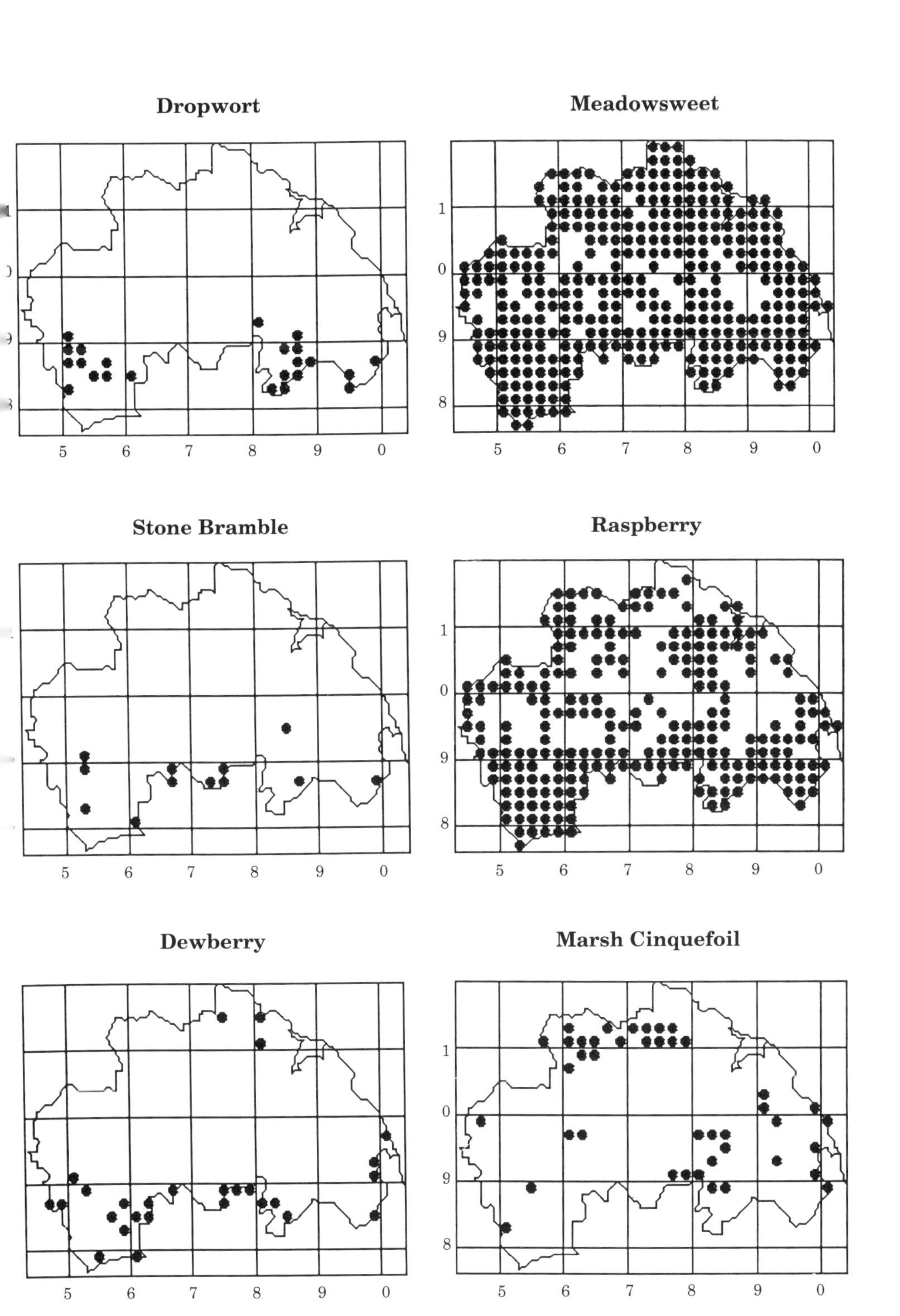
Dropwort
Meadowsweet
Stone Bramble
Raspberry
Dewberry
Marsh Cinquefoil
1
0
9
8
5
6
7
8
9
0

Barren Strawberry 305
Potentilla sterilis
Abundant in free-draining soils on short turf and wayside stony banks; in open woodland and old quarries.

Silverweed 290 M
Potentilla anserina
A common low-growing plant, often plentiful on the roadside splash zone and broken pathways. Tolerant of sheep grazing and trampling, it thrives in railway ballast and any well-drained gravelly ground away from the high moors.

Spring Cinquefoil 0
Potentilla tabernaemontani
[Potentilla neumanniana]
A mid-European plant, rare throughout Britain, which historically was recorded in Cockrah woods. It was again recorded in 1990 on a rocky bank of the River Derwent north of Langdale End but could not be refound the following year. Further searching is required to ascertain if this rarity does grow in this locality.

Tormentil 375 M
Potentilla erecta
Very much a plant of the moors and daleheads, it grows extensively on dry acid heath throughout the uplands. It is also plentiful on forest rides and intake pasture on non-calcareous soils.

Trailing Tormentil 40
Potentilla anglica
Grows on light, slightly acid, sandy soils where it may carpet pathways, open wood edges and grassy banks of less frequented forest rides.

Creeping Cinquefoil 255
Potentilla reptans
Extensive ground cover is formed by this plant on grassy verges, rail ballast, gardens and waysides.

A range of hybrids between the above three species has been observed.

Wild Strawberry 257 M
Fragaria vesca
Common on base-rich and calcareous well-drained soils. Usually found on sloping banks, cut tracksides in the forest and in short turf. In grazed areas, it survives and fruits in miniature form.

Hautbois Strawberry 1
Fragaria moschata [Fragaria muricata]
Introduced as a garden plant and naturalised in a disused quarry near Hutton-le-Hole.

Wood Avens 285 M
Geum urbanum
Common on a wide range of fertile soils in lightly shaded woods, on grassy verges, at the foot of hedgerows and on forest rides.

Water Avens 147 M
Geum rivale
Large colonies occur on fertile soils on river banks, in wet shady grassland and alder carrs.

Geum x *intermedium (G urbanum* x *G rivale)* occurs in proximity of both parents.

Common Agrimony 142 M
Agrimonia eupatoria
Grows intermittently amongst coarse roadside vegetation, on hedgebanks and grassy field edges on well-drained calcareous soils. Occurs as individual plants or in small clumps.

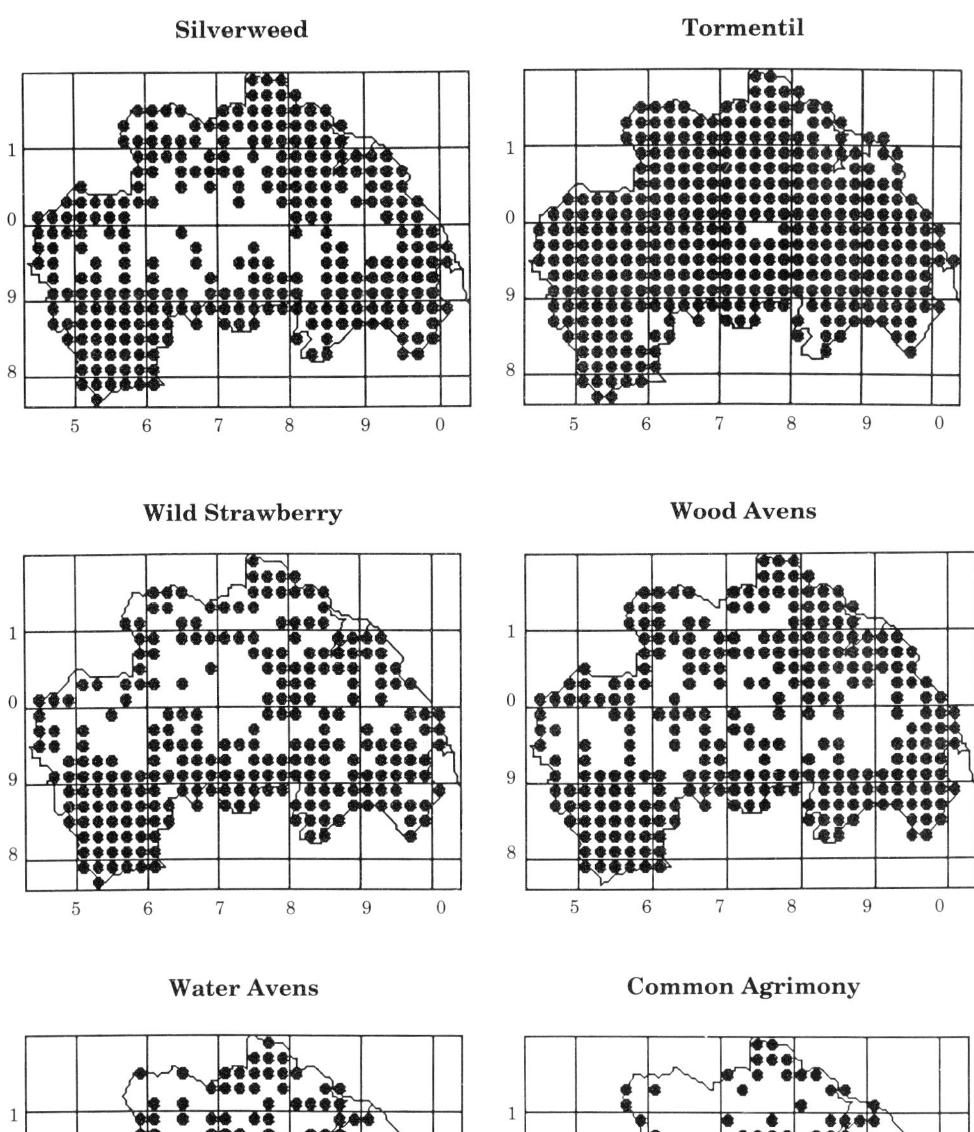
Silverweed
Tormentil
Wild Strawberry
Wood Avens

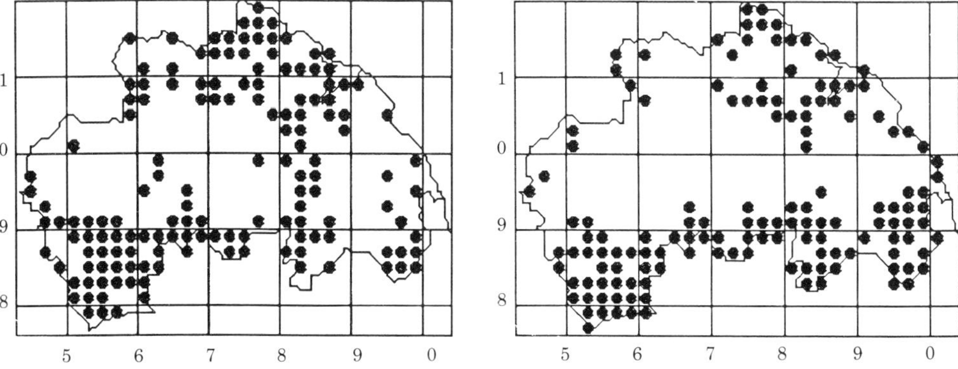
Water Avens
Common Agrimony

Fragrant Agrimony 14 M
Agrimonia procera
Much less frequent than the previous species, this more robust plant has been found on heavier and rather acid soils, in sheltered locations such as open woodland and valleysides.

Lady's Mantle
Alchemilla filicaulis 72
Shows a preference for grazed grassland on limestone hillsides.

Alchemilla xanthochlora 197 M
Common in grassy places on lighter soils, especially amongst fieldside vegetation and away from exposed uplands.

Alchemilla glabra 86
Found on dry, sparse grassland and rocky banks with less acid soils.

Alchemilla mollis
This vigorous garden plant is occasionally naturalised on verges and waste ground where rubbish has been deposited.

Parsley Piert 167 M
Aphanes arvensis
An unobtrusive, small plant, widely distributed in gardens and pathways as well as arable fields. It grows profusely during the first year or two after arable land has been set-aside.

Slender Parsley Piert 10
Aphanes microcarpa
[Aphanes inexspectata]
Found infrequently on grazed heath, moorland trackways and forest rides, on more acid soils than the previous species.

Great Burnet 83 M
Sanguisorba officinalis
Frequent in damp grassland, it can dominate the vegetation on some heavier alkaline soils, especially in unimproved riverside pastures.

Salad Burnet 103 M
Sanguisorba minor
Flourishes in unimproved calcareous pastures, meadows, grassy verges, in old quarries and on rocky outcrops, where its deep penetrating roots assist survival in drought conditions.

ROSES

Field Rose 35 M
Rosa arvensis
This distinctive white-flowered rose has to be looked for in hedgerows and thickets on fertile non-acid soils. It is quite plentiful in the Helmsley area and Raindale and scattered elsewhere. Almost at the northern limit of its range, it favours a sheltered location.

Burnet Rose 14
Rosa pimpinellifolia
Another white-flowered rose, encrusted with spines and low-growing, it is a rare plant in this area. Single bushes have been found at a few places on the northern escarpment of the Tabular Hills, on coastal cliffs at Runswick and alongside the North Yorkshire Moors Railway track.

(The taxonomy of roses is full of complexities. For simplicity all other native roses have been identified to group. Further work is needed to assess the distribution of subspecies.)

Dog Rose 349
Rosa canina group
The commonest rose type encountered, it has been found in hedgerows, thickets, unmanaged pasture and woodland edge throughout, except on high moorland. It colonises under-grazed grassland and has been seen high up some of the moorland gills.

Fragrant Agrimony

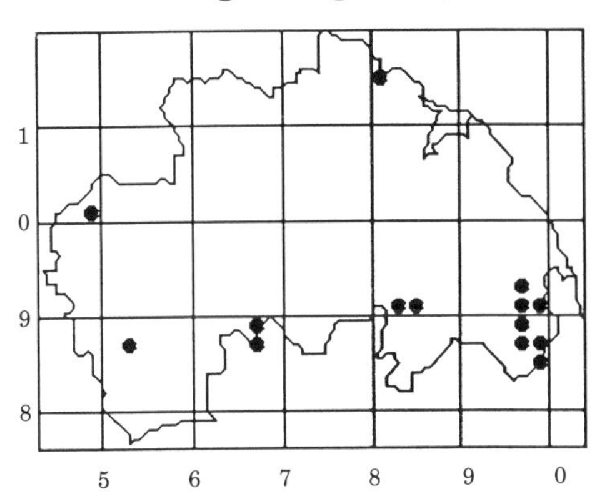

Lady's Mantle *Alchemella xanthochlora*

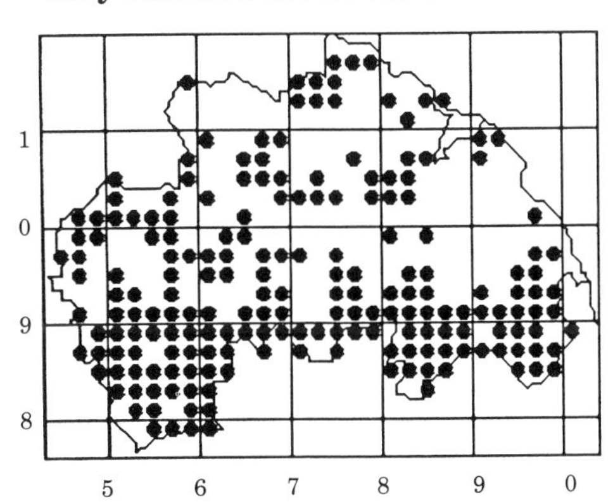

Parsley Piert

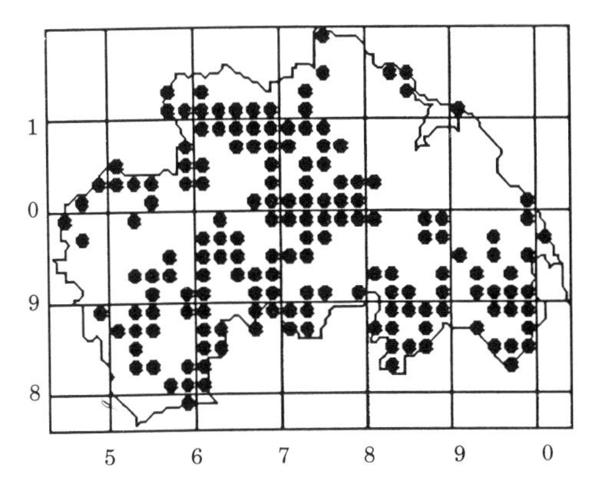

Great Burnet

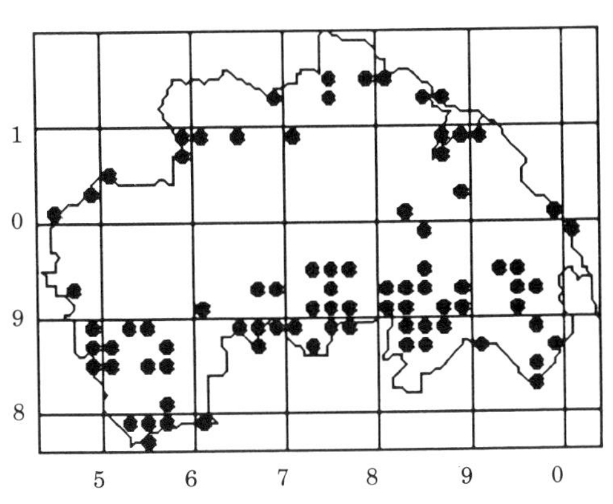

Salad Burnet

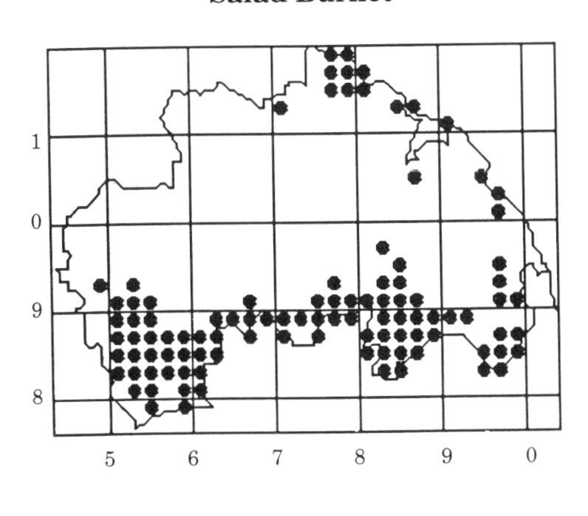

Field Rose

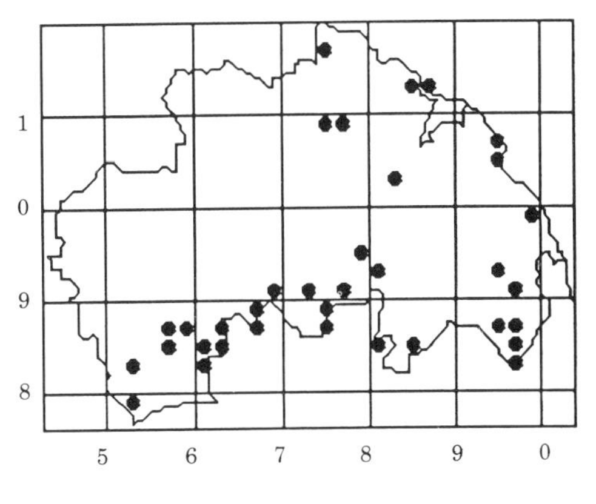

Downy Rose 134 M
Rosa tomentosa group
In similar situations to dog rose but more of a hedgerow shrub and far less common. *Rosa sherardii* is plentiful in old hedges above East Ayton.

Sweet Briar 8 M
Rosa rubiginosa group
A rare plant in this area, it grows in scrubby woodland on alkaline soils at the top of Hackness Windings, at Boonhill, Farwath, Goathland, Forge Valley and Hawnby.

Rosa multiflora
A charming floribunda type garden rose, which has been long-established in a Westerdale hedgerow – presumably originally bird-sown.

Rosa rugosa
A sturdy garden plant which grows rarely on wasteland.

Blackthorn 324
Prunus spinosa
A widespread and vigorous shrub, it grows in profusion in boulder clay on windswept coastal cliffs where it develops a characteristic leeward lean. It forms dense thickets on road and rail verges and its suckering habit enables it quickly to engulf abandoned pasture. As a hedgerow shrub, when allowed to grow to maturity its early blossom is a welcome harbinger of spring, though not infrequently in the dales its early white flowers are accompanied by a covering of snow.

Bullace 61 M
Prunus domestica
Introduced, and formerly planted to produce plums for domestic use, it is widely naturalised in hedgerows, usually near habitation. Both ssp. *insititia* and ssp. *domestica* have been noted.

Wild Cherry or **Gean** 172 M
Prunus avium
Frequent in hedgerows on fertile base-rich soils, where it has often been allowed to grow to maturity. This is perhaps a legacy from the pre-combine era of stacking and threshing, when wild cherry was valued as a source of good thatching spars. It regenerates freely from suckers and is frequently planted as an attractive wayside tree and as a component of new woodland planting schemes.

Sour Cherry
Prunus cerasus
Possibly derived from gardens, an occasional old gnarled specimen of this tree has been seen in derelict steadings.

Bird Cherry 147 M
Prunus padus
Closely following the river valleys, this handsome small tree is abundant in the Hawnby – Bilsdale area. Specimen trees abound, while in some fields it is cut and trimmed as a hedging plant. It occurs widely throughout the Park, except on the coastal plain, and is a tree rarely seen in the south of Britain.

Cherry Plum 16 M
Prunus cerasifera
Introduced from the Balkans as a source of fruit, this early-flowering tree can be found in a few old hedgerows along the southern fringe. Its prevalence in the Kilburn, Ampleforth and Coxwold area may result from plantings by the monks of Byland Abbey. Some trees are close by the old watercourse which served the Abbey.

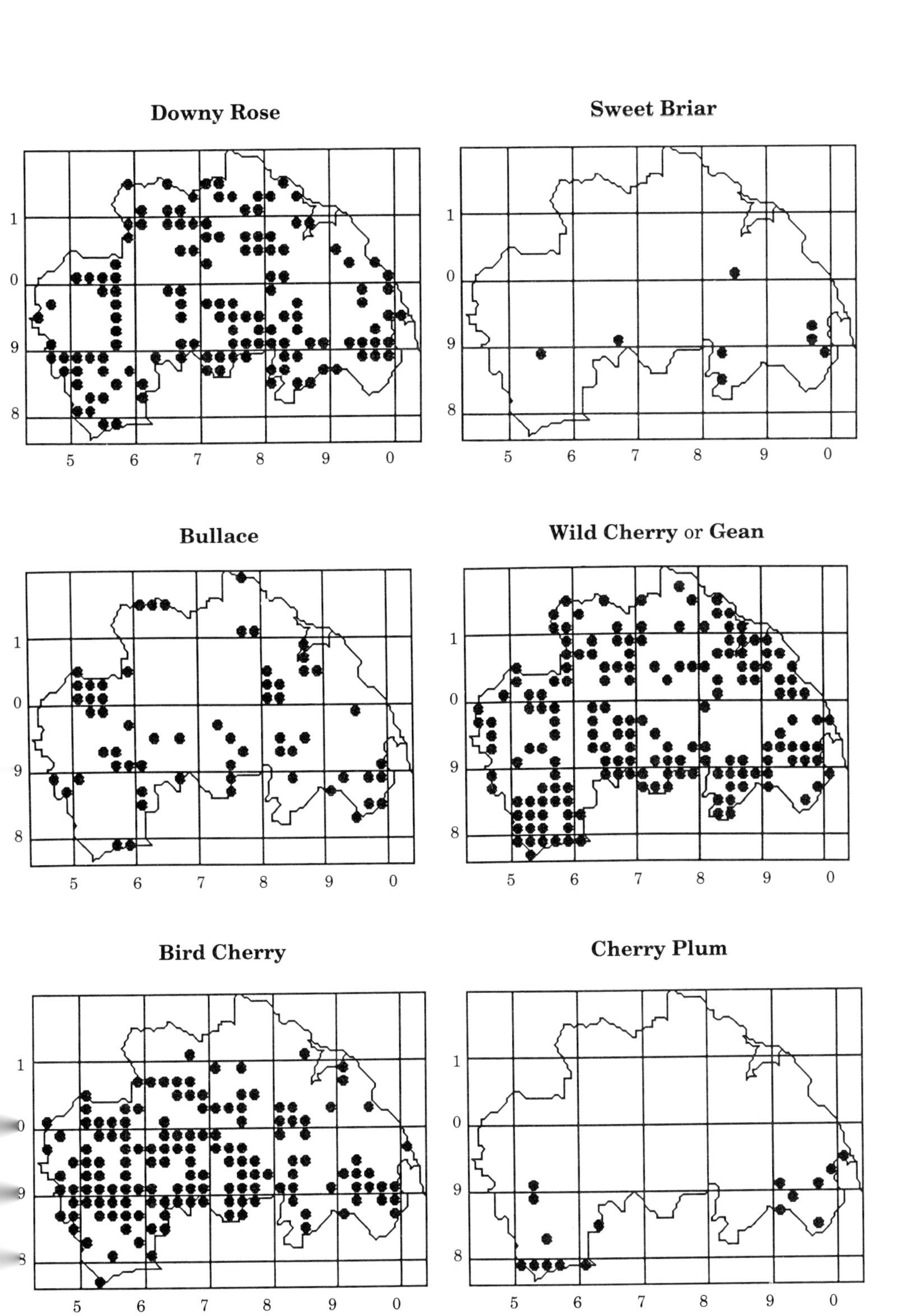

Downy Rose
Sweet Briar
Bullace
Wild Cherry or Gean
Bird Cherry
Cherry Plum

Cherry Laurel
Prunus laurocerasus
This small evergreen tree from the Balkans is occasionally planted and becomes naturalised in open woodland such as Riccaldale.

Bridewort 11 M
Spiraea spp.
Varieties of this attractive pink-flowered shrub, introduced from eastern Europe, are established in numerous hedgerows around Staintondale, Harwood Dale, Rosedale, Roseberry and Ampleforth.

Cotoneaster spp.
Planted by the Forestry Commission for roadside amenity; also occasionally naturalised where garden rubbish has been dumped.

Hawthorn 378 M
Crataegus monogyna
The commonest hedging plant, especially in enclosure boundaries. Soon appears in under-grazed grassland reverting to scrub.

Midland Hawthorn
Crataegus laevigata
Not a shrub normally encountered this far north but isolated specimens and hybrids with *C. monogyna* have been found in woodland fringes at Roxby, Waupley, Easington and Lownorth.

Rowan 368 M
Sorbus aucuparia
Often the sole surviving tree species as gills give way to open moor. Rowan is essentially a tree of upland oak/birch woods. It grows on lanesides, in hedgerows and daleheads; is planted around dales farmsteads; and a solitary specimen occasionally escapes sheep nibbling on open moorland. Absent from very wet areas and moors subject to regular burning. Old trees in close proximity to farmsteads may reflect a once widespread belief in the power of rowan to dispel evil spirits.

Whitebeam
Sorbus aria
Not native in this area though occasionally planted in estate woodland and on forest edges.

Service Tree 2
Sorbus torminalis
A southern tree not occurring naturally this far north but occasionally seen edging forest plantations as in Raindale.

Pear
Pyrus pyraster
The origins of two apparently wild pear trees in upper Bilsdale are unknown – they may have been planted or bird-sown.

Crab Apple 201 M
Malus sylvestris
The small yellow fruits remaining on branches well into the winter reveal numerous crab apple trees in old uncut hedgerows, on the sides of hollow-ways, green lanes and outlying field boundaries. The native crab apple – ssp. *sylvestris* – has a hairless flower stalk and sepals which distinguish it from cultivated apples – ssp. *domestica* – often found as ancient orchard trees indicating the site of an abandoned dwelling.

STONECROP FAMILY
CRASSULACEAE

Houseleek 3
Sempervivum tectorum
A rock garden plant which occasionally becomes established on old walls and asbestos roofs.

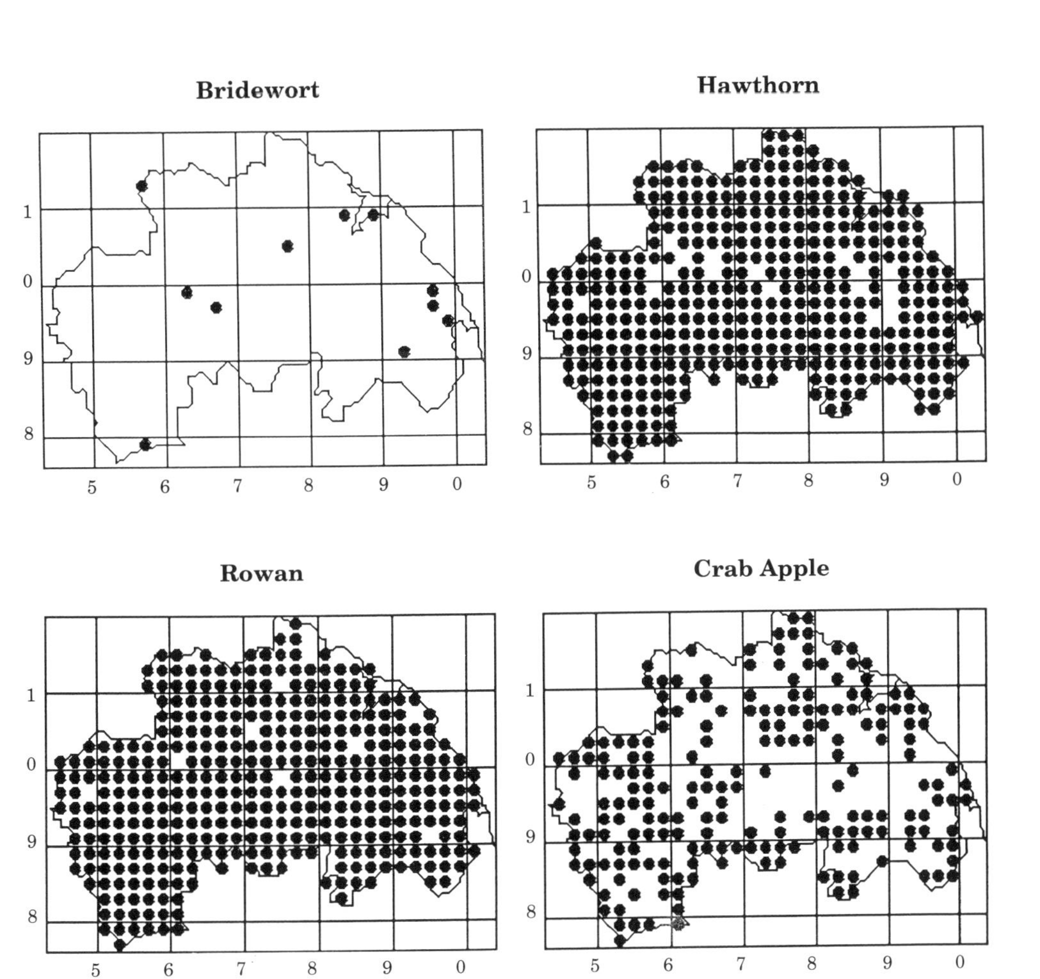
Bridewort
Hawthorn
Rowan
Crab Apple
1
0
9
8
5
6
7
8
9
0

English Stonecrop 7
Sedum anglicum
Occasionally found away from habitation but probably derived from garden refuse.

White Stonecrop 31 M
Sedum album
Another garden plant which has spread on to rail ballast, walls and rocks.

Reflexed Stonecrop
Sedum reflexum [Sedum rupestre]
Sometimes becomes established on old retaining walls and churchyard precincts. Yet again a garden escape.

Wall Pepper 31 M
Sedum acre
Broken concrete hutment bases at Lownorth are carpeted with this attractive golden-flowered sedum. Elsewhere it thrives on low roofs, walls, derelict buildings and in paving cracks.

Orpine 1
Sedum telephium
Grows in open woodland at Duncombe Park, possibly a legacy from ornamental gardens.

Pigmyweed 3
Crassula helmsii
A recent introduction from Australia, it was sold as a pond oxygenator in 1927 and was first noticed in Yorkshire some 50 years later in pools at Cayton and Sheriff Hutton. Later discoveries have been in water at Rigg Mill, Danby Lodge and Faceby, presumably dispersed by birds.

SAXIFRAGE FAMILY
SAXIFRAGACEAE

Rue-leaved Saxifrage 12 M
Saxifraga tridactylites
An early-flowering annual which spreads itself liberally on tops of limestone walls, in sandy verges and quarries, then withers into oblivion a few weeks later. Abundant on old masonry at Helmsley Castle, Mount Grace Priory and Byland Abbey.

Meadow Saxifrage 23 M
Saxifraga granulata
This once common saxifrage is hard to find as its favoured habitat of unimproved rough damp grassland is now scarce. It survives in a few riverside pastures and grassy slopes and apparently thrives in fields subject to cattle trampling. Around Hawnby, Mickleby, Hackness and Gerrick.

Opposite-leaved Golden Saxifrage 312 M
Chrysosplenium oppositifolium
Very common in shady wet gullies, carr woodland, rocks with dripping water, streamsides and damp hedge bottoms. It often covers extensive areas.

Alternate-leaved Golden Saxifrage 71 M
Chrysosplenium alternifolium
Often growing with the above species but nowhere near as plentiful. It favours less acid ground and old established woodland, as well as waterfalls, springs and flushes with moving water.

Pick-a-Back Plant
Tolmiea menziesii
A house plant, naturalised in the wild beside Danby Beck at Botton village.

White Stonecrop

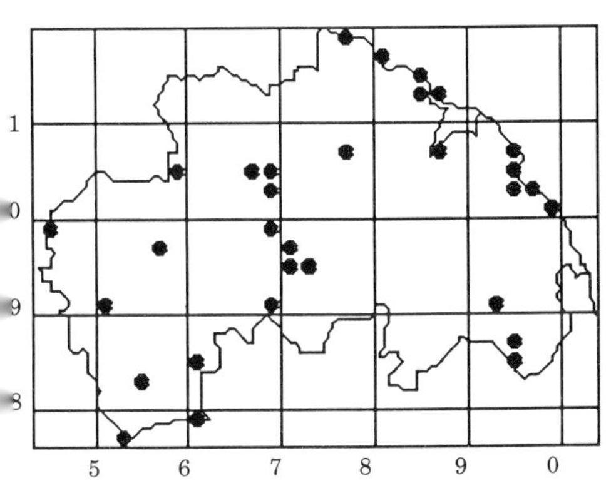

Wall Pepper

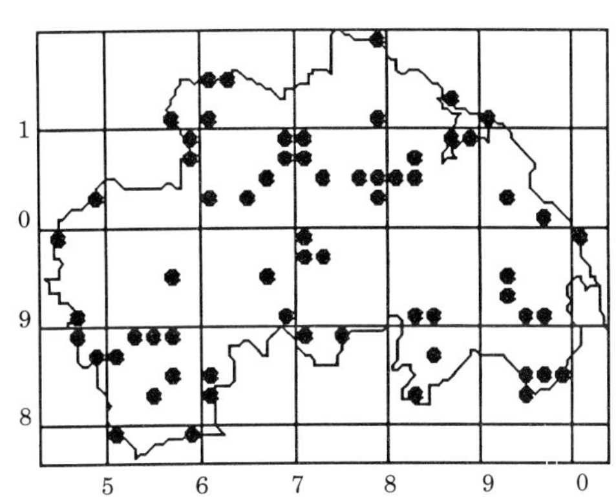

Rue-leaved Saxifrage

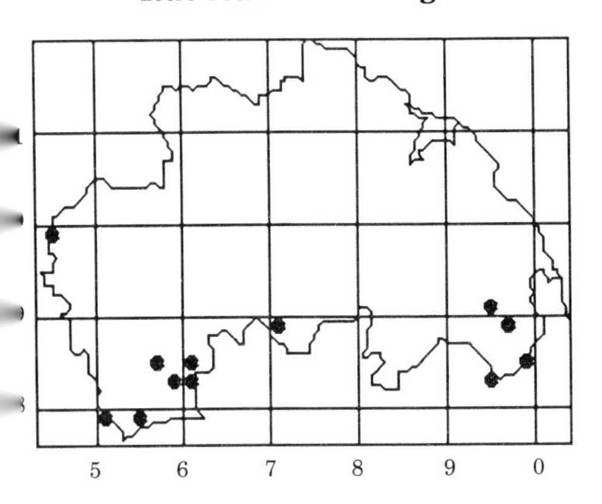

Meadow Saxifrage

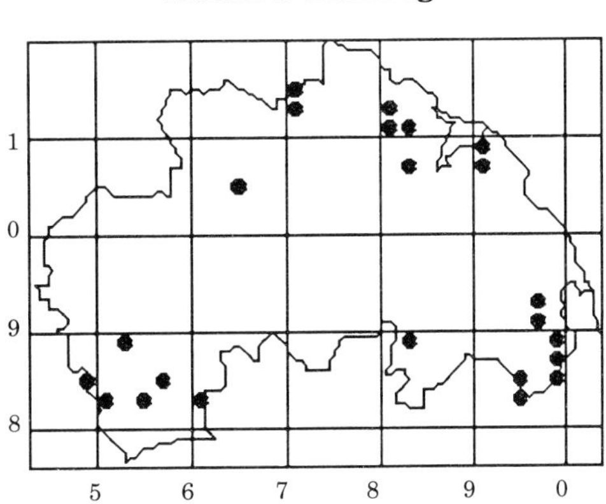

Opposite-leaved Golden Saxifrage

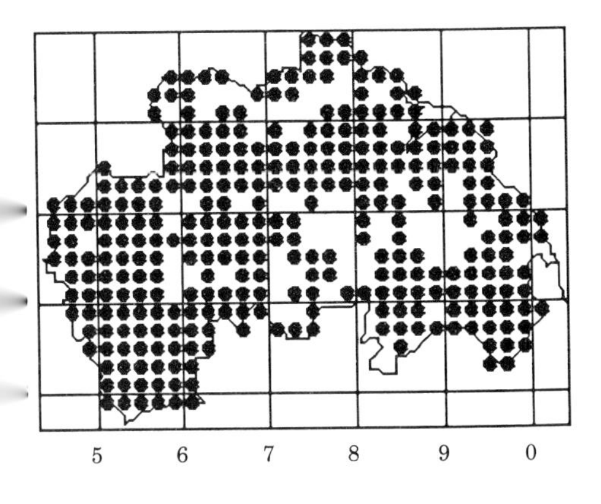

Alternate-leaved Golden Saxifrage

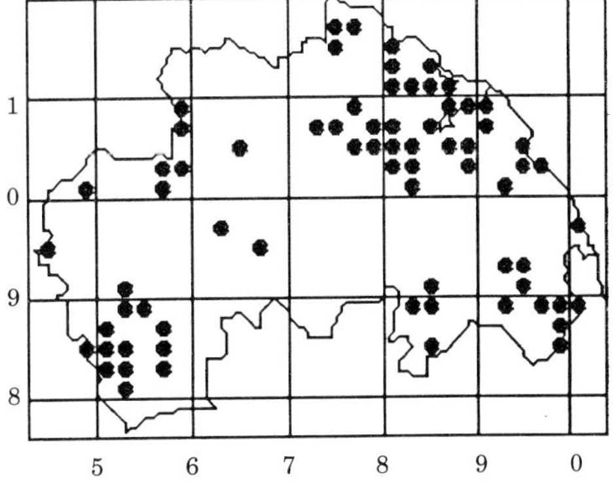

Fringecups
Tellima grandiflora
A garden escape occasionally naturalised. It may have been planted in Crunkly Gill.

Foam Flower
Tiarella spp.
Another garden plant successfully established in the wild – this one on the banks of the Esk below Blue Scar.

London Pride
Saxifraga x *urbium*
A few clumps of this familiar garden plant have been seen naturalised far from habitation such as in Raindale and on Rievaulx Moor.

PARNASSUS FAMILY
PARNASSIACEAE [SAXIFRACACEAE]

Grass of Parnassus 49 M
Parnassia palustris
Despite its name, there is nothing grass-like about this beautiful flower or its leaves. It thrives on the coastal cliffs and inland in marshes, moorland flushes and wet grassland on base-rich soils.

CURRANT FAMILY
GROSSULARIACEAE

Gooseberry 223 M
Ribes uva-crispa
Wild gooseberry is a frequent and widespread shrub in older hedgerows, often producing a useful crop of fruit. It forms an impenetrable tangle in hedges subject to flail cutting.

Black Currant 25 M
Ribes nigrum
An uncommon plant, found in wet woodlands and streamsides in Iburndale, Raisdale, Oldstead, Skelder and Castleton.

Red Currant 100 M
Ribes rubrum
Quite a frequent shrub in moist ancient woodland and shady streambanks in undisturbed and sheltered valleys.

Mountain Currant 9 M
Ribes alpinum
Woodland on limestone in Yorkshire is one of the few native haunts for this rare shrub in Britain. Locally it has been found in scrub woodland and old hedgerows around Helmsley, Rievaulx, Raisdale and Scugdale. It may have been planted at Hackness, Crunkly Gill and Easby.

Flowering Currant
Ribes sanguineum
A garden shrub which establishes in the wild infrequently.

SUNDEW FAMILY
DROSERACEAE

Round-leaved Sundew 147 M
Drosera rotundifolia
In sphagnum bogs and moorland flushes, it grows in abundance. Its carnivorous diet allows it to survive on water-logged, nutrient-poor, bare peat and ditchsides which are often devoid of other vegetation. It is absent from the drier heather-dominated areas.

Long-leaved Sundew 0
Drosera anglica [Drosera longifolia]
Formerly recorded in Sievedale fen and Battersby slack but has not been seen in recent years.

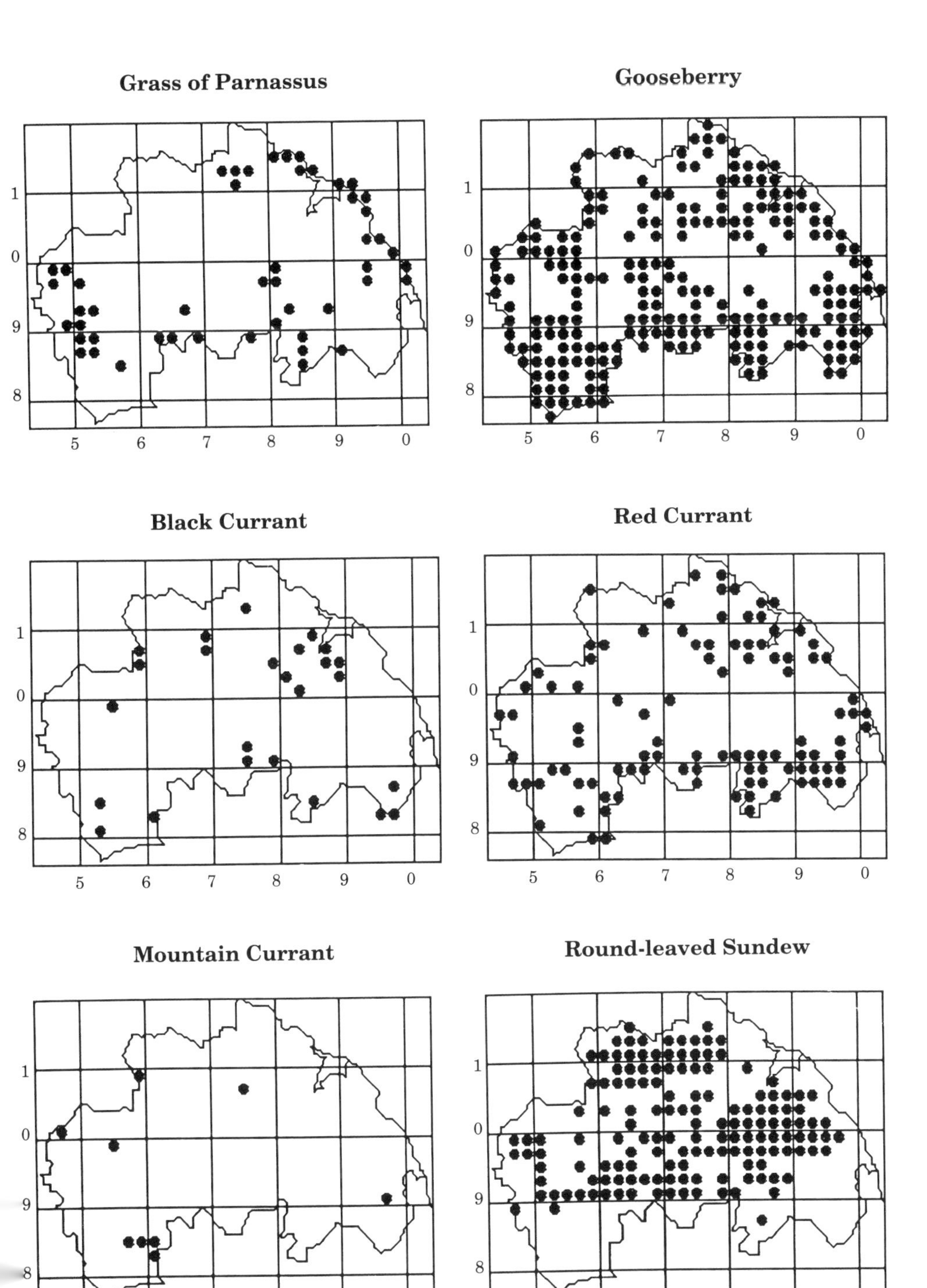
Grass of Parnassus
Gooseberry
Black Currant
Red Currant
Mountain Currant
Round-leaved Sundew
1
0
9
8
5
6
7
8
9
0

LOOSESTRIFE FAMILY
LYTHRACEAE

Purple Loosestrife 7 M
Lythrum salicaria
With much recent land drainage, suitable sites for this once common plant are now scarce. Small populations survive in marshes and shallow becks at Coxwold, Everley, Harwood Dale, Eskdaleside and Throxenby but the long-term survival of this attractive marsh plant is in jeopardy.

Water Purslane 6 M
Lythrum portula
Infrequent by muddy pools and lake edge. Arden, Kepwick, Elleron, Lunshaw Beck, Lythe and Hilla Green.

DAPHNE FAMILY
THYMELAEACEAE

Spurge Laurel 24 M
Daphne laureola
More a plant of southern British beechwoods, its local distribution is sparse in undisturbed older hedgerows, open woods and scrub on base-rich soils and in sheltered locations.

Mezereon 1
Daphne mezereum
Known only in a disused limestone quarry north of Pickering, where a few plants struggle to survive encroaching vegetation. A short-lived shrub, it appears to regenerate adequately in this one location but has not managed to disperse from there.

OLEASTER FAMILY
ELAEAGNACEAE

Sea Buckthorn 5
Hippophae rhamnoides
It has been found at various places on coastal cliffs northwards from Boggle Hole. Although it is believed that the plants have been introduced, this species has naturalised well in the salt-laden winds which assault these cliffs.

Eleagnus umbellata
Several bushes of this popular garden shrub are incorporated in fieldside hedging near Silpho.

WILLOWHERB FAMILY
ONAGRACEAE

Great Hairy Willowherb 252 M
Epilobium hirsutum
Known locally as "Codlins and Cream", this stalwart plant is widespread in shallow streams, marshes and pond edges with more or less permanent water and fertile soil. Mainly a lowland species and often prolific in ditches with nitrogen-enriched run-off from agricultural land.

Lesser Hairy Willowherb 90 M
Epilobium parviflorum
Occasional on stream banks, wet wasteland and marsh.

Broad-leaved Willowherb 315 M
Epilobium montanum
A very common plant on waste ground, walls, ditches and in gardens, absent only from high moorland.

Small-flowered Willowherb 6
Epilobium roseum
A locally rare plant found in damp disturbed soils on woodland edge.

Purple Loosestrife

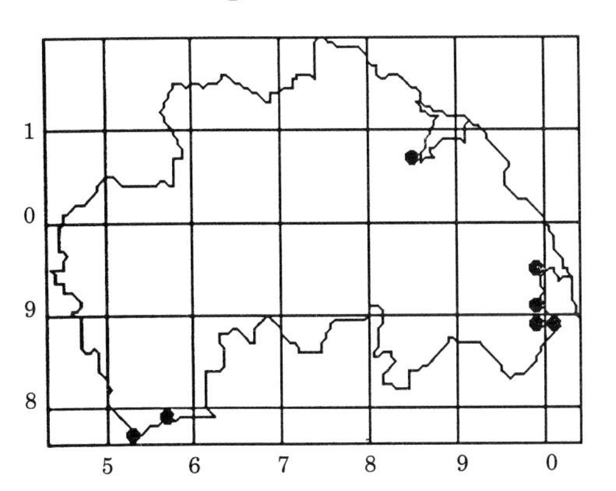

Water Purslane

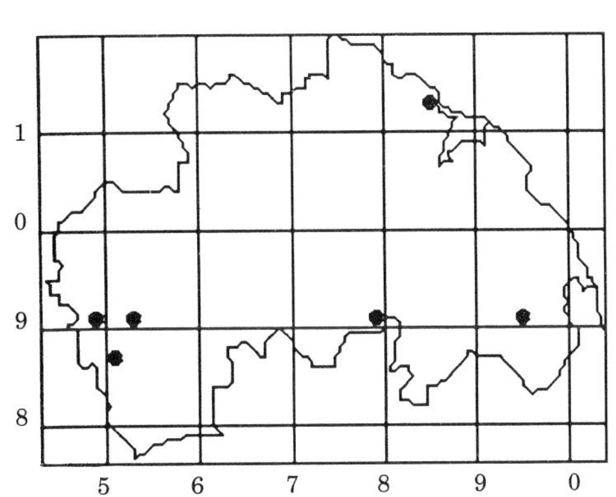

Spurge Laurel

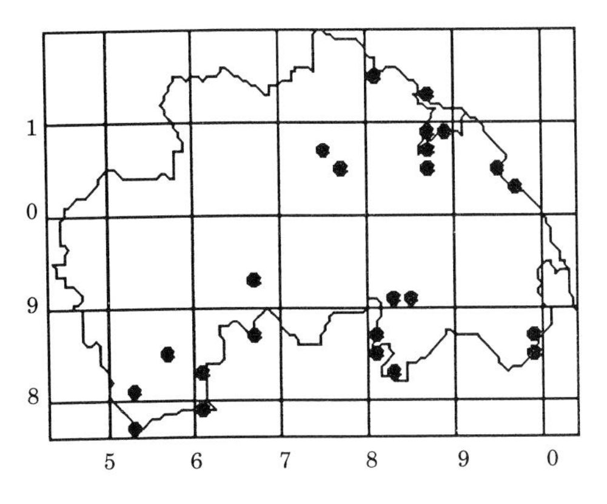

Great Hairy Willowherb

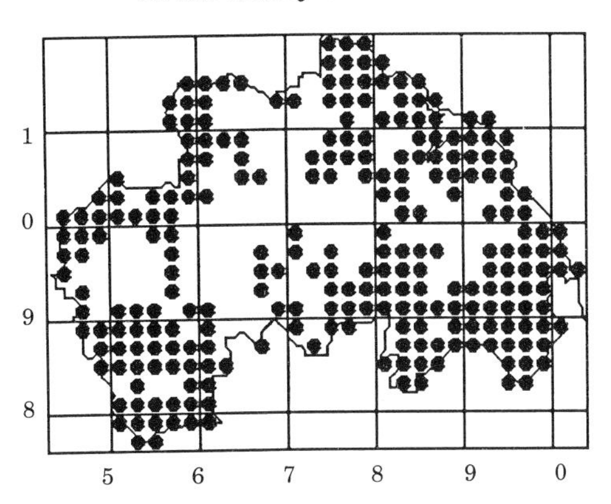

Lesser Hairy Willowherb

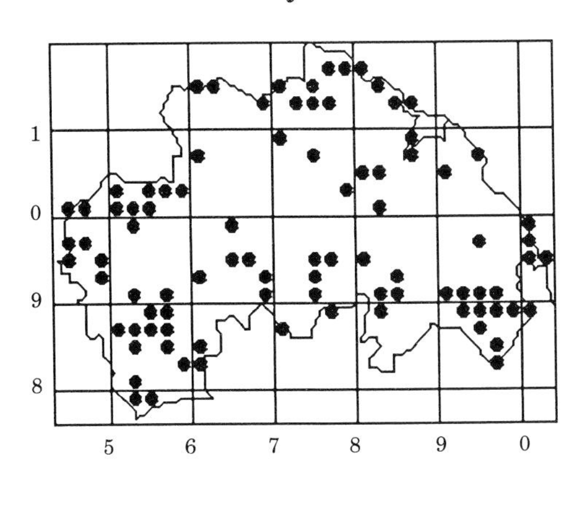

Broad-leaved Willowherb

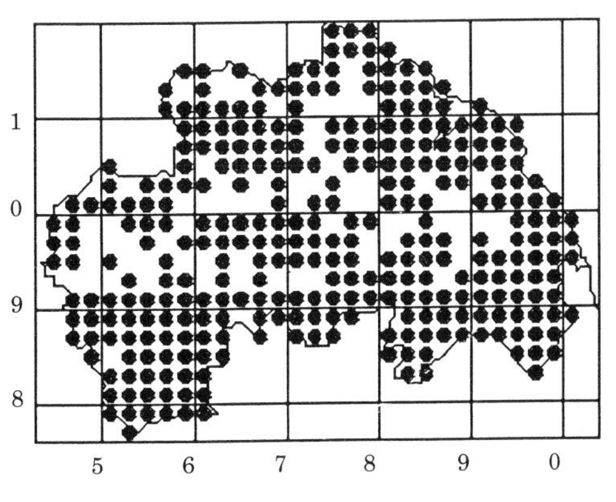

American Willowherb 84 M
Epilobium ciliatum
First recorded in Britain in 1891, the efficient air-borne seed dispersal system of this plant has ensured its countrywide spread. It is noticeably abundant along the Esk Valley railside, presumably wafted along in the slipstream of passing trains. Commonly found on wasteland, roadsides and woodland edges throughout the lower land.

Square-stemmed Willowherb 27
Epilobium tetragonum
Grows by streamsides and in damp wooded areas.

Dull-leaved Willowherb 20
Epilobium obscurum
Like the above species, it has been recorded only sparsely, and in similar habitats. It may well be that some willowherbs have been under-recorded owing to difficulties in identification when not flowering.

Marsh Willowherb 253 M
Epilobium palustre
Found extensively in acid bogs, marshes, moorland flushes and ditches. It is usually almost hidden by more vigorous wetland plants.

New Zealand Willlowherb 52 M
Epilobium brunnescens
Another recent arrival to Britain, it was brought in as a rock garden plant in 1908 and soon took to the wild. It is a familiar and, when flowering, decorative addition to the moorland flora, sprawling around damp hollows, wheelruts, peaty banks and forest rides. In vegetative form it can be confused with bog pimpernel.

Rosebay Willowherb 361
Chamerion angustifolium
Widespread and abundant on disturbed ground, rubbish tips and roadsides. It quickly colonises felled forest compartments until it is out-competed by bramble thicket.

Evening Primrose 3
Oenothera spp.
Varieties of this garden plant grow wild in a few wasteland locations.

Enchanter's Nightshade 213 M
Circaea lutetiana
Occasionally a persistent garden weed, its normal habitat is moist shady woodland, where large colonies prosper in humus-rich soils.

WATER MILFOIL FAMILY
HALORAGACEAE

Spiked Water Milfoil 1
Myriophyllum spicatum
Occurs in less acid water. Recorded in Boltby reservoir. Records for this species in the lower river systems require confirmation.

Alternate-flowered Water Milfoil 18 M
Myriophyllum alterniflorum
A plant of upland acid or peaty water, often growing in the higher reaches of rivers and in northern reservoirs.

MARESTAIL FAMILY
HIPPURIDACEAE

Marestail 13 M
Hippuris vulgaris
Not a common water plant in this area but it has been found in several nutrient-rich streams such as in Dalbydale, Sleddale, Kirkdale, Bransdale and elsewhere. Often planted in new fishponds and ornamental lakes.

American Willowherb

Marsh Willowherb

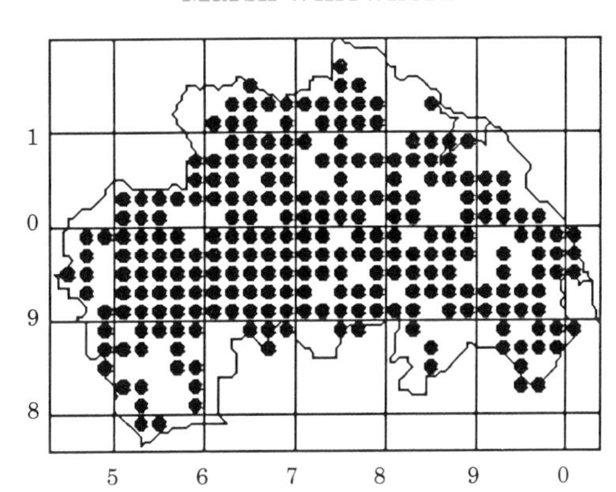

New Zealand Willlowherb

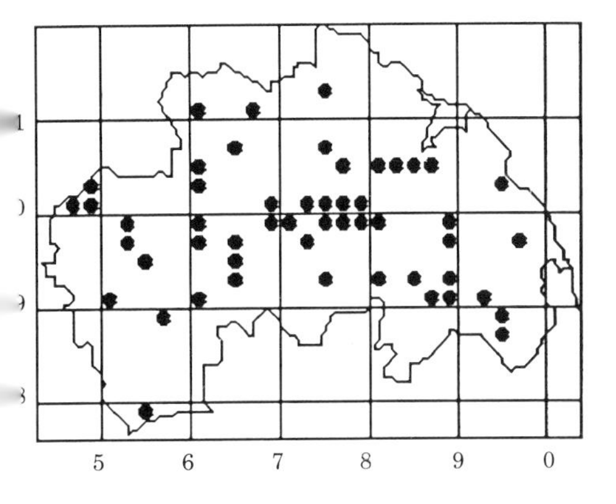

Enchanter's Nightshade

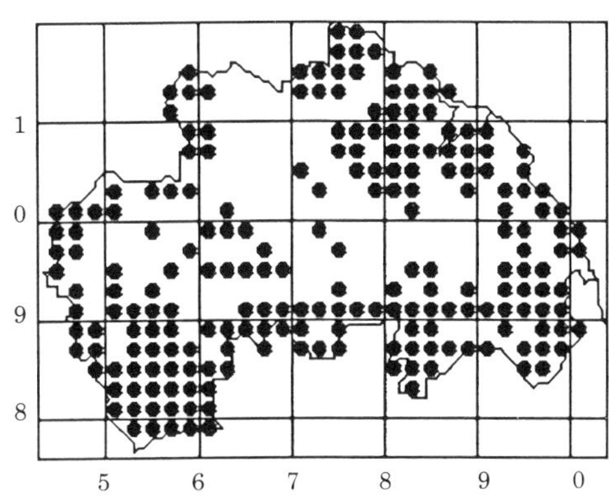

Alternate-flowered Water Milfoil

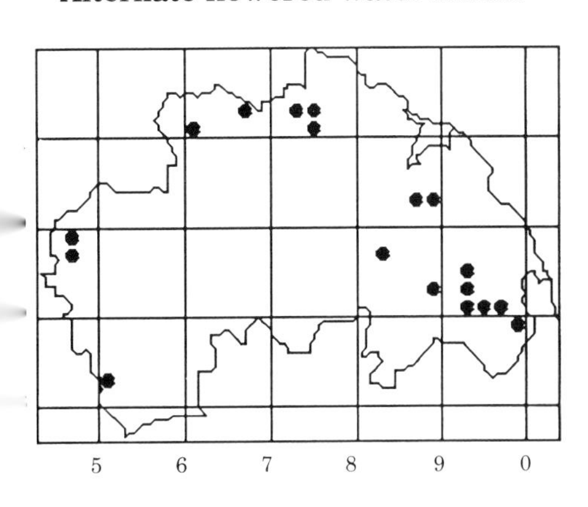

Marestail

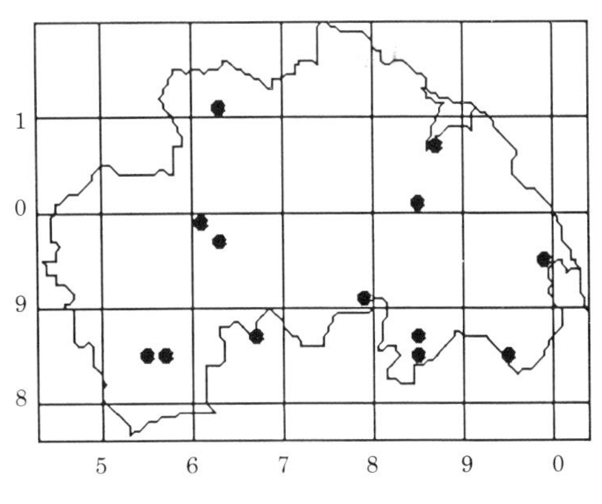

STARWORT FAMILY
CALLITRICHACEAE

The following starworts have been noted but insufficient records exist to map them separately.

C. hammulata,
C. stagnalis,
C. hermaphroditica
Abundant in most shallow waterways and semi-permanent puddles.

DOGWOOD FAMILY
CORNACEAE

Dogwood 33 M
Cornus sanguinea
At the northern limit of its range, this distinctive shrub grows in older mixed hedgerows and scrub on the limestone belt. Seen at its best in uncut spinneys such as in Riccaldale, Appleton-le-Moors and Ampleforth.

Dwarf Cornel 3
Cornus suecica
A relic of post glacial arctic vegetation and dispersed on high Scottish moorlands and Scandinavian mountains, the only English populations have survived on north-facing slopes of the Hole of Horcum, Blakey Topping and until re-afforestation, Crosscliff.

IVY FAMILY
ARALIACEAE

Ivy 294 M
Hedera helix
Abundant on walls, banksides, open woodlands and around buildings. Wayside trees are frequently almost smothered with ivy up to the canopy, although it uses the tree for support rather than sustenance. In mixed deciduous woods it grows extensively up trees and along the ground. It avoids very wet acid soils and is absent from upland woods with low winter temperatures. Sparse also in birch and conifer woodland.

CARROT FAMILY
UMBELLIFERAE [APIACEAE]

Pennywort 205 M
Hydrocotyle vulgaris
Widespread across the wetter moors, its low-growing, almost circular leaves cover extensive patches in acid shallow pools, flushes, runnels and roadside ditches, though its flowers are seldom seen.

Sanicle 172 M
Sanicula europaea
Frequent in old deciduous woods on calcareous and base-rich soils. Often found quite deep into a wood, provided a modicum of light penetrates.

Rough Chervil 145 M
Chaerophyllum temulentum
[Chaerophyllum temulem]
A grassy verge plant, which comes into flower as cow parsley dies back, but less numerous and not as widespread. It favours light free-draining soil on lower land and is most plentiful in the shelter of hedgerows on the coastal plain.

Cow Parsley 322 M
Anthriscus sylvestris
Despite mowing, herbicide spraying, parking of cars etc, cow parsley continues to flourish on most grassy road verges away from the moors, providing a spectacular springtime display, and described colloquially as "Queen Anne's Lace".

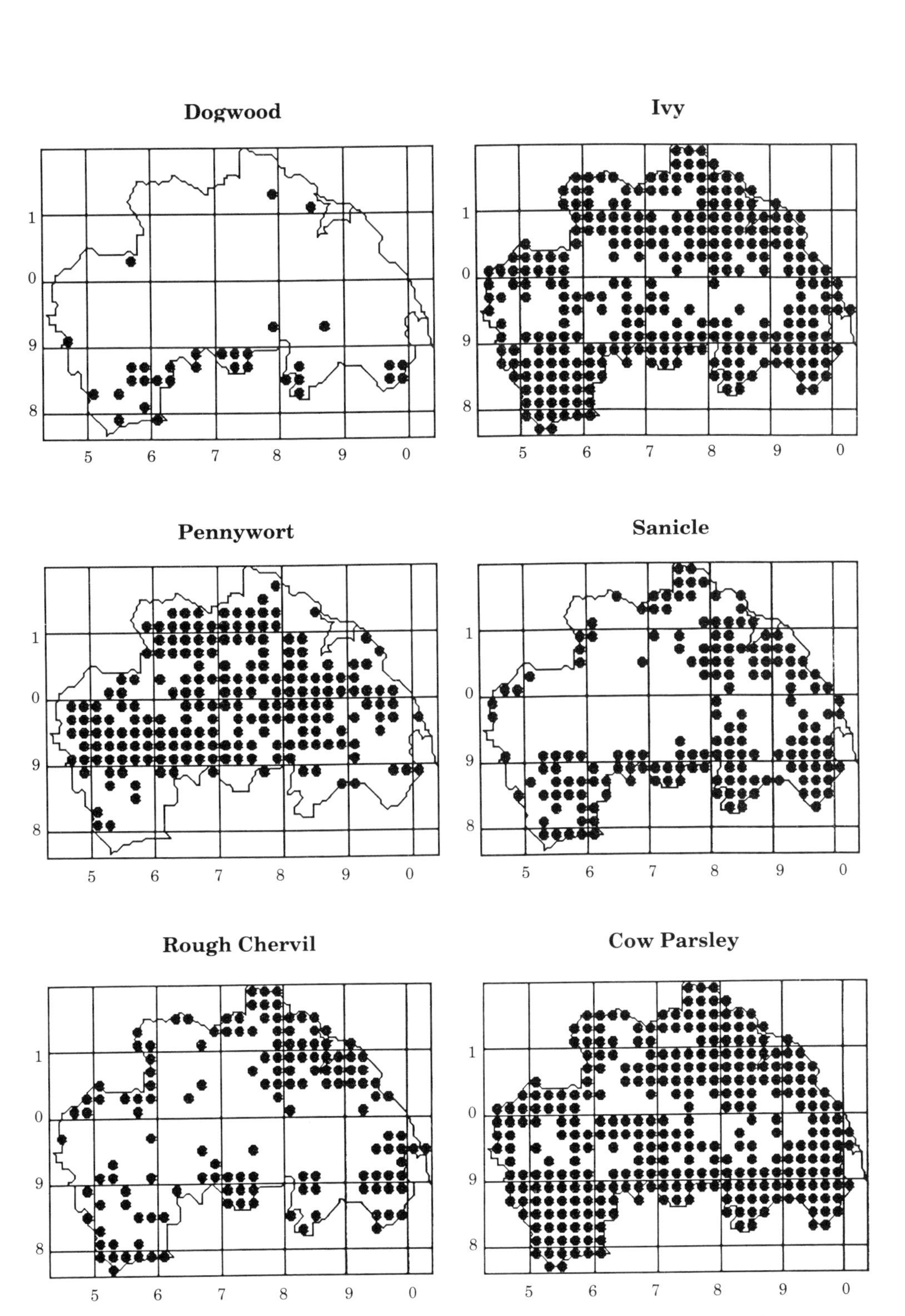
Dogwood
Ivy
Pennywort
Sanicle
Rough Chervil
Cow Parsley
1
0
9
8
5
6
7
8
9
0

Shepherd's Needle
Scandix pecten-veneris
Described as "common" in *The Natural History of the Scarborough District,* published in 1953, not a single plant has been found during the recent survey, presumably eliminated by herbicide sprays. It will be interesting to observe, on land now being set-aside from food production, if viable seed has remained dormant to enable this plant to return.

Sweet Cicely 152 M
Myrrhis odorata
An alien from the mountains of southern Europe, it is widely established as a roadside plant, often in a dampish situation. It can be prolific on verges approaching river bridges, though seldom grows far down the river bank. Its strong aniseed aroma and luxuriant growth make it noticeable on many waysides. Abundant on seepage lines near Cold Kirby church.

Alexanders 22 M
Smyrnium olusatrum
An introduced herb formerly eaten like celery, it grows in abundance on waysides and grassy verges, always within a mile or two of the coast. In some places on the sea cliffs it is the dominant vegetation.

Pignut 339 M
Conopodium majus
Widespread in old grassland, hedgebanks and open woods, especially on lighter soils. Absent from high moorland.

Burnet Saxifrage 52 M
Pimpinella saxifraga
Quite frequent in dry, rough calcareous grassland, especially old unimproved pastures and disused limestone quarries.

Greater Burnet Saxifrage 20 M
Pimpinella major
More of a lowland plant and virtually confined to the Ampleforth – Coxwold area where it grows abundantly on alkaline soil. On mown verges, damage to the rooting system stimulates prolific vegetative growth.

Ground Elder 221
Aegopodium podagraria
Believed to have been introduced by the Romans, this plant seeks out nitrogen-rich soil and then manages to oust most other vegetation. Hence the problem it causes in many gardens and the large patches which occur on wasteland and roadsides near buildings.

Water Parsnip 18 M
Berula erecta
To be found in most clear running water on fertile, alkaline soils. Often growing with fool's watercress, it appears to be less hardy and is confined to lowland streams and pools in the south of the Park.

Fine-leaved Water Dropwort 1
Oenanthe aquatica
Able to withstand long dry periods, this vigorous plant grows rapidly when water returns; it tolerates grazing and trampling by cattle around West Ayton pond, its only known location.

Hemlock Water Dropwort 5
Oenanthe crocata
Rare on flood banks by the Esk at Ruswarp, on cliffs between Saltwick and Hawsker Highlight and in Newton Wood, Roseberry.

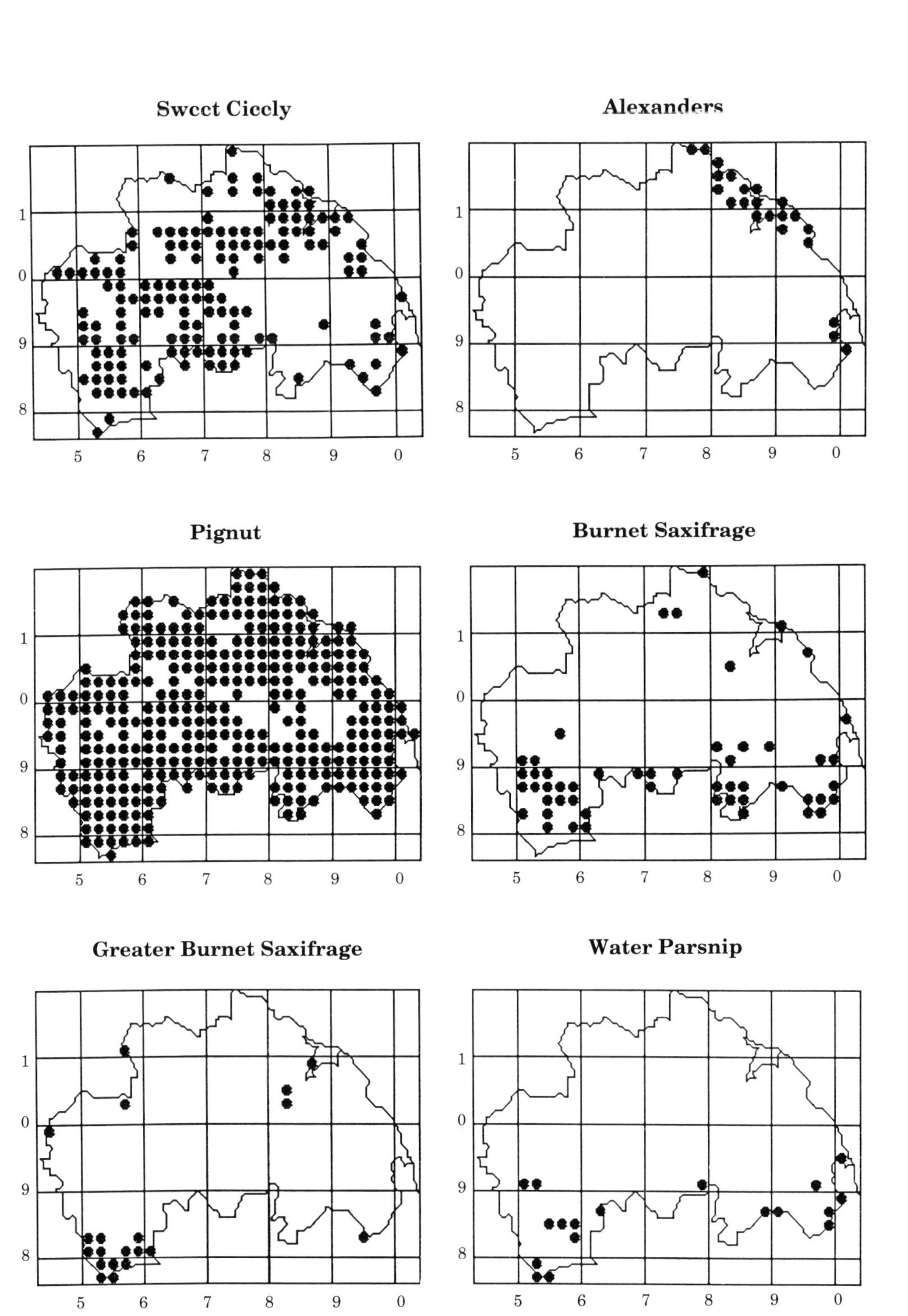

Sweet Cicely
Alexanders
Pignut
Burnet Saxifrage
Greater Burnet Saxifrage
Water Parsnip
1
0
9
8
5
6
7
8
9
0

Fool's Parsley 50 M
Aethusa cynapium
A frequent weed of waste ground, fields and gardens on sandy or limestone soils in lower land. A late flowering annual, it is sometimes abundant in autumn stubble fields.

Pepper Saxifrage 23 M
Silaum silaus
An indication of unimproved herb-rich pasture is provided by this uncommon yellow-flowered plant. It has been found in damp fields, heaths such as Appleton Common and rough grassy banks as at Waupley, Raindale and Hawsker Bottoms.

Hemlock 58 M
Conium maculatum
This highly poisonous plant is quite widespread on heavy damp soils, especially the coastal boulder clay. It grows on road verges, streamsides, rubbish tips and in arable fields.

Wild Parsnip 4
Pastinaca sativa
Only around Staithes, Grosmont and Briggswath has this plant been seen. It may have originated as a garden throw-out, but is well established in its wild locations.

Fool's Watercress 34 M
Apium nodiflorum
In shallow nutrient-rich streams and ditches this plant grows liberally, almost choking the waterway on occasions. It seems to prefer clear, slightly moving water.

Lesser Marshwort 3
Apium inundatum
Rare in still or slow-moving water, it occurs in ponds at West Ayton, Appleton Common and at Lake Gormire, and quickly revives after lengthy periods of drought.

Parsley 2
Petroselinum crispum
An introduced garden herb, which has spread to a few locations on the cliffs from Staithes to Boulby.

Wild Angelica 322 M
Angelica sylvestris
A sturdy wetland plant widely distributed wherever water stands for most of the year in grassland, ditches and marshy ground.

Wild Celery 2
Apium graveolens
Very rare, at its northern limit in Britain, it has been found on the banks of the Esk around Ruswarp.

Hogweed 360
Heracleum sphondylium
A very common and robust plant found on rough grassland, verges and field edges throughout the valleys and farmed area. A distinctive narrow-leaved form, var. *angustifolia*, is quite widespread.

Giant Hogweed 1
Heracleum mantegazzianum
This poisonous giant of a plant has been planted beside Crosscliff Lake, but being virtually inaccessible and apparently not spreading, it causes no problem – unlike the specimens which appear from time to time in more populous places.

Upright Hedge Parsley 221 M
Torilis japonica
Common on hedgebanks and grassy road and rail verges away from the moors.

Knotted Hedge Parsley 1
Torilis nodosa
A plant of light sandy soils, it has been recorded only once, in a disused quarry at Beedale, where it flourishes on sheep-grazed, stony pasture.

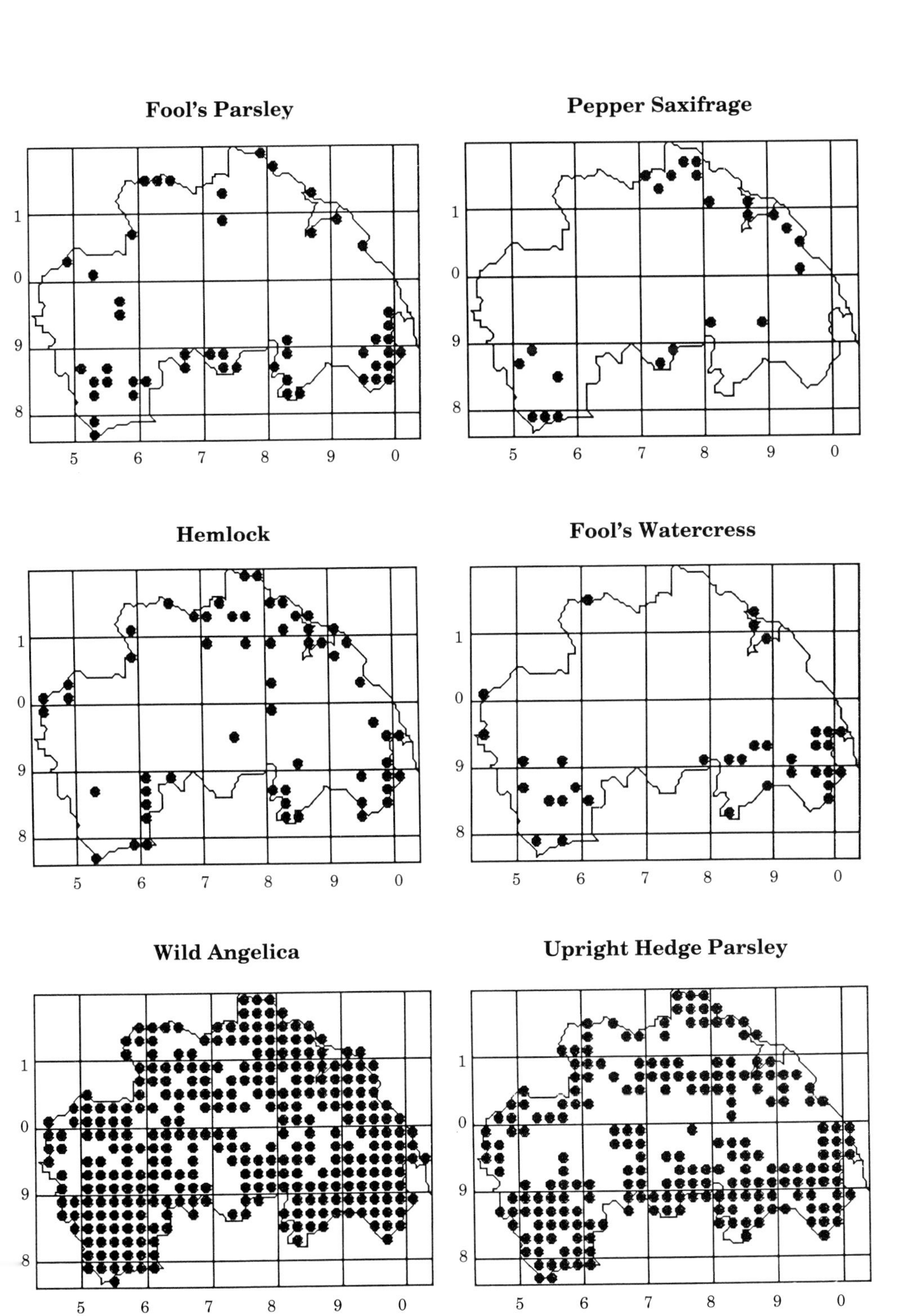
Fool's Parsley
Pepper Saxifrage
Hemlock
Fool's Watercress
Wild Angelica
Upright Hedge Parsley
1
0
9
8
5
6
7
8
9
0

Wild Carrot 31 M
Daucus carota
This lime-loving plant occurs sporadically in grassland on coastal cliffs, also further inland on embankments, laybys and verges with calcareous soils.

Caraway
Carum carvi
Appeared briefly on farmland at Mowthorpe, possibly introduced with grass seed.

Fennel
Foeniculum vulgare
A culinary herb quite widely grown in gardens, and established in the wild at Briggswath and Irton moor.

MELON FAMILY
CUCURBITACEAE

White Bryony 10
Bryonia dioica
Approaching its northern limit, single plants have been found climbing up sheltered hedgerows in Sanddale, Wass, Sleightholmedale, Riccaldale and along the coast.

SPURGE FAMILY
EUPHORBIACEAE

Dog's Mercury 293 M
Mercurialis perennis
Regarded as an indicator of ancient woodland, it grows in large populations on neutral soils in deciduous woods and nearby hedgebanks. It seems to survive after removal of tree cover as it is quite often seen in unimproved pastures.

Sun Spurge 71 M
Euphorbia helioscopia
A common weed on enriched arable land, in gardens and waysides.

Petty Spurge 65 M
Euphorbia peplus
Frequent in farm and garden on disturbed soil and may often be found at the foot of walls and fences.

Dwarf Spurge 4
Euphorbia exigua
Once an abundant cornfield weed, this plant is now listed as rare throughout the country. In this area it was found on set-aside land at Murton, also in a forest glade at Cropton and in two arable fields.

Sweet Spurge
Euphorbia dulcis
A garden escape, found established beside a ride in Allerston Forest.

Caper Spurge 1
Euphorbia lathyrus
A garden plant naturalised on wasteland near Ingleby Greenhow.

DOCK FAMILY
POLYGONACEAE

Knotgrass 329 M
Polygonum aviculare agg.
A widespread weed in trampled or disturbed ground such as gateways, paths and tracks. *Polygonum arenastrum* has been noted but not mapped separately.

Bistort 50 M
Polygonum bistorta [Persicaria bistorta]
A native plant formerly used as a pot herb as indicated by its common name of Easter ledges. It flourishes in patches on verges and field edge, often near habitation. Its prominent flowering spikes create a colourful addition to grassy roadsides at Cropton, Sleights, Byland, Seave Green, Boltby and lower Eskdale. It also flourishes on river banks in Rosedale and Farndale.

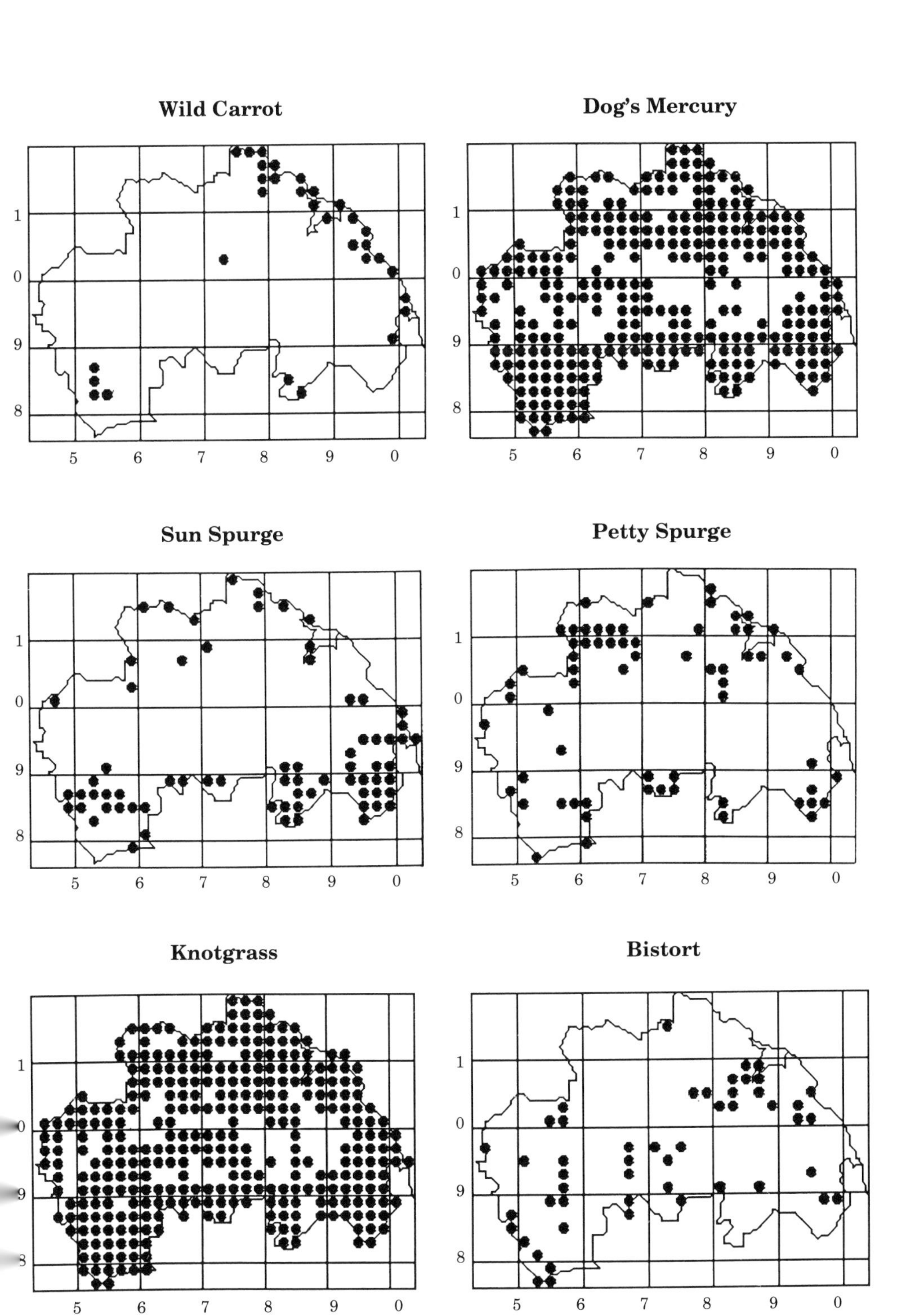
Wild Carrot
1
0
9
8
5
6
7
8
9
0
Dog's Mercury
1
0
9
8
5
6
7
8
9
0
Sun Spurge
1
0
9
8
5
6
7
8
9
0
Petty Spurge
1
0
9
8
5
6
7
8
9
0
Knotgrass
1
0
9
8
5
6
7
8
9
0
Bistort
1
0
9
8
5
6
7
8
9
0

Amphibious Bistort 16
Polygonum amphibium
[Persicaria amphibia]
Both amphibious and terrestrial forms of this plant have been noted. It has a very limited distribution in marshy meadows and slow-running streams with non-calcareous water. Pond edges at Throxenby, Appleton Common, the old Abbey watercourse at Byland and in Leven Vale.

Redshank or **Persicaria** 281 M
Polygonum persicaria
[Persicaria maculosa]
Very common on disturbed ground throughout the farmed area. It shows resistance to herbicides and may carpet an infested field on poorer soil.

Pale Persicaria 91 M
Polygonum lapathifolium
[Persicaria lapathifolia]
Often growing with, but far less common than redshank. It is found in poorly drained arable land, permanent pasture and waste ground.

Water Pepper 44 M
Polygonum hydropiper
[Persicaria hydropiper]
On damp arable land, shallow ditches, wet hollows in pasture and occasionally by moorland streams. Its occurrence is local but, on sandy soil with a high seasonal water table, it can be extensive and persistent.

Tasteless Water Pepper 2
Polygonum mite [Persicaria laxiflora]
Rare, found only in Troutsdale and in a slack on Stony Marl moor.

Japanese Knotweed 31
Reynoutria japonica [Fallopia japonica]
An introduced plant, which has spread alarmingly further south but in this area, although established in many places, it does not appear to create a problem. It was brought into Victorian gardens from Japan but, because of its exceptionally rampant growth form, further planting in this country is illegal.

Himalayan Knotweeds
Polygonum polystachum [Persicaria wallichii] – a garden escape naturalised in a few places.

Polygonum campanulatum [Persicaria campanulata] – rarely recorded in this country, an established colony has been found by Ingleby Beck.

Black Bindweed 98 M
Fallopia convolvulus
Frequent on arable land and on rubbish heaps, where the soil is acidic but nutrient-rich.

Sheep's Sorrel 336
Rumex acetosella
Indicating impoverished acid soil, it is widespread in the uplands. On old shale heaps, forest clear-fells and severely burnt moorland, scarlet patches are created by its maturing leaves and flowers.

Slender Sheep's Sorrel 7
Rumex tenuifolius
Occasional on low-nutrient soils or sand, especially on bare, windswept or fire damaged heath.

Sorrel 376 M
Rumex acetosa
Common on neutral to acid grassland in field, wood, ditch and wayside.

Curled Dock 229 M
Rumex crispus
Although it can be a troublesome farm or garden weed, its location is fairly selective, being concentrated on the coastal plain and absent from very exposed, acid or wet ground.

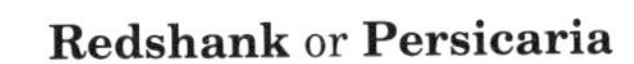

Redshank or **Persicaria**

Pale Persicaria

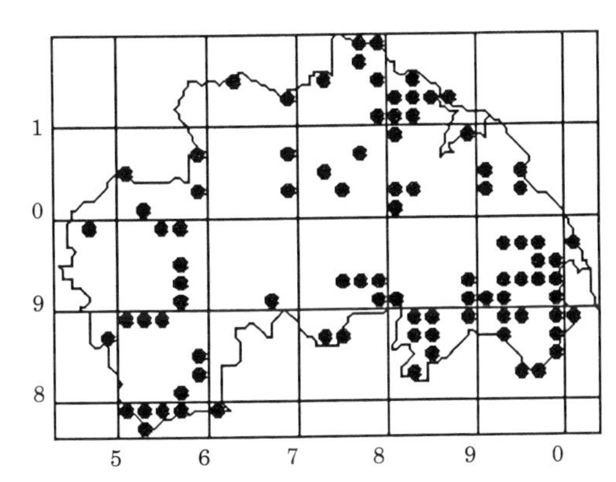

Water Pepper

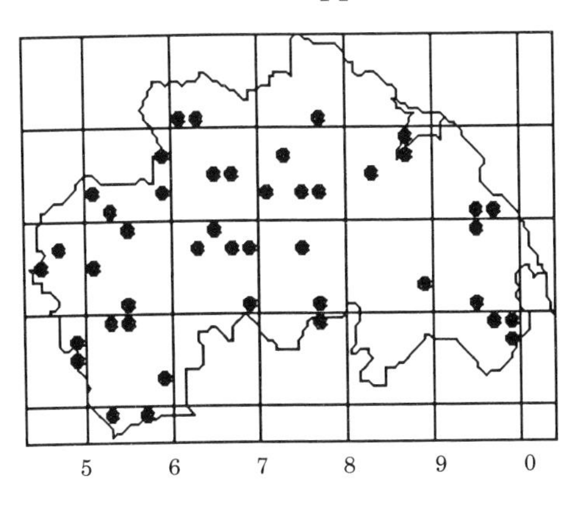

Black Bindweed

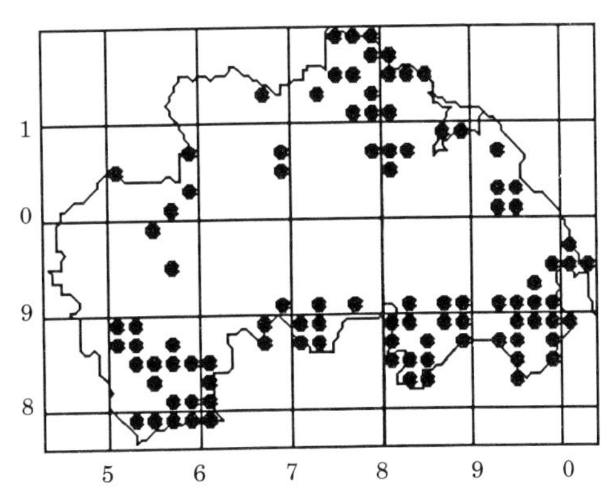

Sorrel

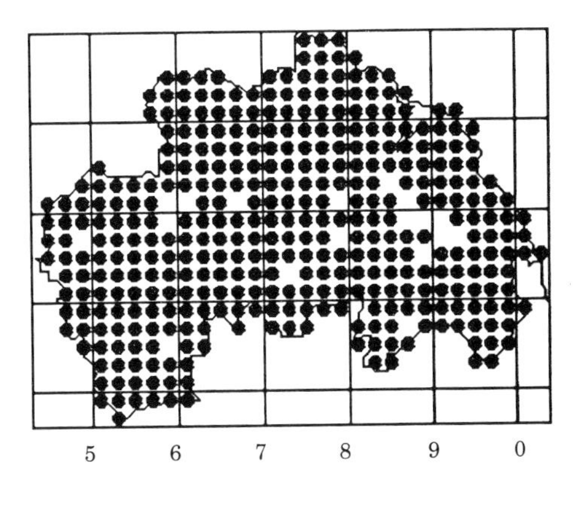

Curled Dock

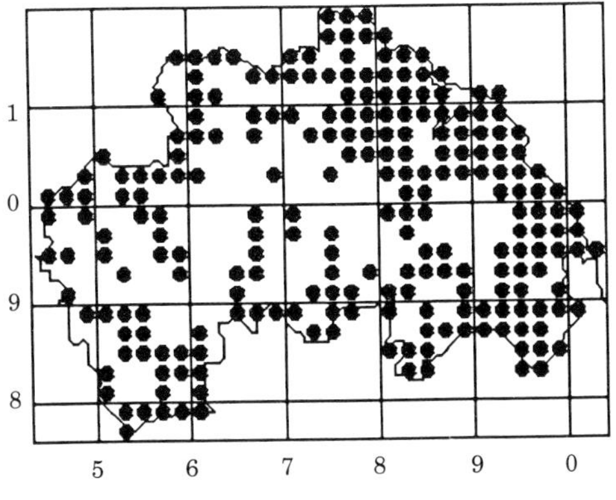

Broad-leaved Dock 362 M
Rumex obtusifolius
A very common dock throughout the area except on acid peat. It grows on roadsides, around buildings, gateways, in old pastures and disturbed ground, its deep penetrating root ensuring survival in most unlikely situations.

Red-veined or **Wood Dock** 142 M
Rumex sanguineus
Predominantly a plant of old damp valley woods, it thrives in heavy soils beneath moderate shade of deciduous trees and on nearby waysides and verges. Red veining in its leaves is not always apparent.

Sharp Dock 47
Rumex conglomeratus
Found infrequently in wet rough grassland, on ditch banks and damp wood margins.

Golden Dock 1
Rumex maritimus
Recorded some 50 years ago in Suffield Mere, this handsome plant was refound there in the hot summer of 1990, when it appeared to be struggling for survival in dried-out mud.

NETTLE FAMILY
URTICACEAE

Pellitory of the Wall 10 M
Parietaria judaica
An insignificant plant which manages to flourish in apparently impoverished situations. With a preference for the coast and churchyard walls, it grows around Whitby Abbey, Saltwick, Ruswarp, Newholm, Robin Hood's Bay and Boggle Hole, and inland at Hutton Buscel, Hackness and Yoadwath. Often rooted in old mortar, at wall footings or on exposed rock.

Annual Nettle 36 M
Urtica urens
Found occasionally on disturbed ground with sandy or free-draining soil, especially in gardens and allotments. More plentiful further south, in this area it is more or less restricted to warmer lower land and the moderating influence of the coast.

Stinging Nettle 386
Urtica dioica
Abundant in enriched ground, often near habitation and farmyards. It soon appears on rubble heaps, bonfire sites and drainage outlets. Benefiting from high nitrogen, it frequently grows with elder by walls and derelict buildings where sheep shelter in the upper dales.

HEMP FAMILY
CANNABACEAE

Hop 12 M
Humulus lupulus
Rare this far north, single plants have been found scrambling over hedgerows and old walls in upper Farndale, Scugdale, Staithes, Hundale Point, Ridge Lane near Roxby and Osmotherley.

ELM FAMILY
ULMACEAE

Wych Elm 229 M
Ulmus glabra
Frequent in mixed woodland, hedgerows, wet copses and streamsides. This elm largely withstood the ravages of dutch elm disease, only isolated trees being affected.

Broad-leaved Dock

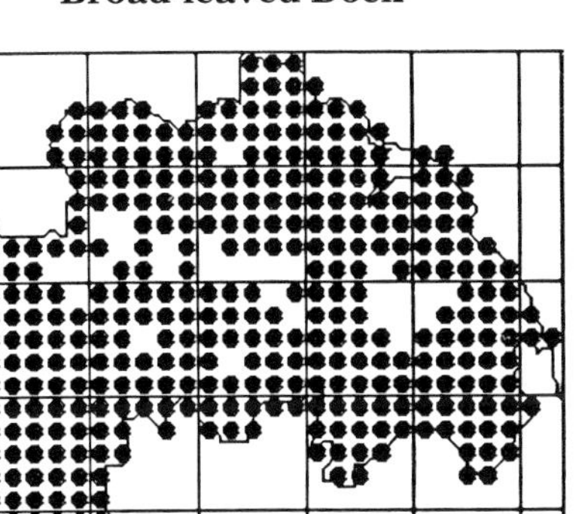

Red-veined or Wood Dock

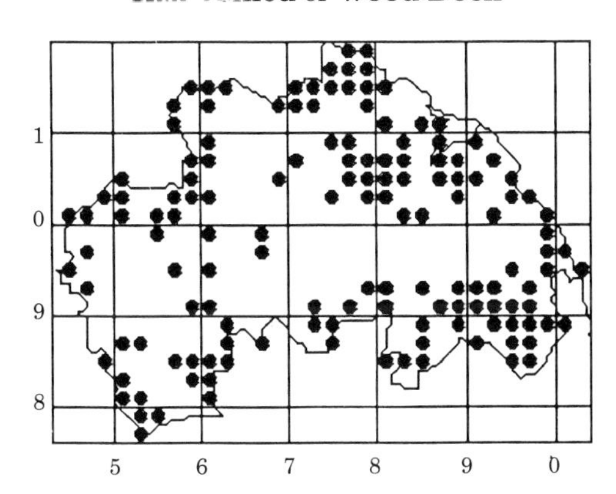

Pellitory of the Wall

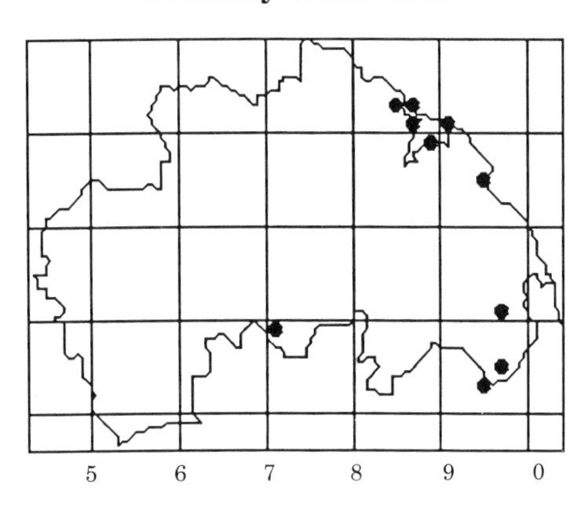

Annual Nettle

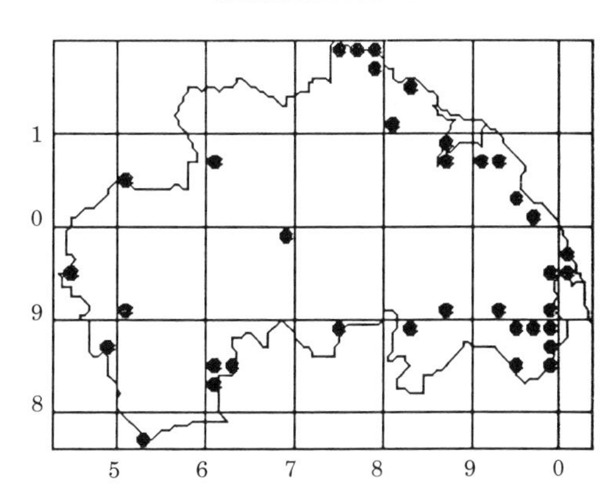

Hop

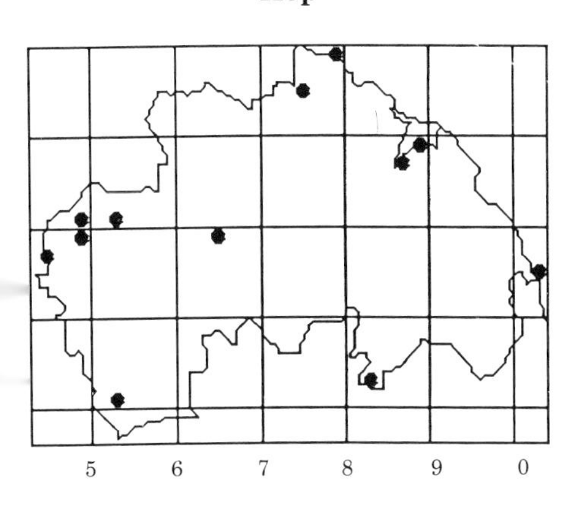

Wych Elm

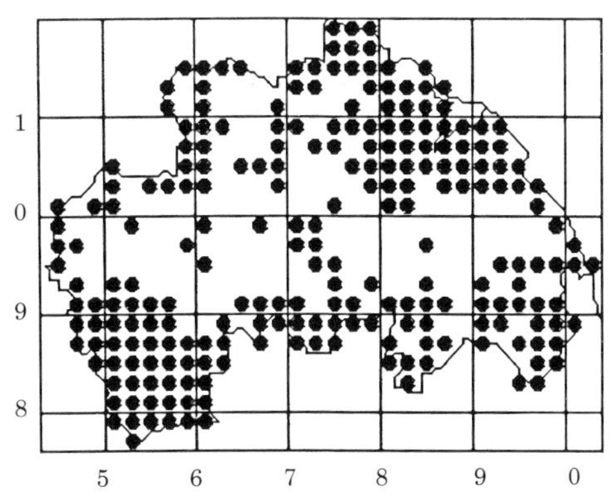

English Elm 47 M
Ulmus procera
Although dutch elm disease severely affected this species during the 1970s, not all were killed off. Quite a few mature trees subsequently started regrowth from ground level.

Smooth Elm
Ulmus minor
This tree has been found in Partridge Hill Wood, Sneaton, and at Hay Brow, Scalby, but is believed to have been planted in both locations.

SWEET GALE FAMILY
MYRICACEAE

Sweet Gale or **Bog Myrtle** 51 M
Myrica gale
Forms large stands in acid bogs with moving ground water and minimal sheep grazing. To date it has only been found south and east of a line from Shaken Bridge near Hawnby on the Rye to Overdale Wyke near Sandsend on the coast, presumably unable to tolerate the wind exposure and more extreme temperatures of the higher moorland. Its aromatic foliage is still picked and used for home brewing of gale beer.

BIRCH FAMILY
BETULACEAE

Silver Birch 324 M
Betula pendula
A common tree on lighter, well-drained soil, away from shade and seaspray. In scrub woodland, on dalesides, forest edge and ungrazed moor, young trees soon spring up and create a birch thicket until stronger species start to dominate. A quick coloniser of newly felled forest compartments.

Downy Birch 258 M
Betula pubescens
Along with oak, this is the principal tree of upland gills and dalehead valleys, often growing in wet peat or clinging precariously to steep rocky crevices.

Although an attempt has been made to map the birches separately, there is considerable hybridisation between them, and a range of characteristics has been observed on different trees, often growing in the same habitat.

Alder 338 M
Alnus glutinosa
Perhaps the commonest native tree in the Park, if the thousands which fringe the banks of practically every waterway could be counted. Rarely more than one or two deep, they nevertheless form an almost unbroken tree corridor throughout the river systems. Absent only from the high moorland, lower limestone valleys and calcareous boulder clay. In a national context, widespread drainage has severely reduced the amount of alder woodland, thus the several alder carr woods which remain in this area are valuable habitats. Some occur at the foothills of the northern escarpment, others are scattered in the larger southern dales.

Oregon Alder *(Alnus rubra)*, Italian Alder *(Alnus cordata)* and Grey Alder *(Alnus incana)* have been planted occasionally as amenity trees.

HAZEL FAMILY
CORYLACEAE [BETULACEAE]

Hornbeam 19 M
Carpinus betulus
Not a native tree this far north but occasionally planted in parks and gar

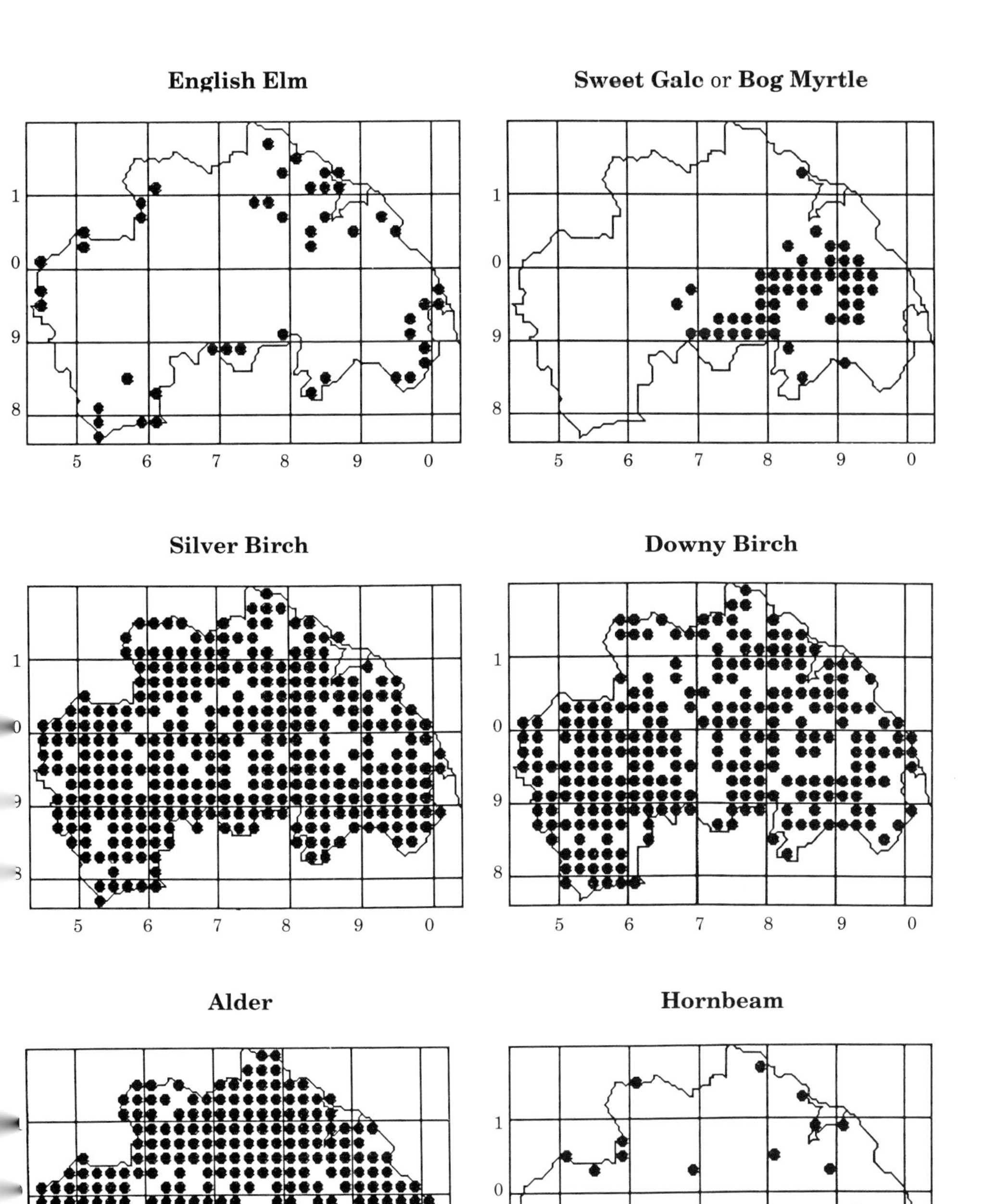
English Elm
Sweet Gale or Bog Myrtle
Silver Birch
Downy Birch
Alder
Hornbeam

dens. A large hornbeam plantation at Ingleby Manor is believed to be unique in this area.

Hazel 339 M
Corylus avellana
Widespread in hedgerows, open woodland and scrub on less acid soil. In several of the ancient woodland remnants on the southern limestone, large old coppiced stools of hazel have grown into sizeable multi-stemmed trees. Hazel coppicing has been re-introduced in woods at Hawnby and elsewhere.

BEECH FAMILY
FAGACEAE

Beech 242 M
Fagus sylvatica
A southern tree and not regarded as native in these parts, it nevertheless regenerates freely from the many mixed plantations and hedgerow trees which have been planted.

Sweet Chestnut 26
Castanea sativa
Brought to Britain by the Romans but an unusual tree in this area where it is used for amenity planting in villages and on forest edges.

Oak 354 M
Quercus x *rosacea (hybrids of Pedunculate and Sessile oak)*
So much hybridisation has occurred in the oak population that it has proved impractical to map their distribution as separate species. Nearly every tree displays intermediate characteristics. The map therefore shows the overall distribution of *Quercus* x *rosacea*. Oak is a co-dominant with birch and, to a lesser extent, rowan in the gills and daleheads. In roadside hedgerows and field boundaries there are many old mature oaks but there is a serious lack of young replacement trees where mechanical hedge cutting is practised. In grazed woodland particularly on moorland edges, juvenile oaks are few. Landowners are being encouraged to fence to allow natural regeneration. Planting schemes are under way and saplings in their protective plastic tubes are a familiar sight on hillsides and field corners.

Turkey Oak 4
Quercus cerris
Occasionally planted in mixed woodland at Sycarham, Bousdale and Borrowby.

WILLOW FAMILY
SALICACEAE

Black Poplar 13 M
Populus x *canadensis*
Colloquially known as black poplar, this hybrid is planted on forest edge and in estate woodland. Some mature trees of this hybrid have previously been recorded as *Populus nigra* but the recent survey has found no native black poplar within the National Park boundary, the nearest being in the grounds of Whitby Hospital.

Balsam Poplar
Populus trichocarpa
Occasionally planted as an amenity tree, quite numerous around Byland Abbey.

Aspen 64 M
Populus tremula
Small clumps occur in open woods and wide lane verges on nutrient-poor moist soils. Deepdale Gill, Sinnington Woods and Wrench Green are among its

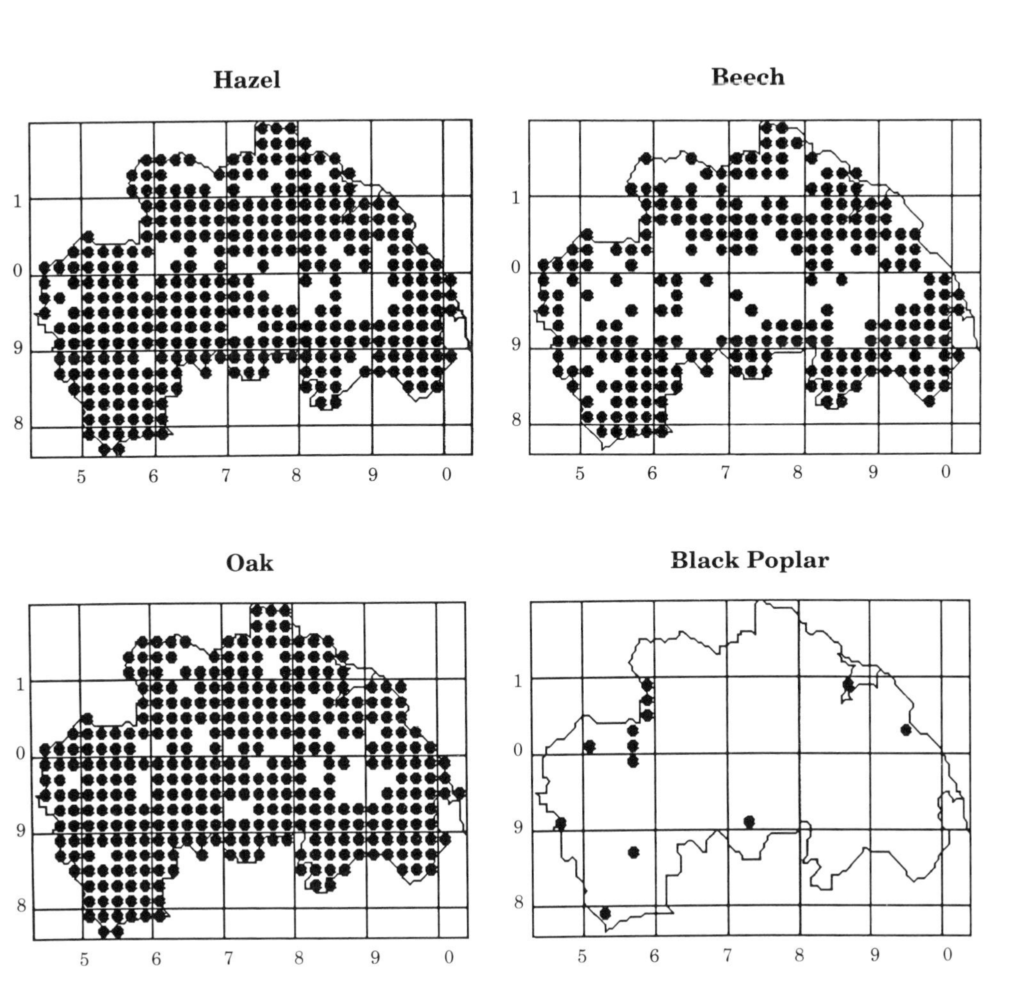
Hazel
Beech
Oak
Black Poplar
1
0
9
8
5
6
7
8
9
0

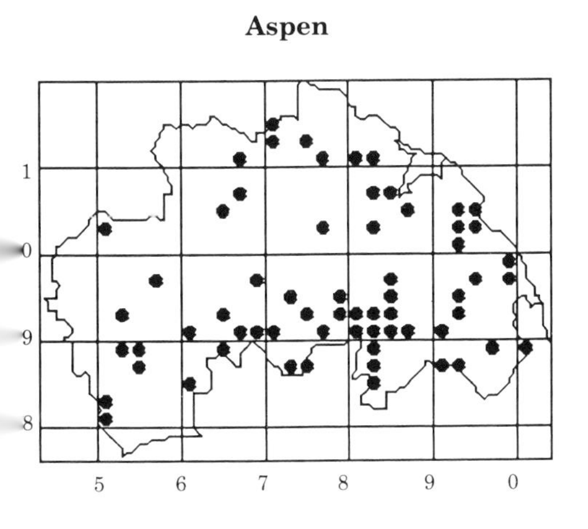
Aspen
1
0
9
8
5
6
7
8
9
0

numerous locations. The presence of this tree seems to indicate an undisturbed habitat, where its suckers soon form a copse.

Bay Willow 36 M
Salix pentandra
The glossy leaves and golden catkins of this attractive willow provide a remarkable springtime display along the streamsides it inhabits which include Raisdale, Scarth Nick, Harwood Dale, Stape and Westerdale.

White Willow 26
Salix alba
Possibly native alongside the Esk, where many fine old trees enhance the riverbanks but frequently planted by new pools.

Crack Willow 105 M
Salix fragilis
In low lying fields where water stands for much of the year, this tree grows to amazing size, new shoots arising from the many broken branches which give the tree its name.

Osier 50
Salix viminalis
Not known to occur naturally in this area but often planted by ponds and waterside.

Goat Willow 336 M
Salix caprea
Large groups grow vigorously on streamsides and in rough land, where the water level fluctuates but rarely dries out. They tolerate stagnant pools like those at Ravenscar quarries and less submerged parts of alder carr. Also grows as a hedgerow shrub in moist situations.

Sallow 319 M
Salix cinerea
In similar habitats to, and often growing with, goat willow though it seems to prefer wetter conditions.

Eared Willow 145 M
Salix aurita
Widespread in acid soils on the edge of forest rides and in moorland scrub.

Creeping Willow 41 M
Salix repens
This small willow can often be found in the undergrowth of scrubby banks, drier parts of moorland flushes and in unburnt fringes of the heather moors such as Wheeldale, Waupley, Ugthorpe, Stape, Saltergate.

Purple Willow 3
Salix purpurea
Not known to occur naturally but has been planted alongside a few forest roads.

Dark-leaved Willow
Salix nigricans [Salix myrsinifolia]
Formerly recorded in damp scrub at Ashberry Pastures near Rievaulx but has not been refound in the recent survey.

The taxonomy of local hybrid willows requires further study. Amongst those noted were:
Salix x *sericans (caprea* x *viminalis)* at Sawdondale
Salix x *rubens (alba* x *fragilis)* at Sleights
Salix x *reichardtii (cinerea* x *caprea)* at Eastmoors
Salix x *ambigua (repens* x *aurita)* at Biller Howe Dale

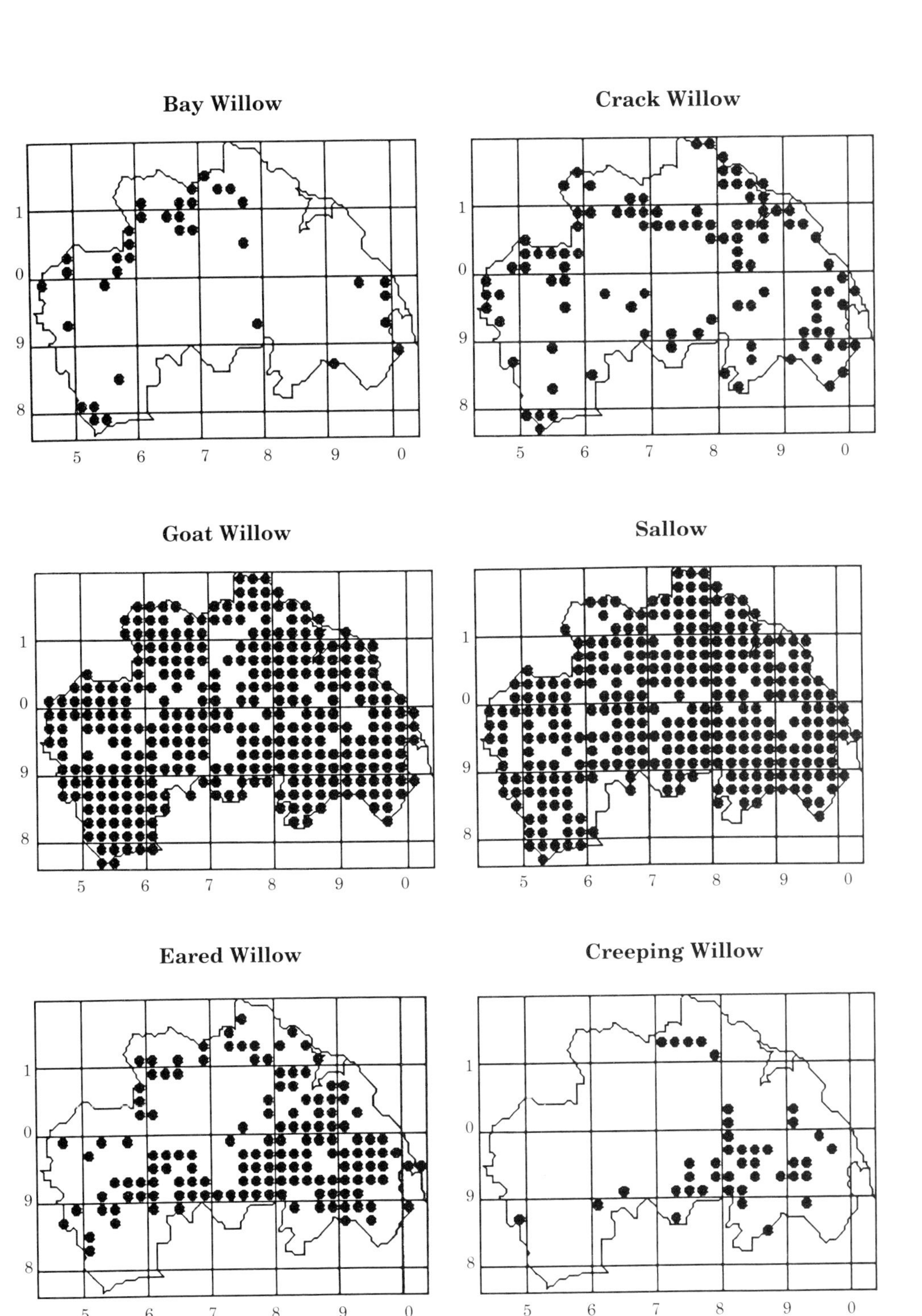
Bay Willow
Crack Willow
Goat Willow
Sallow
Eared Willow
Creeping Willow
1
0
9
8
5
6
7
8
9
0

HEATHER FAMILY
ERICACEAE

Rhododendron 79 M
Rhododendron ponticum
Brought to this country in the 18th century as an ornamental garden shrub, its bid for freedom has been devastatingly successful. This invasive shrub tends to eliminate all ground flora and threatens to choke the shrub layer out of existence. Its brief springtime glory belies its long-term detrimental effect on native woodland. A lover of acid soils, it encroaches into numerous plantations, and is prolific on open heath such as Kepwick Bank.

Marsh Rosemary
Andromeda polifolia
May Moss on Fylingdales Moor is the only known site in the Park for this alpine-arctic relic of post glacial vegetation. It flourishes in company with cloudberry on a raised bog, not subject to cyclical burning, and where a constant high water table maintains a growing sphagnum and cottongrass community.

Bearberry
Arctostaphylos uva-ursi
A plant more usual in northern mountains, it is believed to have lingered on locally after the last ice age, having been recorded on north-facing slopes of the Hole of Horcum. Recent searches have failed to locate it, but its superficial similarity to *Vaccinium* spp., with which it grows, may mean it has been overlooked and still survives.

Heather or **Ling** 344 M
Calluna vulgaris
The plant for which the North York Moors National Park is so well known, attracting thousands of visitors to admire its purple splendour in late summer. It is one of the few plants to thrive on the impoverished acidic soils and in the wet and windy conditions which characterise the uplands. It usually exists as a monoculture where rotational burning favours its dominance over other plants but unmanaged stands can allow development of a more complex plant community. A grey, softly hairy form of ling *(C. vulgaris* var. *hirsuta)* is widespread on parts of the moors.

Cross-leaved Heath 260 M
Erica tetralix
This pale, pink-flowered moorland shrub indicates the presence of wet peat. It flourishes around acid pools, flushes and sphagnum bogs. In some of the wettest moors, it all but replaces heather.

Bell Heather 257 M
Erica cinerea
By contrast to the above species, this dark purple-flowered heathy shrub thrives only on well drained peaty soils. It is often to be seen fringing banks of tracks and moor roads where water can seep away, and occupies drier hummocks throughout the moors, though it is noticeably less common on the highest ground such as Urra and Cringle moors.

Cowberry 73 M
Vaccinium vitis-idaea
A plant abundant in the Scottish Highlands but local on the North York Moors. Nearly always on sloping ground, it seems to favour drier peat on the moorland fringe, away from heavy grazing pressure. Where established it grows in profusion and may be the dominant plant, as in parts of Rosedale and Wheeldale and on Westerdale and Lockton Low Moors.

Heather or Ling

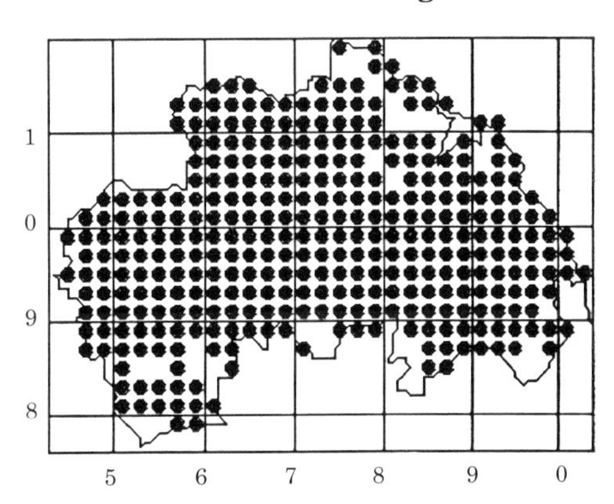

Cross-leaved Heath

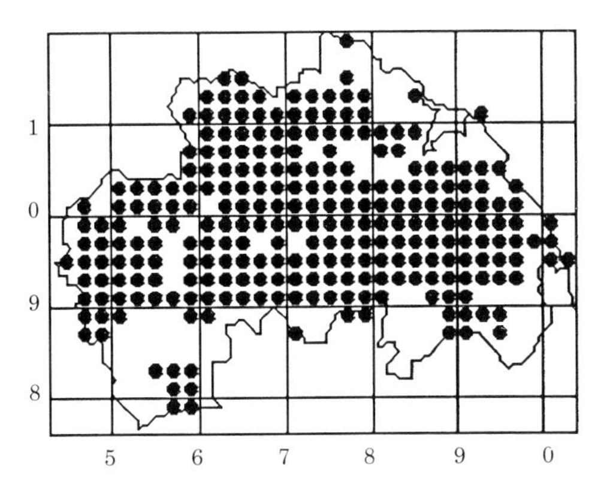

Bell Heather

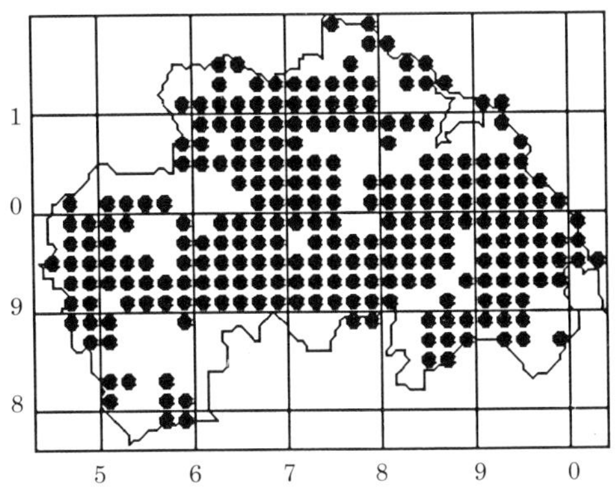

Cowberry

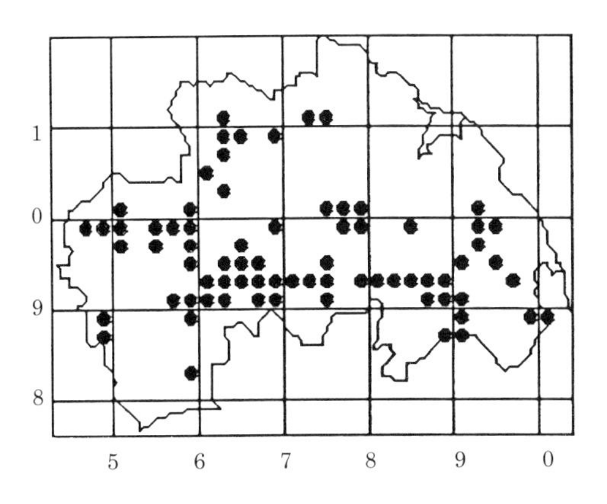

Bilberry 345 M
Vaccinium myrtillus
Tolerant of wind and shade, it grows abundantly in light woodland on acid soils, at the edge of forest rides and on moorland margins, often in association with heather. Bilberry patches, where the shrub dominates the ground vegetation, yield a liberal harvest of dark purple berries much sought after in late summer.

Cranberry 33 M
Vaccinium oxycoccus
A shy creeping member of the moorland flora, it is difficult to detect when not showing its exquisite flowers, thus may be more widespread than records show. It trails over sphagnum and wet heath, being most plentiful in base-rich flushes.

Prickly Heath
Pernettya mucronata
[Gaultheria mucronata]
This prickly evergreen bush is a native of Chile but is frequently planted here in gardens. Presumably birds were responsible for dropping seed alongside the old railway at Ravenscar, where this plant is now established.

WINTERGREEN FAMILY
PYROLACEAE

Common Wintergreen 6 M
Pyrola minor
More a plant of Scottish pinewoods, it has been found rarely in undisturbed pockets on woodland fringe and in conifer plantations. It needs semi-shade with a nutrient and humus rich soil. Small colonies grow on forest rides at Sutherland and Silpho and on woody banks in Sleightholmedale and Cockmoor.

Intermediate Wintergreen 3 M
Pyrola media
A rare plant throughout Britain, it grows locally near forest plantations at Silpho, Raindale and Flaxdale.

BIRD'S NEST FAMILY
MONOTROPACEAE

Yellow Bird's Nest 1
Monotropa hypopitys
A saprophytic plant rare in British beech and pine woods, its only known location in the Park is in the Flaxdale area of Dalby Forest. It was not refound there in the beech plantation where it was recorded in 1914 but a new and sizeable colony was discovered in 1989 beneath pine trees surrounding an old quarry nearby. Another old record for this plant in Forge Valley awaits confirmation.

CROWBERRY FAMILY
EMPETRACEAE

Crowberry 234 M
Empetrum nigrum
At the southern end of its eastern range in Britain, it is dispersed across the heather moorland, occasionally covering extensive patches of drier heath as on Murk Mire Moor. It grows in open birch woodland and tends to displace heather under heavy grazing pressure.

SEA LAVENDER FAMILY
PLUMBAGINACEAE

Thrift
Armeria maritima
Not known as a native plant along this coast but a single clump has been found at the edge of Newton Mulgrave plantation, presumably naturalised from garden rubbish.

Bilberry

Cranberry

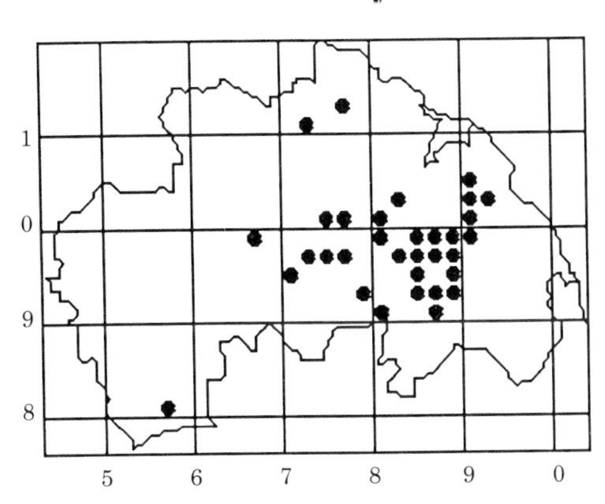

Common Wintergreen

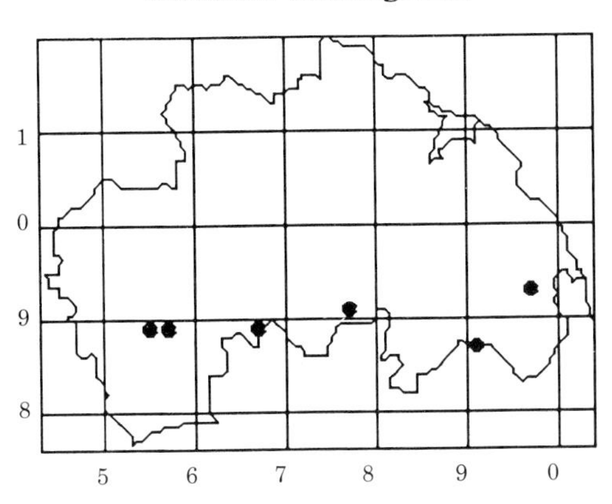

Intermediate Wintergreen

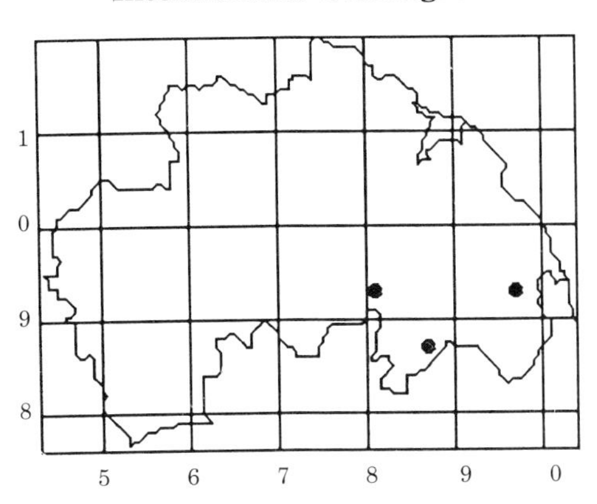

Crowberry

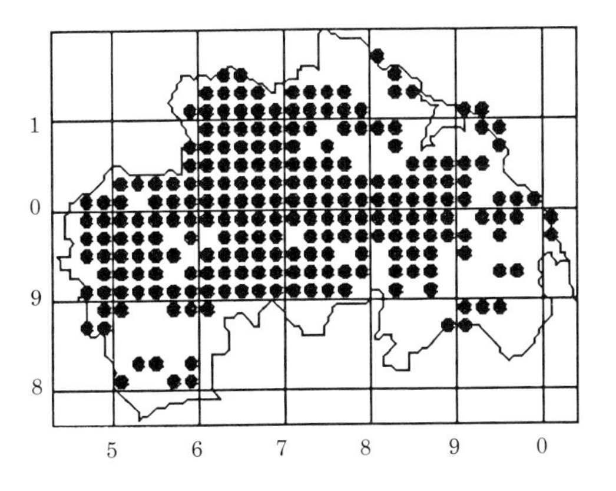

PRIMROSE FAMILY
PRIMULACEAE

Birdseye Primrose 5 M
Primula farinosa
Rare in short damp calcareous grassland and flushes, also in wet hollows of grassy forest rides. Colonies of this charming pink primrose can be found in valleys around Helmsley and Rievaulx.

Cowslip 157 M
Primula veris
Since roadside verge maintenance has been less vigorous, later and infrequent cutting has encouraged this plant to seed and return to many old haunts, much to the delight of passers-by. It can be found flourishing in old pastures, scrubby woodland and hedgebanks on less acid soils. It has re-appeared on set-aside land at Appleton-le-Moors which had been under the plough for more than two decades.

Primrose 321 M
Primula vulgaris
Although persistent picking of its flowers has reduced roadside populations, there are still many secluded banks and woods where it flourishes unmolested. It prefers a dampish heavy soil in light shade and is often prolific after woodland felling. Occasionally pink-flowered clumps are found.

Hybrids of the above two species occur frequently, producing what is known as a "false oxlip".

Yellow Pimpernel 296 M
Lysimachia nemorum
Its yellow star-like flowers brighten many a sombre woodland track. Widely distributed, it trails amongst low-growing vegetation on moist acid soils along shady streamsides and woodland floors.

Creeping Jenny
Lysimachia nummularia
Found only rarely in damp grassland where it could have originated from garden rubbish. It has naturalised on the shores of Elleron Lake, Scaling Dam and Lunshaw Beck.

Yellow Loosestrife 1
Lysimachia vulgaris
Only known from a marshy area near the ruined abbey in Baysdale.

Dotted Loosestrife 25 M
Lysimachia punctata
Widely planted in gardens and by new ponds, yellow-flowered clumps are quite often seen by a roadside where this plant has become established in the wild.

Tufted Loosestrife 1
Lysimachia thyrsiflora
A small colony on the shores of Lake Gormire is one of few locations in Britain for this Baltic plant. It has a good vegetative spread but flowers only sparsely.

Chickweed Wintergreen 129 M
Trientalis europaea
Essentially a plant of Scandinavian forests, its occurrence in the Park is almost its southern limit in Britain. Frequenting mainly the drier heath, its distribution marks the moorland fringe either where oak/birch woodland remains or where woodland has been replaced by bracken. It is rarely found on the exposed heather dominated moor but may be abundant in partially shaded dalesides, secreted amongst leaf and bracken litter until its white starry flowers appear in spring.

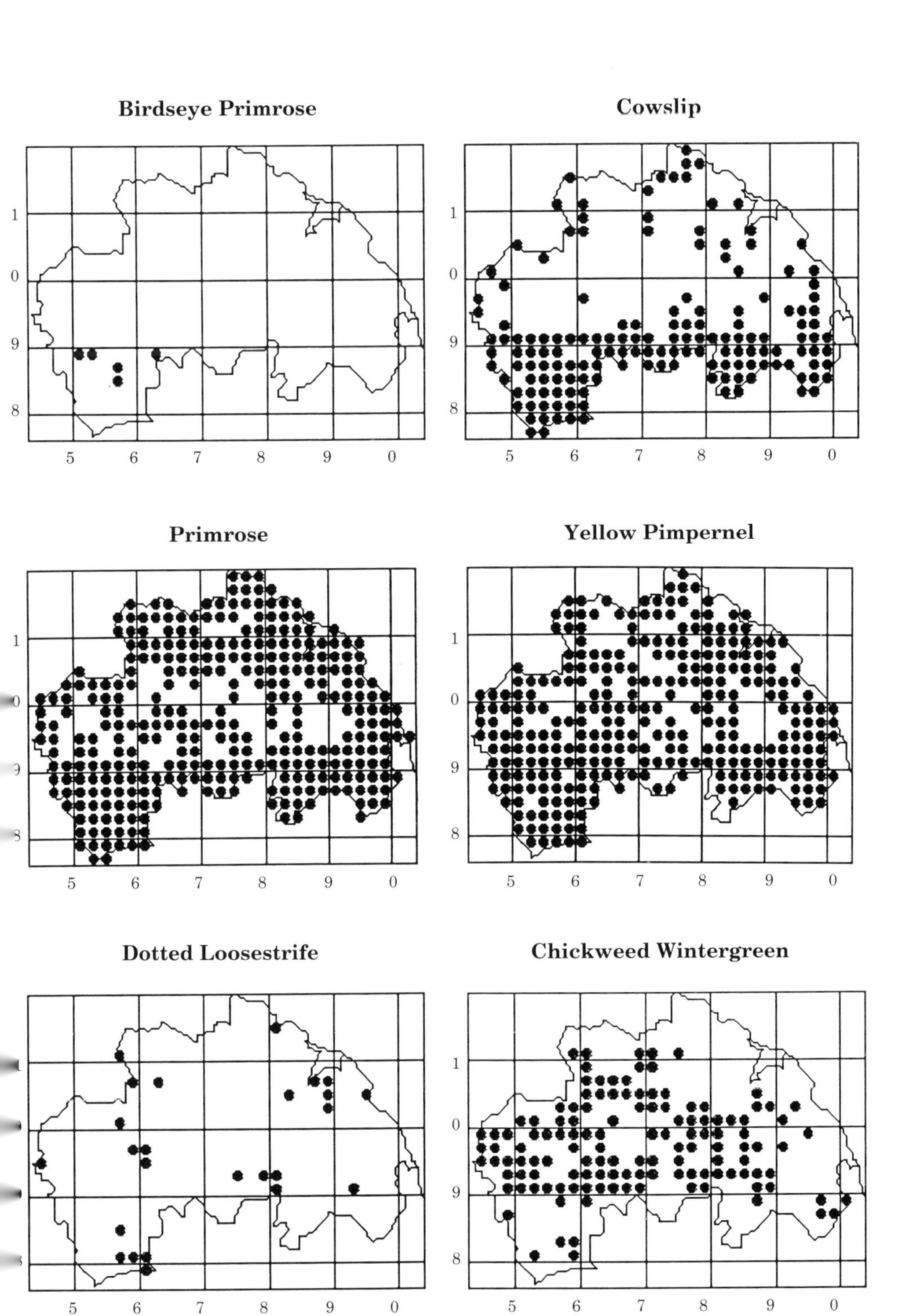
Birdseye Primrose
Cowslip
Primrose
Yellow Pimpernel
Dotted Loosestrife
Chickweed Wintergreen
1
0
9
8
5
6
7
8
9
0

Bog Pimpernel 113 M
Anagallis tenella
A diminutive plant of wet heath, it scrambles over sphagnum bogs and is associated with impeded drainage on moorland slacks and seepage zones on flushes.

Scarlet Pimpernel 74 M
Anagallis arvensis
Occurs as an arable weed on light, well drained land. A summer annual, its shy red flowers appear occasionally on waste ground, in gardens, quarries and gateways on calcareous soils. Widespread but rarely abundant.

Sea Milkwort 2
Glaux maritima
Limited by lack of suitable habitat, only found on the strandline of tide-washed shores between Ruswarp and Whitby.

OLIVE FAMILY
OLEACEAE

Ash 349 M
Fraxinus excelsior
Widespread as a roadside tree, ash is also common in hedgerows, where it survives any amount of cutting, and in woodlands on calcareous soil. It regenerates easily and its open canopy allows a rich ground flora to flourish as in some of the ash-dominated woods on the southern zone.

Wild Privet 24 M
Ligustrum vulgare
Infrequent in lowland hedgerows, open woods and copses on lime-rich soil. It indicates an undisturbed habitat and possibly the site of ancient woodland.

PERIWINKLE FAMILY
APOCYNACEAE

Lesser Periwinkle 7
Vinca minor
A garden plant naturalised at Grosmont car park and on occasional verges.

Greater Periwinkle 1
Vinca major
Also a garden outcast occasionally covering a roadside bank near where rubbish has been tipped.

GENTIAN FAMILY
GENTIANACEAE

Common Centaury 114 M
Centaurium erythraea
Benefiting from lack of competition on nutrient-poor forest rides, it often forms a colourful border to conifer plantations. It is widespread on coastal cliffs and on the dry sandy soil of disused quarries.

Yellow-wort
Blackstonia perfoliata
A plant of calcareous sandy grassland and dunes, it is mainly coastal this far north. Although it grows on sea cliffs at Cloughton, and again at Skinningrove, its only known location in the Park is in Harwood Dale where it has been introduced with hardcore for a forest ride and is naturalised alongside the track.

Field Gentian 2
Gentianella campestris
Formerly known on several grassy banks in the Newtondale vicinity, it was refound in 1991 at Gallock Hill and a thriving colony was located on unimproved grassland north of Helmsley. It seems to have disappeared from several earlier known sites.

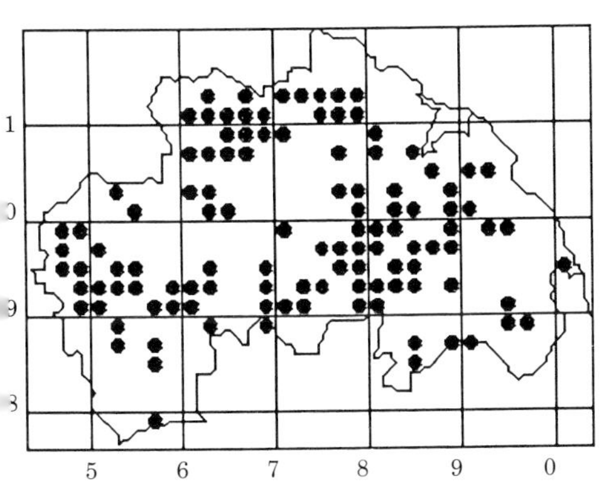

Scarlet Pimpernel

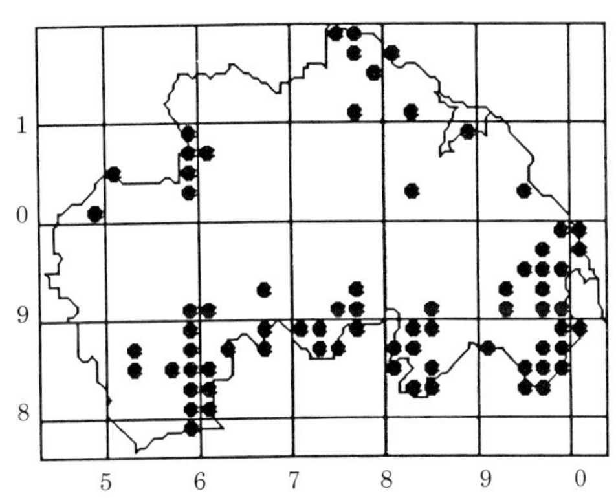

Ash

Wild Privet

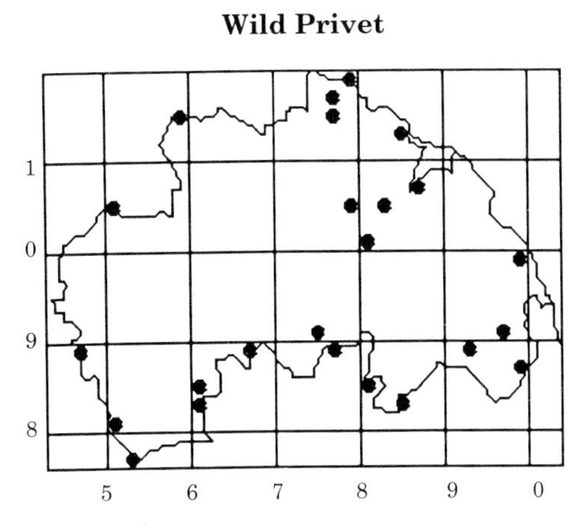

Common Centaury

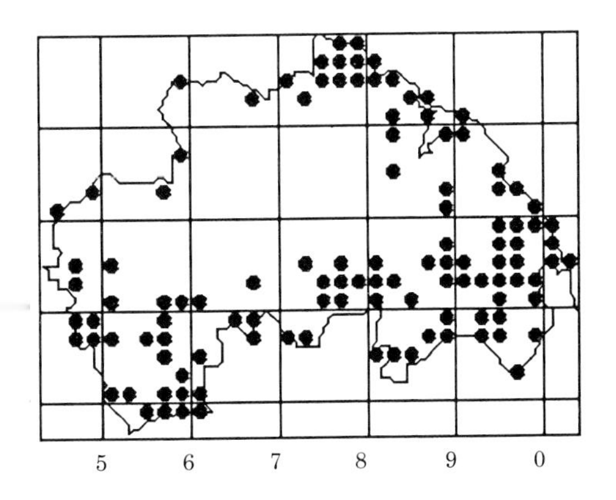

Felwort 49 M
Gentianella amarella
This autumn-flowering gentian is both widespread and abundant, especially on the Hambleton Hills. It grows on short, well-drained calcareous grassland, some sheep-grazed roadsides, in old limestone quarries and on the side of forest tracks made from limestone chippings.

Marsh Gentian
Gentiana pneumonanthe
Previously recorded in wet grassland near Cropton and Sutherland Becks but not seen in recent years. It must be presumed extinct in this area, a victim of recent field drainage, the last known site having been destroyed inadvertently during the 1980s.

BOGBEAN FAMILY
MENYANTHACEAE

Bogbean 57 M
Menyanthes trifoliata
Widespread in sphagnum bogs, shallow pools and moorland slacks, also in wet open carr woodland on organic soils. It has disappeared from a number of previously known sites on the moors due to drainage.

Fringed Water Lily 1
Nymphoides peltata
Planted and naturalised in a farm pond near Raincliffe.

JACOB'S LADDER FAMILY
POLEMONIACEAE

Jacob's Ladder
Polemonium caeruleum
Listed as a British rarity, this species was known to grow in a quarry on Pexton Moor but has not been seen there in recent years. It is believed to be locally extinct as a native plant. Garden escapes have become established on a roadside at Kildale and quite recently, after sheep proof fencing was erected, on a verge of the A169 on Sleights Moor.

BORAGE FAMILY
BORAGINACEAE

Borage 4
Borago officinalis
A garden escape naturalised in Ramsdale and at Yoadwath, Hutton Buscel and Lythe.

Abraham, Isaac and Jacob 1
Trachystemon orientalis
A blue-flowered plant, similar to borage, it was introduced to British gardens around 1750. Several colonies have naturalised along the banks of Stainsacre Beck in the shady lush vegetation of Cockmill Wood.

Houndstongue 5 M
Cynoglossum officinale
This hairy plant with its strong smell of mice has been found occasionally in rough calcareous grassland. Hutton Common, Caydale, Shallowdale and Duncombe Park.

Russian Comfrey 79 M
Symphytum x *uplandicum*
This hybrid comfrey is widely dispersed as a roadside plant, its purple-flowered tussocks being a familiar summertime sight on verges, especially in Eskdale. Its usual proximity to habitation may derive from its former use as a medicinal herb.

Felwort

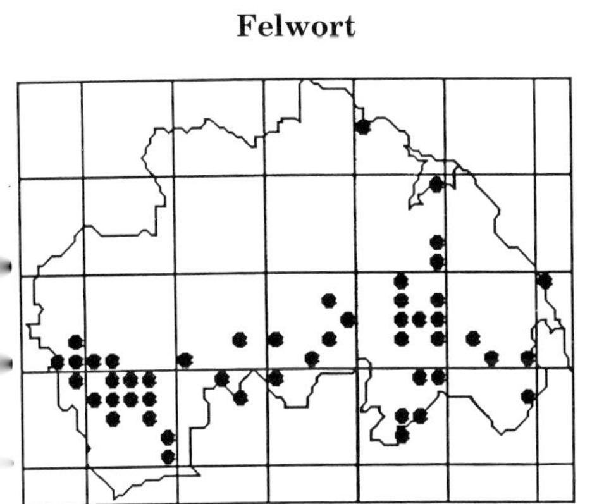

Bogbean

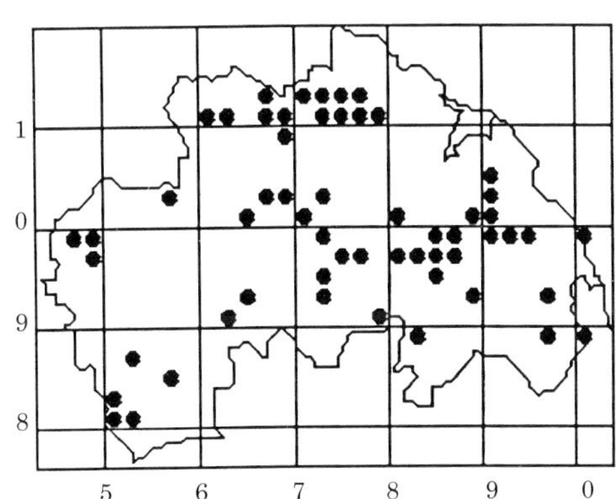

Houndstongue

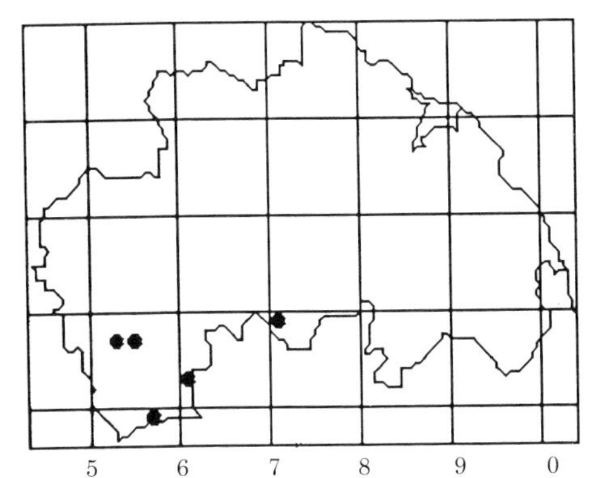

Russian Comfrey

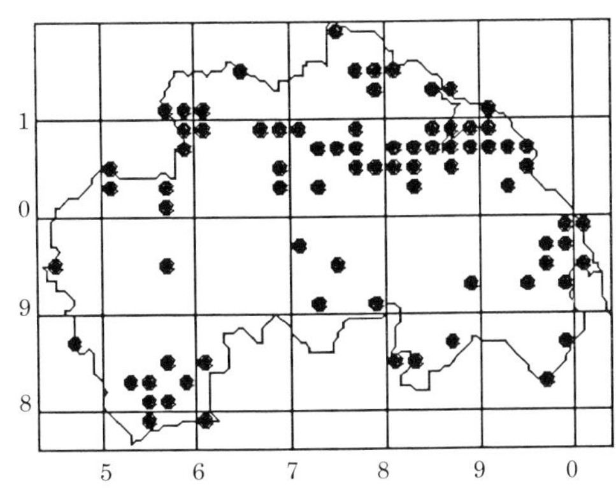

Tuberous Comfrey 3
Symphytum tuberosum
A garden escape which grows in quarries or on verges at Helmsley, Coomboots and Forge Valley.

Alkanet 42 M
Pentaglottis sempervirens
A mediaeval introduction for gardens, widely naturalised on wallsides and banks near habitation. The likelihood of its being used as a dyeing and medicinal plant by occupants of Whitby Abbey may explain its frequency in that area.

Bugloss 7 M
Anchusa arvensis
Once a common arable weed on sandy soils, bugloss has succumbed to modern agriculture and its bright blue flowers have been seen only in a few field corners or on wasteland. Battersby, Mowthorpe, Ellerburn, Farwath and Goldsborough.

Fiddleneck
Amsinckia lycopsoides
A rare alien from Canada and believed to have been introduced as rogue seed, it occurs spasmodically in fields from Bickley to Harwood Dale. *Amsinckia micrantha* appeared in disturbed ground at Ruswarp in 1991.

Water Forgetmenot 106 M
Myosotis scorpioides
Frequent in streams, pools and marshes on fertile soils with moving water. Abundant in the Esk and Derwent river systems.

Lesser Water Forgetmenot 22 M
Myosotis secunda
Occasional in acid moorland streams and flushes and in wet upland woods, often where iron seepage occurs.

Tufted Forgetmenot 51
Myosotis laxa ssp. *caespitosa*
Not a common species although it can be found occasionally on stream banks, pond edges and in unimproved marshy pastures.

Wood Forgetmenot 161 M
Myosotis sylvatica
Common in damp woodland on heavy clay soils and frequently established as a garden escape.

Common Forgetmenot 292
Myosotis arvensis
This is well named, for it is the most frequent of the forgetmenot tribe and turns up in a range of habitats on dryish not too acid soils. It quickly colonises disturbed ground.

Changing Forgetmenot 125
Myosotis discolor
Usually found on unimproved grassland on dry calcareous soil, it also inhabits old walls, quarries and sandy arable fields.

Early Forgetmenot 17
Myosotis ramosissima
Sparse on dry sandy waysides and short calcareous turf. On the Silpho to Ayton plateau and spasmodic further west.

Creeping Forgetmenot 13 M
Myosotis stolonifera
Also known as pale forgetmenot on account of its almost white petals, this plant is rare throughout Britain being confined to a few upland areas. It has a stronghold in this area and can be found in acid moorland streams and shallow pools. Hasty Bank, Snowdon Spring, Crosscliff, Hole of Horcum, Farndale, Scugdale and pools on the old railtrack at Rosedale Head.

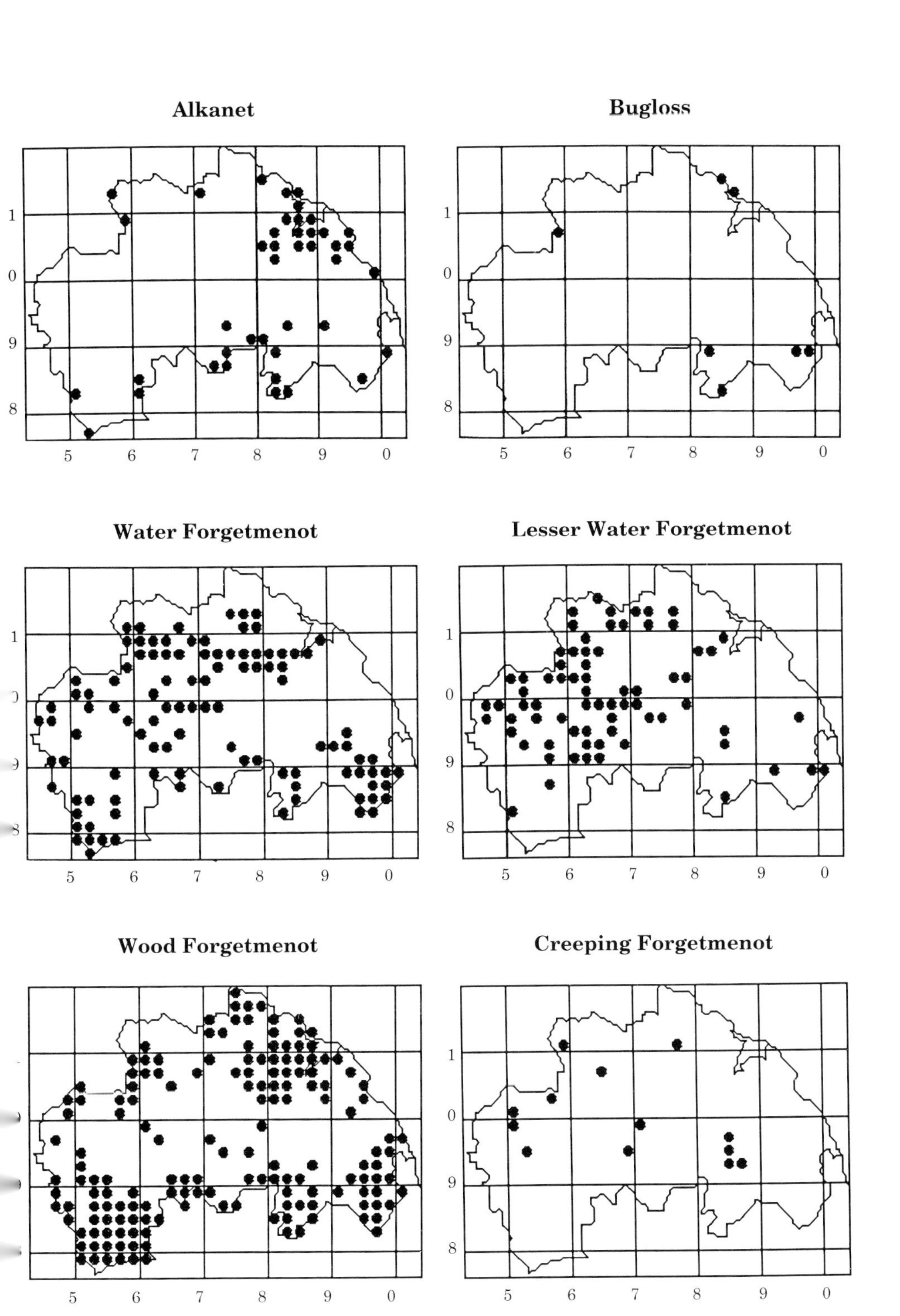

Alkanet
Bugloss
Water Forgetmenot
Lesser Water Forgetmenot
Wood Forgetmenot
Creeping Forgetmenot

Gromwell 4 M
Lithospermum officinale
More a plant of lowland Britain, gromwell grows on coarse, calcareous grassland, gravelly scrub and in old limestone quarries. It has been found only at Newbridge, Forge Valley, Caydale and near Rievaulx.

Viper's Bugloss 11 M
Echium vulgare
This striking plant with its two-tone pink and mauve flowers can be found in a few disused quarries and on rocky outcrops and wasteland with shallow, sandy or calcareous soil.

BINDWEED FAMILY
CONVOLVULACEAE

Field Bindweed 91 M
Convolvulus arvensis
Its pink bell-like flowers may look attractive spread over the ground but this plant can be a pernicious weed in gardens and farmland. It covers the ballast where established on railtracks in Eskdale and Newtondale.

Large Bindweed 171 M
Calystegia sepium ssp. *silvatica*
Introduced as a garden adornment, this plant has taken to the wild in a big way and scrambles over hedges and thickets throughout the lower land and on the coastal plain. In the National Park, it is far more common than the native plant, *Calystegia sepium* ssp. *sepium,* which has been found only on the fringes of the Park around Pickering and Carlton-in-Cleveland and along the coast. A pink-flowered form occurs in Langdale and Kirby Knowle.

Sea Bindweed 1
Calystegia soldanella
This attractive shore-line plant, abundant on western coasts, has been found only at Ruswarp on the North York Moors coast.

Dodder
Cuscuta epithymum
Apparently, some 50 years ago, it was quite common, growing parasitically on gorse and heather. As plenty of these two plants are still around, it is difficult to understand why dodder is no longer apparent. Not a single plant has been recorded.

NIGHTSHADE FAMILY
SOLANACEAE

Duke of Argyll's Tea Plant 11 M
Lycium barbarum
This strangely named plant – erroneously imported instead of tea – is a garden shrub occasionally naturalised in hedgerows near to Rosedale, Stape, Staithes, Stoupe Beck, Boulby and abundant near Hawsker Highlight.

Henbane 2
Hyoscyamus niger
Introduced as a medicinal herb and once a common wasteland plant, it has largely been eradicated on account of its highly poisonous nature. It survives in overgrown quarries at Helmsley and Hutton-le-Hole.

Bittersweet or **Woody Nightshade** 22 M
Solanum dulcamara
More of a lowland plant, this climber occurs in a few woods, ditches and hedgerows on wet, enriched soils away from the hills.

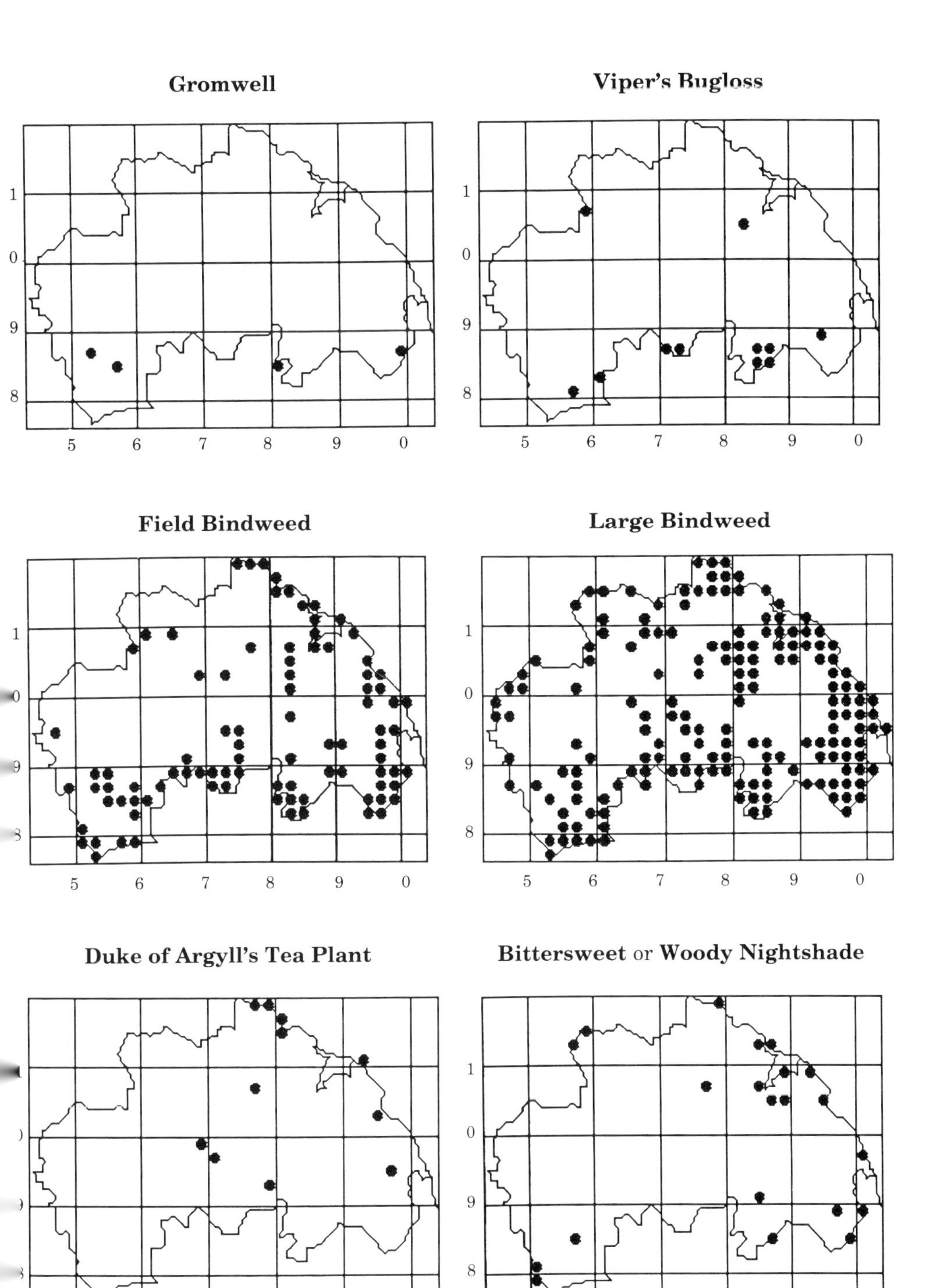
Gromwell
1
0
9
8
5
6
7
8
9
0
Viper's Bugloss
1
0
9
8
5
6
7
8
9
0
Field Bindweed
1
0
9
8
5
6
7
8
9
0
Large Bindweed
1
0
9
8
5
6
7
8
9
0
Duke of Argyll's Tea Plant
5
6
7
8
9
0
Bittersweet or Woody Nightshade
1
0
9
8
5
6
7
8
9
0

Deadly Nightshade 6
Atropa belladonna
An unusual, poisonous plant found in woodland scrub, quarries and on limestone wasteland around Hutton-le-Hole, Rievaulx, Kirkdale and Caydale.

Thorn Apple
Datura stramonium
Once cultivated to use as a cough cure, this herb is rarely seen today but a single plant turned up in a conifer plantation on Lockton High Moor.

FIGWORT FAMILY
SCROPHULARIACEAE

Fairy Foxglove 1
Erinus alpinus
An attractive rock garden plant from the mountains of Europe, it has become established on a few walls in the Helmsley area but does not appear to have spread elsewhere. Its dainty pink flowers are a feature of the old walls of Helmsley Castle.

Great Mullein 25 M
Verbascum thapsus
Uncommon on dry grassy banks and waysides with sandy or calcareous soils. Battersby, Kildale and occasionally on verges of the A172.

Dark Mullein 14 M
Verbascum nigrum
Near its northern limit in Britain, one or two plants appear from time to time on calcareous verges in Hartoft, Glaisdale, Grosmont and on the railside of lower Eskdale.

Yellow Toadflax 44 M
Linaria vulgaris
No longer the common laneside plant of yesteryear, it is only on out-of-the-way uncut verges, field edges and sandy waysides that small populations can be found.

Purple Toadflax 14
Linaria purpurea
This is a more aggressive toadflax and since its introduction from Italy for garden use, it has become well-established in the wild on gravelly waste, wall footings and stony banks near habitation. It is plentiful on railway ballast.

Small Toadflax 19 M
Chaenorhinum minus
A summer annual which flowers in abundance on light dry sandy soil in the absence of stronger competition. It covers a large patch in Hackness village hall car park and grows freely in gravelly railside ballast in Eskdale but is now rare as a cornfield weed.

Ivy-leaved Toadflax 52
Cymbalaria muralis
A rock garden plant which frequently finds a roothold on older walls, covering substantial areas with its dainty two-tone flowers.

Common Figwort 193 M
Scrophularia nodosa
Quite a common plant on moist banks and pathsides in woods, forest and beside road and rail verges.

Water Figwort 76 M
Scrophularia auriculata
Scattered plants are to be found on banks of streams and ditches, in wet scrubby ground and along riversides, usually growing amongst tall lush vegetation.

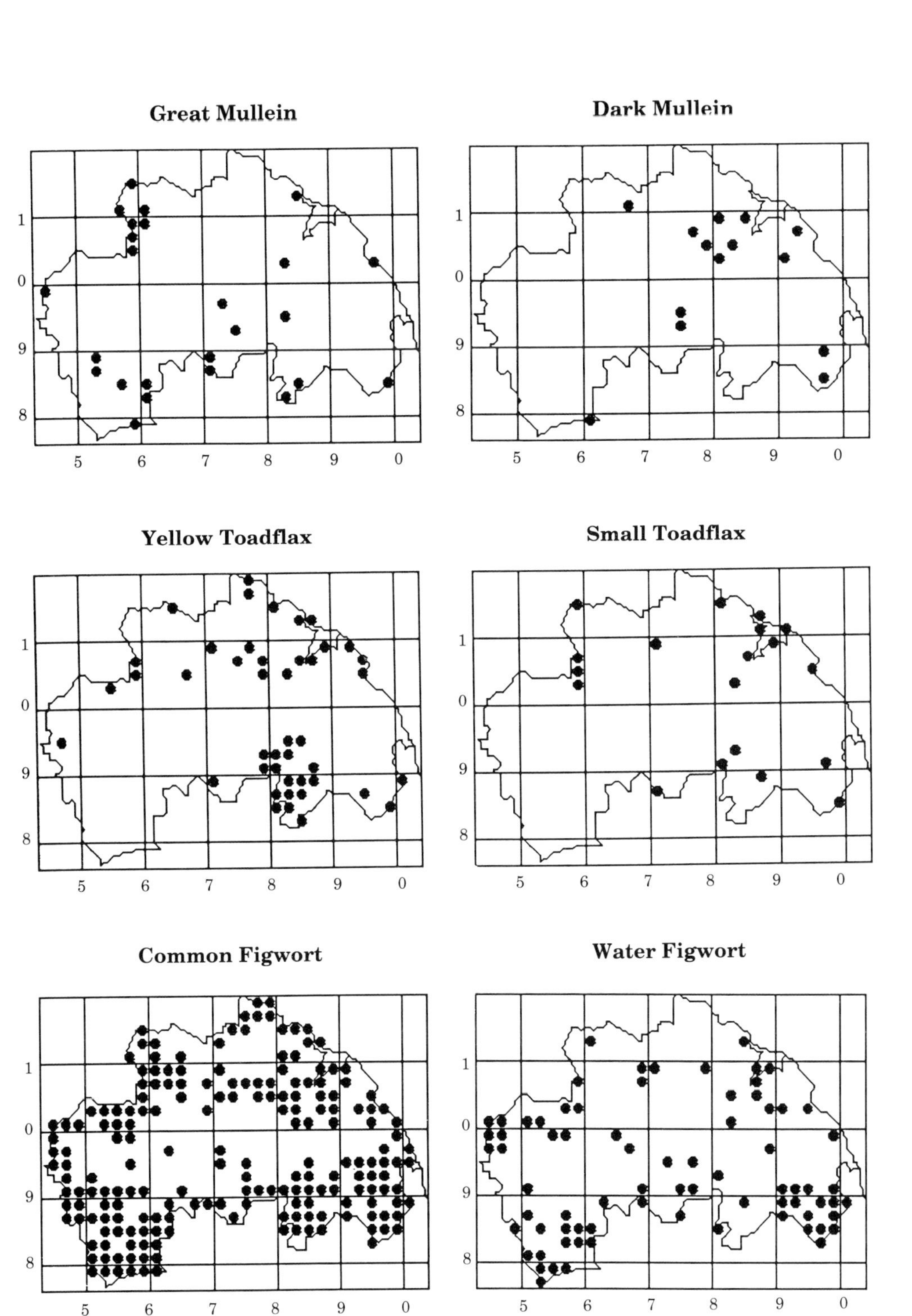

Great Mullein
Dark Mullein
Yellow Toadflax
Small Toadflax
Common Figwort
Water Figwort

Monkey Flower 20
Mimulus guttatus x *luteus*
It is said that most mimulus plants in the wild are sterile hybrids and certainly they display plenty of hybrid vigour spreading over streams and ditches. Old drainage ditches, as at Byland and Rievaulx Abbeys and Mount Grace Priory, are a favoured habitat. Commondale, Troutsdale, Bonfield Gill and the main river systems are among its other locations.

Musk 13 M
Mimulus moschatus
A garden plant brought in from North America, it has naturalised sparsely in Baysdale, Farndale, Thirlby Forest, Westerdale and Iburndale. In Rosedale, however, it flourishes in damp hollows and streamlets up and down the dale. As musk used to be a popular Victorian houseplant, its abundance in Rosedale could be a legacy from the large mining population which occupied the dale in that era. Regrettably, musk no longer retains its perfume in the wild.

Foxglove 321
Digitalis purpurea
The familiar purple-flowered spikes of foxglove are abundant on acid, well-drained soils in open woods, on upland heath, wallsides, verges and in forest clearings.

Brooklime 261
Veronica beccabunga
Abundant in shallow streams, ponds, ditches, wet pastures and wheel ruts, mainly in fertile soil away from the hills.

Marsh Speedwell 18
Veronica scutellata
An elusive plant which secretes itself amongst stronger vegetation in marshy grassland and drainage ditches. Cloughton Hulleys, Wheeldale, Piethorn, Hole of Horcum, Scaling Dam, Ayton Castle pond.

Heath Speedwell 227 M
Veronica officinalis
The pale mauve flowers and hairy leaves of this spreading speedwell are a common sight on dry acid hill pastures, moor edges, stone walls and rocky banks.

Wood Speedwell 218 M
Veronica montana
Plentiful in old woods where its pale green foliage spreads over moist glades and paths, indicating an undisturbed habitat. Its distribution shows a correlation with that of ancient woodland.

Germander Speedwell 362 M
Veronica chamaedrys
The bright blue flowers of this abundant speedwell can be seen at practically any time of the year. It flourishes in a variety of habitats which include short grassland, hedgebanks, fieldsides and paths. Its normal appearance is often distorted by a gall.

Thyme-leaved Speedwell 307 M
Veronica serpyllifolia
This is another very common speedwell, growing in short grass in gardens, forest rides, pathways and damp pasture on more acid soils.

Wall Speedwell 166 M
Veronica arvensis
Despite its name this plant is usually seen on dry bare ground, pathways, and in gardens and sheep grazed turf, although it can be found on old walls. Its miniature blue flowers are easily overlooked.

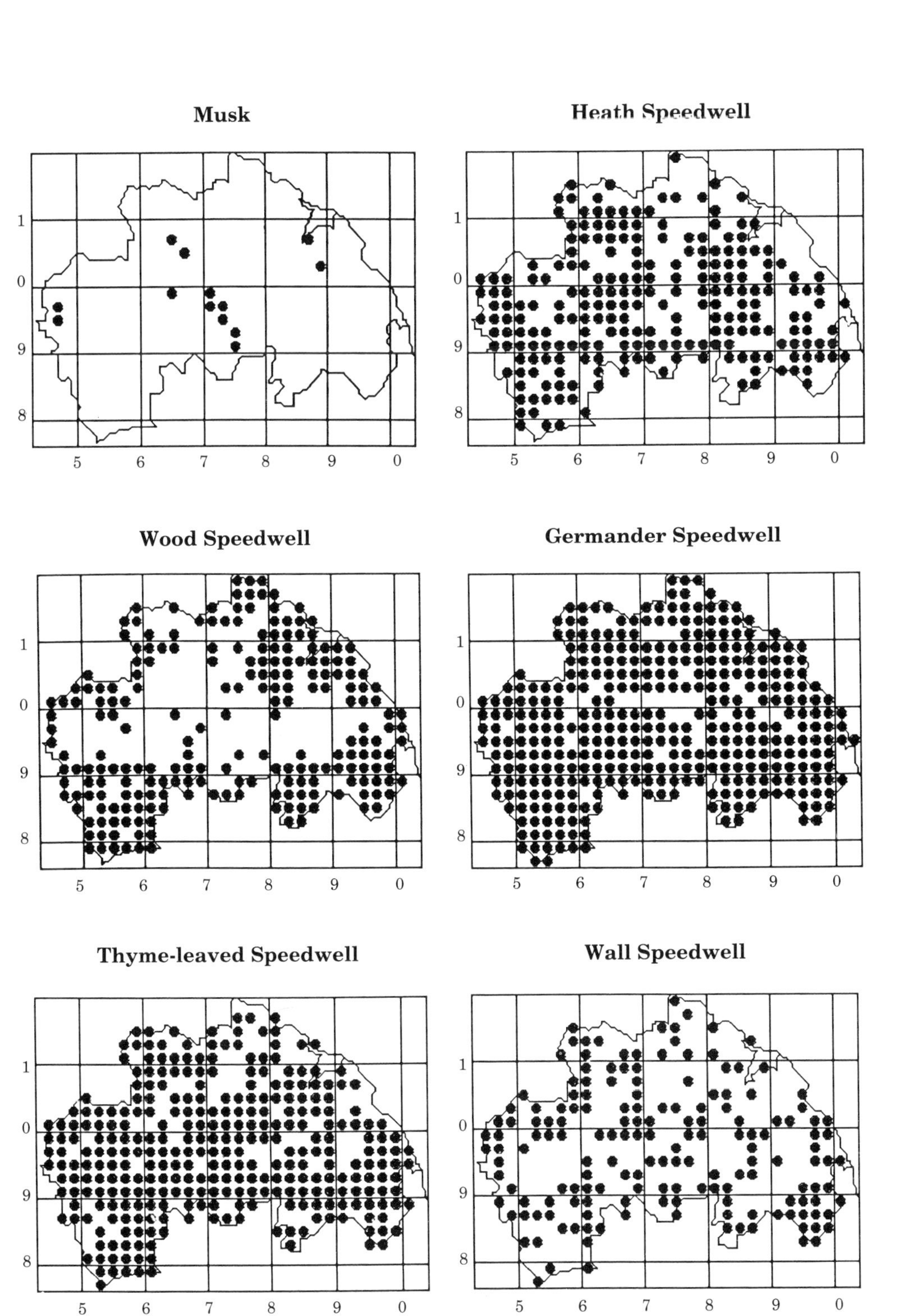

Musk
Heath Speedwell
Wood Speedwell
Germander Speedwell
Thyme-leaved Speedwell
Wall Speedwell
1
0
9
8
5
6
7
8
9
0

Ivy-leaved Speedwell 79
Veronica hederifolia
This is a well named plant with its tiny ivy-shaped leaves. It is often to be found scrambling over light, disturbed ground. Familiar to gardeners, it is also abundant in churchyards as at Coxwold and Pockley. Ssp. *hederifolia* and ssp. *lucorum* have been noted.

Field Speedwell 200
Veronica persica
Introduced to Britain in the 19th century, this speedwell has become a widespread and persistent arable weed. Being somewhat resistant to herbicides, it is found on most cultivated land.

Grey Speedwell 7
Veronica polita
Uncommon in gardens and arable fields on loose sandy soil.

Green Speedwell 16
Veronica agrestis
Found infrequently in arable fields and gardens.

Creeping Speedwell 68
Veronica filiformis
First recorded as a garden escape in 1927 and still rare in 1960, it is now widespread on cut verges, paths, garden lawns and churchyards, usually not far from habitation.

Marsh Lousewort 49
Pedicularis palustris
This uncommon plant of acid wet heath and bog grows as a partial parasite on grass roots.

Common Lousewort 153 M
Pedicularis sylvatica
Much more widespread than marsh lousewort, though they frequently grow together. Also semi-parasitic on grass, it occurs on damp acidic grassland and moor.

Yellow Rattle 176 M
Rhinanthus minor
This is another plant which obtains some of its nutrients by growing parasitically on grasses in old unimproved hay meadows and rough hill pastures on basic, low-nutrient soils. It is often called hay rattle owing to the way its ripe fruits rattle before seed dispersal around haytime.

Common Cow-wheat 76 M
Melampyrum pratense
Occasional on acid humus-rich soils often in moist upland oak/birch woods. It survives on open unburnt moor but is more plentiful in light shade on banks and verges with overhanging trees.

Eyebright 276 M
Euphrasia officinalis agg.
Widespread on short grassland, especially on sheep grazed verges. *E. micrantha* and *E. confusa* have been noted but insufficient records are available to map the variants of this species separately.

Red Bartsia 78 M
Odontites verna [Odontites vernus]
Nowhere common but may have benefited from afforestation as its main stronghold appears to be forest rides. Rarely seen nowadays as a cornfield plant.

BROOMRAPE FAMILY
OROBANCHACEAE

Toothwort 41 M
Lathraea squamaria
Small clusters of this flesh-coloured, parasitic plant infrequently protrude through rich humus on the floor of deciduous woods and at the base of old mixed hedgerows on calcareous fertile soil. Indicative of ancient woodland, it grows on tree roots, usually elm or hazel.

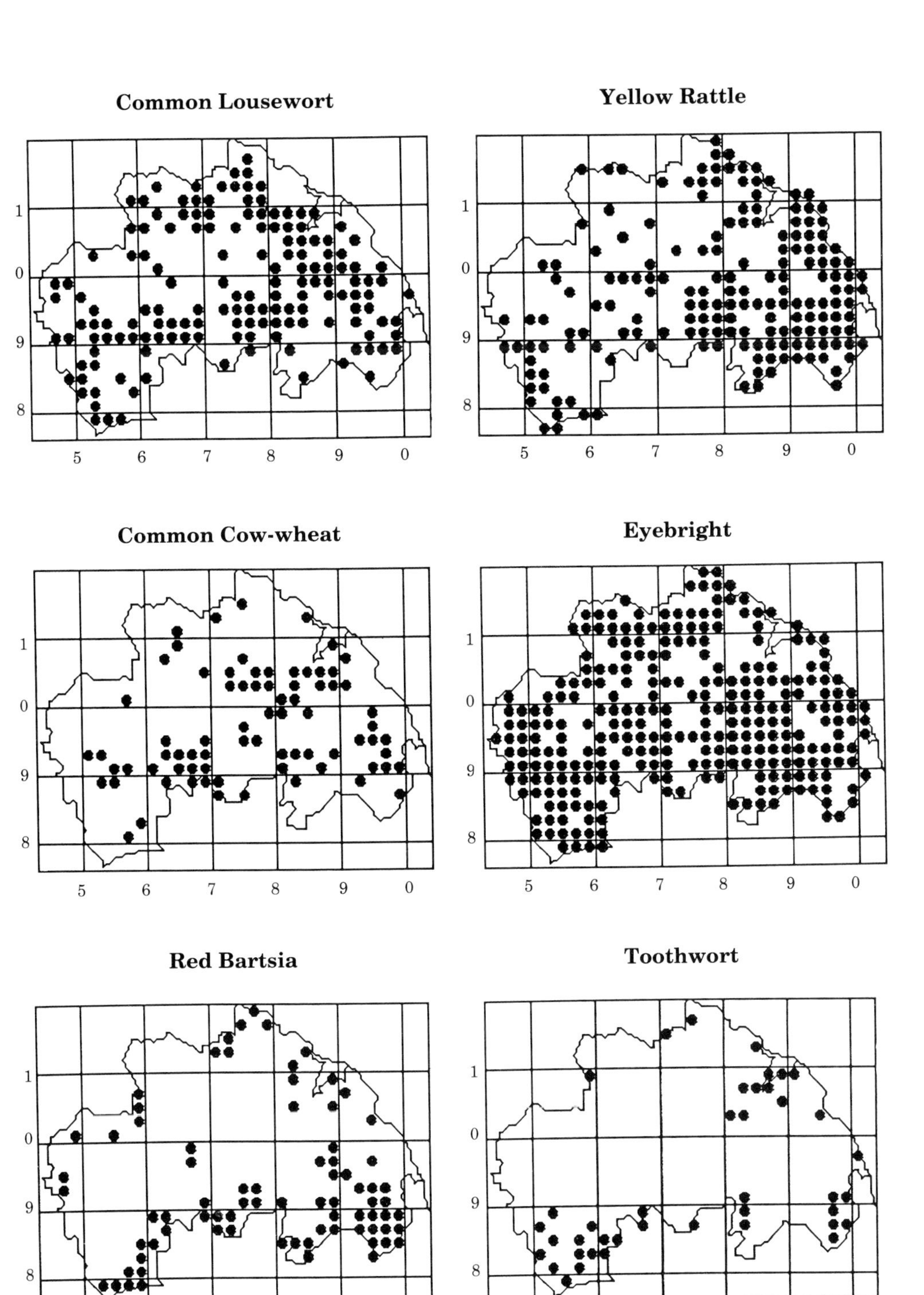

Common Lousewort
Yellow Rattle
Common Cow-wheat
Eyebright
Red Bartsia
Toothwort
1
0
9
8
5
6
7
8
9
0

Tall Broomrape 1
Orobanche elatior
Very rare in this part of the country, its only known site in the National Park is on a laneside bank north of East Ayton where it is parasitic on greater knapweed. This is believed to be its most northerly site in Britain.

BUTTERWORT FAMILY
LENTIBULARIACEAE

Butterwort 86 M
Pinguicula vulgaris
A few plants of this insectivorous species inhabit base-rich moorland flushes and grassy banks with alkaline-seepage. Found also in shallow pools on the edge of limey forest rides. It prefers bare, wet ground devoid of other vegetation.

THYME FAMILY
LABIATAE [LAMIACEAE]

Corn Mint 15 M
Mentha arvensis
A sign of more traditional farming practice, it has been seen rarely on fields at Sneaton, Oldstead, Freeze Gill, Kingthorpe, Commondale, Everley, Waupley, Arden, Farndale and Sleights. Once a common plant, it has now been eliminated from most cultivated ground.

Whorled Mint 14
Mentha x *verticillata*
[M. arvensis x *M. aquatica]*
There is a bewildering array of mint hybrids of which this appears to be the most frequent. It grows along damp roadsides, fringes of ponds and streams and in wet grassland.

Mentha x *smithiana [M. aquatica* x *arvensis* x *spicata]*
A rare hybrid, found in two patches east of Newton Mulgrave.

Water Mint 238 M
Mentha aquatica
This is a very common plant in wet grassland, along streamsides and in alder/willow carr where its presence is revealed by a strong mint fragrance.

Peppermint 4
Mentha x *piperita*
[M. aquatica x *spicata]*
Recorded in shallow becks and damp grassland at Glaisdale, Baysdale and Raisdale.

Spearmint 25 M
Mentha spicata
This commonly cultivated garden mint appears occasionally in the wild, either on streamside or grassy verge near habitation.

Apple Mint 15 M
Mentha suaveolens
A garden plant which has naturalised in a few places. It sometimes forms an extensive mat on sheep-grazed moorland turf where its felted leaves remain uneaten.

Also recorded was *Mentha* x *gentilis [M. arvensis* x *spicata]*

Gipsywort 6 M
Lycopus europaeus
This plant of wet woodland and riverside marsh thrives on fertile mineral or peaty soil and is unusual this far north in Britain. In the Park it was found in a few sheltered locations beside the River Derwent at Hilla Green and West Ayton, by Scalby Sea Cut and at Gormire and Glaisdale.

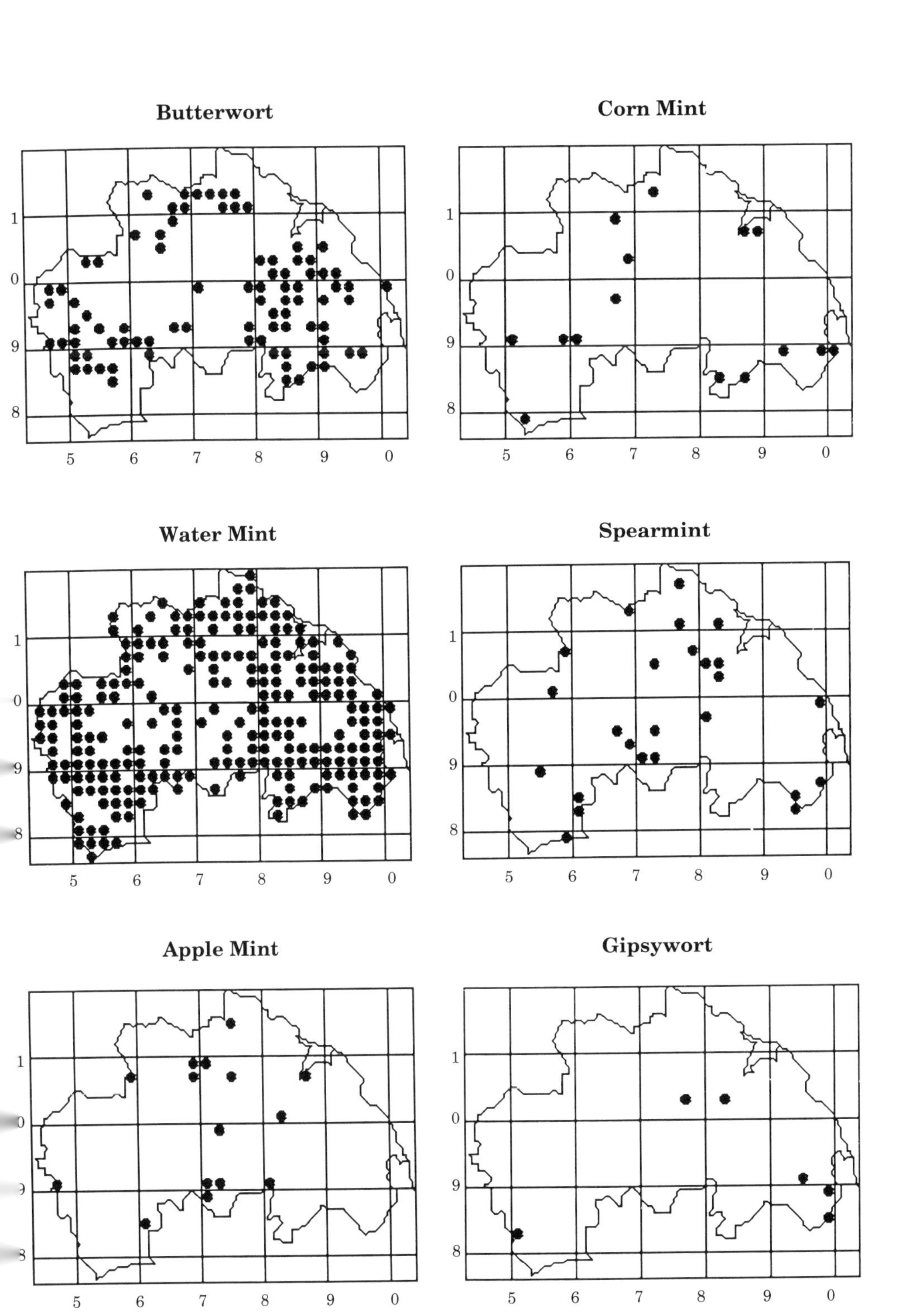
Butterwort
Corn Mint
Water Mint
Spearmint
Apple Mint
Gipsywort
1
0
9
8
5
6
7
8
9
0

Marjoram 67 M
Origanum vulgare
This typical lime-loving plant, well-known to herbalists, grows plentifully in calcareous soils on roadside banks, in rough grassy places and disused limestone quarries.

Wild Thyme 120 M
Thymus praecox [Thymus polytrichus]
Another familiar seasoning herb, wild thyme forms a pink-flowered carpet over many a stretch of short turf on grazed moor edges, in old quarries and on hillside screes, especially on less acid soils. Its deep penetrating roots enable its survival in dry locations devoid of other plants.

Common Calamint 4
Calamintha sylvatica ssp. *ascendens [Clinopodium ascendens]*
At its northern limit climatically, it is not surprising that calamint is rarely seen in the Park. It was found on dry scrubby calcareous grassland and on limestone walls at Hayburn Wyke, Wass, Nabgate and Ruswarp.

Basil Thyme
Acinos arvensis [Calamintha acinos]
This short-lived annual is another plant approaching the northern end of its range. It occurs on dry or bare calcareous ground and has been seen rarely.

Wild Basil 37 M
Clinopodium vulgare
Like marjoram, this plant is a familiar seasoning herb but growing wild it is far less common in this area. It occurs on rough grassland on more calcareous soils. Grows on the coast near Staithes and Runswick and on the southern limestone. Usually only a few plants in each location.

Salvia
Salvia verticillata
Also known as whorled clary, this is a rare species throughout Britain. It is likely that the plants found on disturbed ground at Battersby Junction originated from garden rubbish.

White horehound
Marrubium vulgare
Formerly used as a medicinal herb, this plant is seen occasionally on calcareous waysides but appears to be a short-lived remnant of garden rubbish.

Selfheal 380
Prunella vulgaris
This is a very common component of grassy roadsides, pastures and woodland edge vegetation. It withstands sheep grazing on moorland verges and tolerates moderate shade.

Field Woundwort 21 M
Stachys arvensis
Formerly common in cornfields, field woundwort is now a rarity countrywide. Locally it was found in a few fields on lighter land where herbicide use has been minimal.

Marsh Woundwort 14 M
Stachys palustris
This is quite a scarce plant in the Park. Only a few small colonies were found in shallow streams, roadside ditches and in marshy ground.

Hedge Woundwort 340 M
Stachys sylvatica
This pungent-smelling plant is abundant on coarse grassland, hedgebanks and woodsides, often in semi-shade.

Stachys x *ambigua [S. sylvatica* x *palustris]* has been found in proximity of both parents.

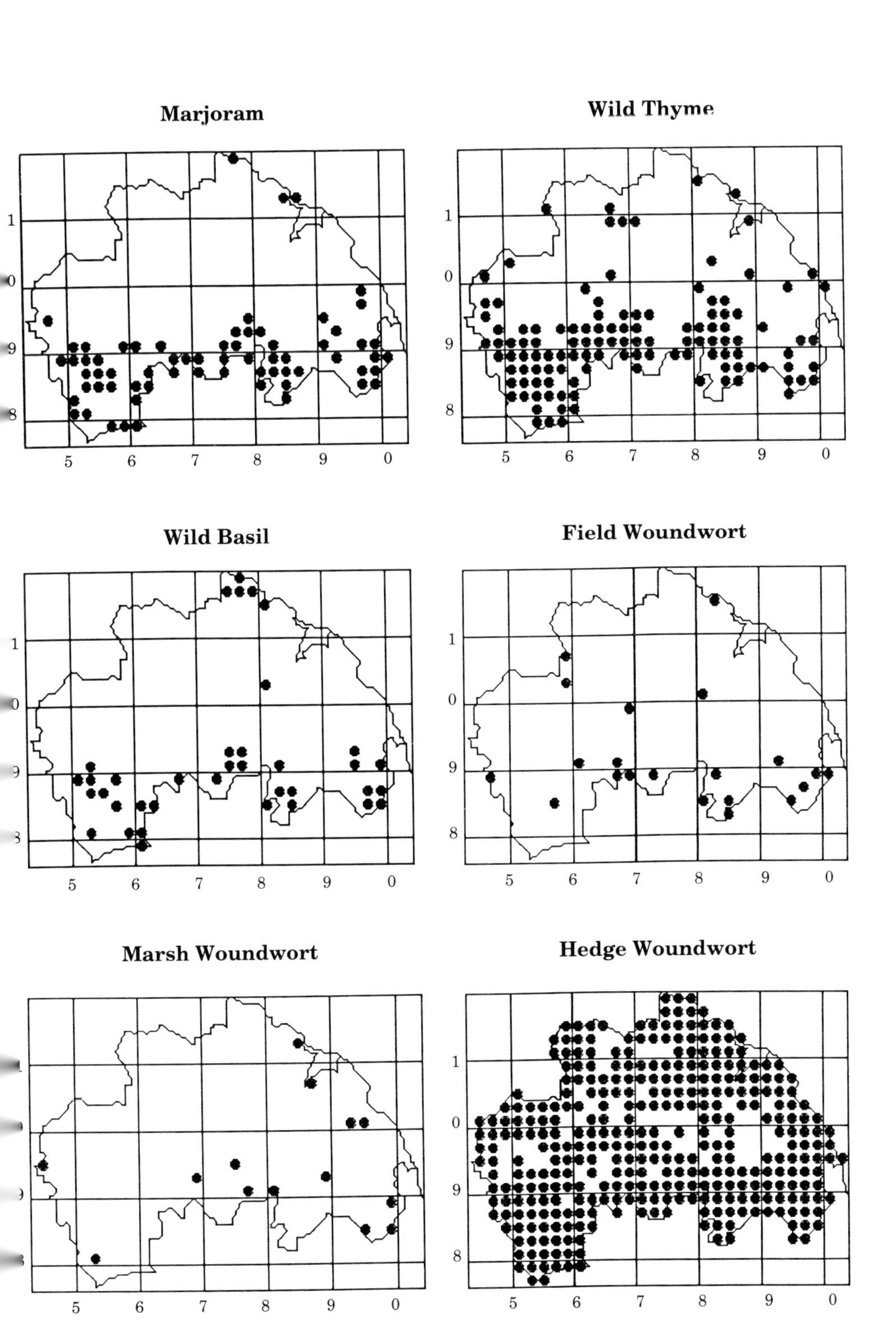
Marjoram
Wild Thyme
Wild Basil
Field Woundwort
Marsh Woundwort
Hedge Woundwort
1
0
9
8
5
6
7
8
9
0

Betony 195 M
Stachys officinalis
The distinctive deep red flowers of betony may be abundant on unimproved permanent pastures and roadside banks. It is a plant which tolerates light grazing.

Black Horehound 19 M
Ballota nigra
This lowland plant grows here and there on waste ground and gravelly verges around West Ayton, Thornton-le-Dale, Helmsley and Whitby. A former medicinal herb, it is rarely found far from habitation.

Yellow Archangel 18 M
Lamiastrum galeobdolon
A plant of ancient woodland, near its northern limit in Britain, it grows on heavy, not too acid, soils in quite deep woodland shade. Most plentiful in Kirkdale and older woods in lower Eskdale.

Henbit 25 M
Lamium amplexicaule
This arable weed appears spasmodically on calcareous or sandy soils.

Northern or **Intermediate Dead Nettle**
Lamium mollucellifolium
[Lamium confertum]
The identification of plants reported to be northern dead nettle and found at Ingleby Greenhow and Mowthorpe requires confirmation. This species is an annual of disturbed ground, found more typically near Scottish coasts.

Cut-leaved Dead Nettle 25
Lamium hybridum
Grows occasionally on enriched cultivated ground.

Red Dead Nettle 258
Lamium purpureum
A very common nettle on any disturbed ground, it proliferates on newly set-aside fields and flourishes on railway ballast, waysides, farmland and in gardens.

White Dead Nettle 148 M
Lamium album
Away from high exposed ground, it covers extensive patches on fertile soils around buildings and on verges and waste ground.

Spotted Dead Nettle 2
Lamium maculatum
A garden escape infrequently naturalised on road verges and wood edges where rubbish has been tipped.

Narrow-leaved Hemp Nettle 1
Galeopsis angustifolia
Described in 1953 as "common in cornfields and waste places", this plant was found only once during the recent survey. A cluster of plants was discovered north of Thornton-le-Dale in a field corner inaccessible to a mechanical sprayer.

Common Hemp Nettle 240 M
Galeopsis tetrahit
Widespread and plentiful on verges, field edge, clearings and waste ground. Flower colour ranges from deep purple to near white. *Galeopsis bifida* has been noted in scattered locations.

Large-flowered Hemp Nettle 3
Galeopsis speciosa
Occasional in arable fields, especially on peaty soils. Kempswithen, Baysdale, Coxwold and Mowthorpe.

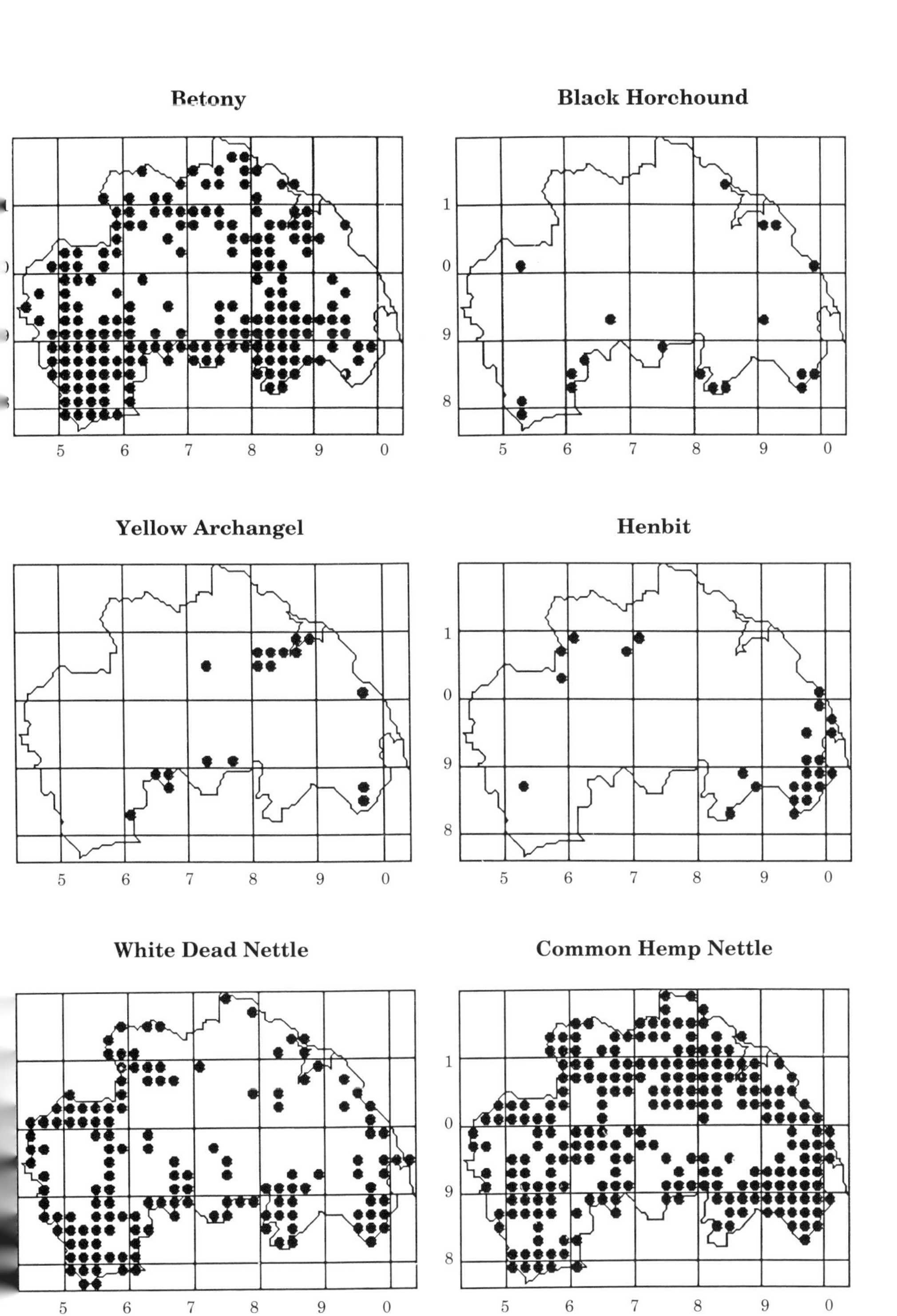

Betony
Black Horchound
Yellow Archangel
Henbit
White Dead Nettle
Common Hemp Nettle
1
0
9
8
5
6
7
8
9
0

Ground Ivy 240 M
Glechoma hederacea
Forms extensive ground cover on shady hedgebanks, road and rail verges and woodland clearings on fertile heavy soils but avoids exposed high ground.

Common Skullcap 24 M
Scutellaria galericulata
Quite large colonies grow in marshes at Throxenby Mere and Gormire. Elsewhere it is dispersed along shady streamsides and in light damp woodland, its shy flowers often secreted amongst more vigorous wetland vegetation.

Wood Sage 299 M
Teucrium scorodonia
Thrives in light shade on gravelly banks, woodland edges and free-draining wasteland, on shale heaps in old alum quarries, railway ballast and old brickworks at Ravenscar.

Bugle 321
Ajuga reptans
A common ground cover plant to be found in damp woodland, pastures, forest rides and streamsides.

PLANTAIN FAMILY
PLANTAGINACEAE

Broad-leaved Plantain 387
Plantago major
A wayside plant found on all but very acid disturbed ground. It tolerates trampling on paths and gateways and can be a tiresome invader of lawns and paving.

Hoary Plantain 85 M
Plantago media
The prominent pink flower spikes of this calcicolous plantain adorn large patches in disused limestone quarries, verges and calcareous grassland.

Ribwort Plantain 378
Plantago lanceolata
Common in most grassy places from rank roadside verge to closely grazed turf. Its leaves form a flattened rosette on overgrazed swards but in fertile pastures stand boldly upright. Absent from very acid soils.

Sea Plantain 26 M
Plantago maritima
Common on sea cliffs, where it grows in trampled turf alongside the Cleveland Way, and amongst grassland vegetation from shoreline up to cliff top fields.

Buckshorn Plantain 19 M
Plantago coronopus
Mainly a coastal plant, growing on short turf and sand well into the sea spray zone. Also on edges of moor roads subject to winter salting.

Shoreweed 10
Littorella uniflora
Abundant in mud and shallow water around reservoirs such as Scaling Dam, Scarth Wood, Boltby and Lockwood; also in Crag pond, Farndale and Ugthorpe moor pond.

BELLFLOWER FAMILY
CAMPANULACEAE

Ivy Campanula
Wahlenbergia hederacea
This tiny bellflower common in the west of England was said to have been seen on Scarth Wood Moor in the 1980s but subsequent searches have failed to locate it.

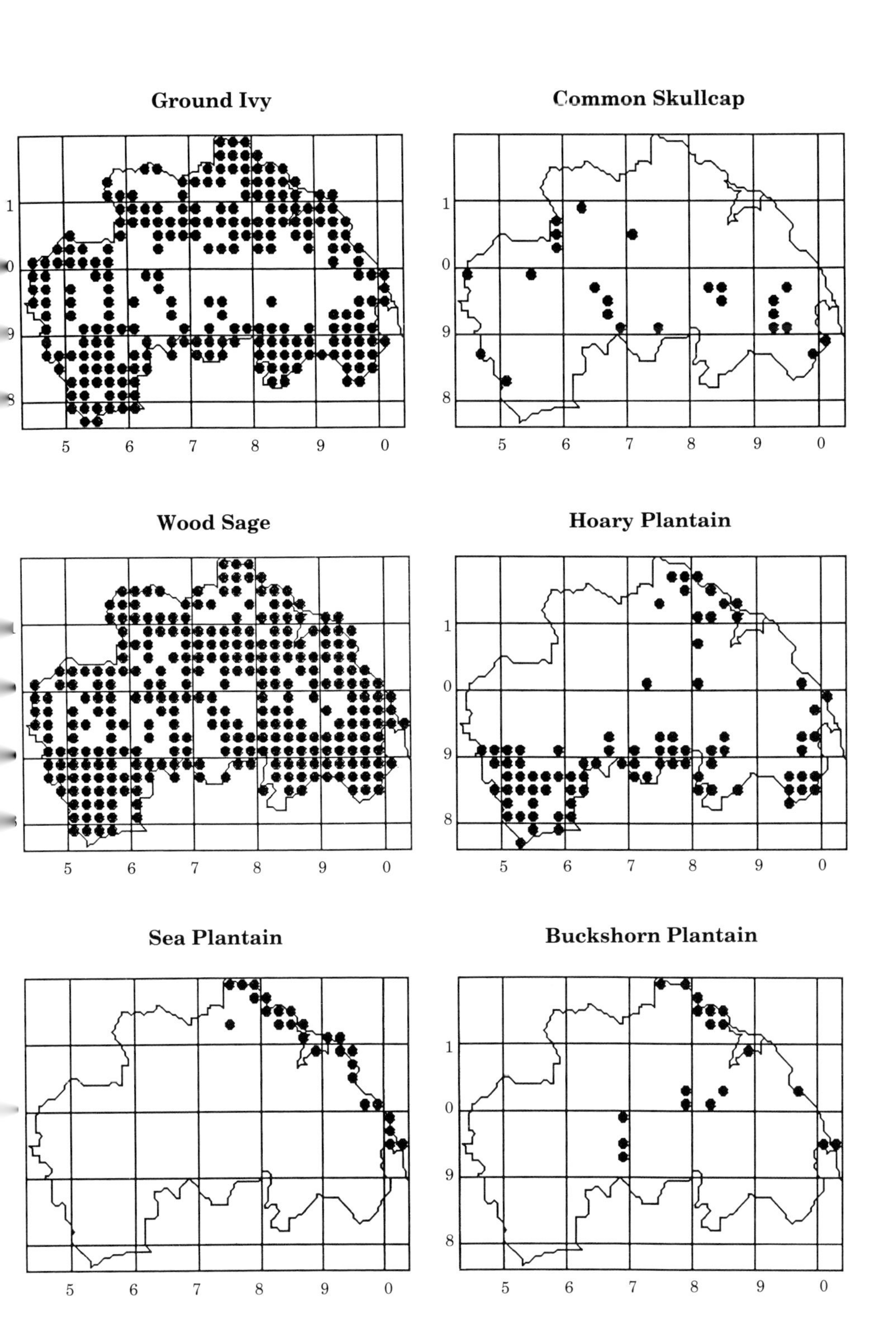
Ground Ivy
Common Skullcap
Wood Sage
Hoary Plantain
Sea Plantain
Buckshorn Plantain
1
0
9
8
5
6
7
8
9
0

Giant Bellflower 108 M
Campanula latifolia
Only common in the north of England, this handsome plant with its tall flowering spikes is frequent in the Park on neutral undisturbed soils. Mainly on lower land, it prefers light shade, and grows in sizeable colonies in older woods and hedgebanks with overhanging trees.

Creeping Campanula
Campanula rapunculoides
A rock garden plant which occasionally establishes on verges.

Clustered Bellflower 5
Campanula glomerata
As a native plant, it is confined to a few sites on short calcareous turf in the Hawnby area and in Forge Valley. It is naturalised from garden waste on a Hutton Buscel laneside.

Harebell 322 M
Campanula rotundifolia
Plentiful in the upper dales but absent from moor tops and wet or enriched habitats. It flowers in short dry grassland, quarries, rail and roadside verges and on coastal cliffs with nutrient-poor shallow soils.

Milky Bellflower
Campanula lactiflora
A showy garden plant which is naturalised on islets in Hodge Beck in Sleightholmedale.

Venus' Looking Glass 3
Legousia hybrida
In serious decline throughout the country, this chalkland plant appears fleetingly in this area on calcareous arable land. It has been recorded at Thornton-le-Dale, Murton and East Ayton and reappeared in a set-aside field where it had last been noted 20 years ago.

BEDSTRAW FAMILY
RUBIACEAE

Field Madder 34
Sherardia arvensis
Occurs in various habitats on shallow calcareous soils. No longer common on arable land, though it quickly reappears in set-aside fields. It is most often seen in disused limestone quarries, embedded in short grazed turf, on forest ride edges and in close cut lawns and verges.

Sweet Woodruff 153 M
Galium odoratum
A frequent ground flora plant found in damp deciduous woods on calcareous or base-rich soils. It is often extensive in undisturbed ancient woodland.

Crosswort 292 M
Galium cruciata [Cruciata laevipes]
A familiar plant on hedgebanks, verges, scrub and rough grassland with non-acid soils.

Hedge Bedstraw 23 M
Galium mollugo
A southern species uncommon in this area. Single clumps are found infrequently on rough grassy verges and hedgebanks with fertile soil in a sheltered situation.

Lady's Bedstraw 155 M
Galium verum
Once used for stuffing pillows, this prominent yellow-flowered plant grows in many disused limestone quarries and on hedgebanks, field edges and rough grassy places with non-acid soils.

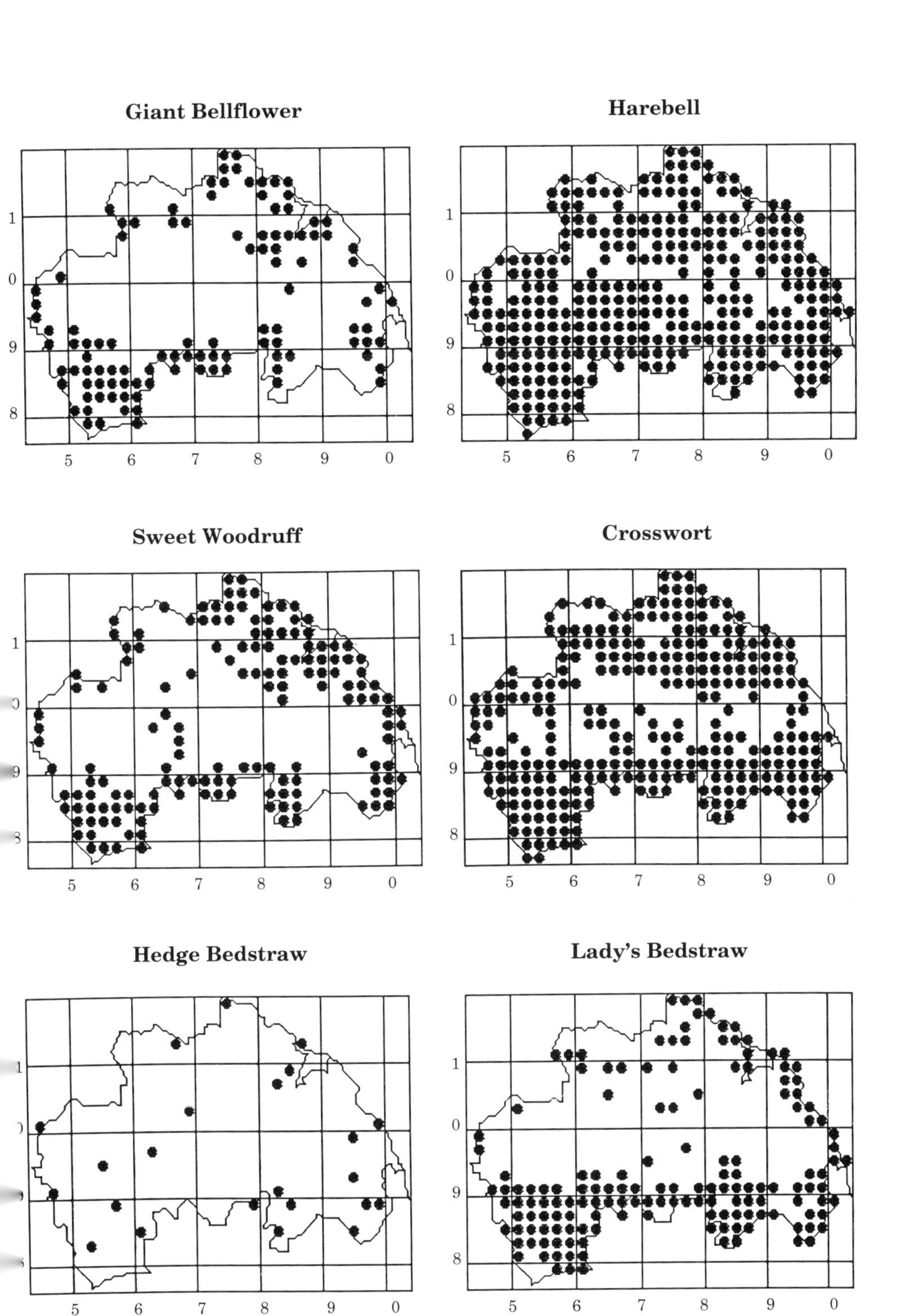
Giant Bellflower
1
0
9
8
5
6
7
8
9
0
Harebell
1
0
9
8
5
6
7
8
9
0
Sweet Woodruff
1
0
9
8
5
6
7
8
9
0
Crosswort
1
0
9
8
5
6
7
8
9
0
Hedge Bedstraw
5
6
7
8
9
0
Lady's Bedstraw
1
0
9
8
5
6
7
8
9
0

Heath Bedstraw 354 M
Galium saxatile
In company with tormentil, this is the commonest flower on upland hillside grazing and moorland fringe. It is abundant on short acidic well-drained grassland. On dampish pasture it covers the drier soil of molehills and is one of the few plants to be found some way inside forest plantations.

Marsh Bedstraw 253 M
Galium palustre
Frequent in marshes, grassland with standing water, swamps and on stream banks.

Fen Bedstraw 81 M
Galium uliginosum
Often almost hidden amongst reeds and sedges, it straggles about in fen and calcareous, wetland vegetation. Plentiful in slacks on Pamperdale, Cringle and Roxby High Moors.

Goosegrass 331
Galium aparine
A deep rooted scrambling plant, very common in fertile soil. It clambers over hedges, grassy banks and waste land.

HONEYSUCKLE FAMILY
CAPRIFOLIACEAE

Red-berried Elder 1
Sambucus racemosa
Grows in the forest around Sutherland, possibly brought in by roosting starlings.

Danewort
Sambucus ebulus
Formerly recorded in a hedgerow at Thornton-le-Dale, but not refound during the recent survey.

Elder 327 M
Sambucus nigra
Common in disturbed ground with nutrient enrichment, it is often found by rabbit warrens and old buildings where sheep shelter. Quite frequently establishes in hedgerows, presumably bird-sown. It is known locally as Bourtree.

Wayfaring Tree 4
Viburnum lantana
A southern shrub which is not native in this area but is sometimes naturalised from garden plantings as at Hackness.

Guelder Rose 156 M
Viburnum opulus
Alluvial soils in the valley bottoms provide the preferred habitat for this attractive shrub which can be found scattered in older woodland and hedges on lower land. It often grows in glades with light shade.

Snowberry 97
Symphoricarpos rivularis
[Symphoricarpos albus]
Planted as a garden shrub and for game cover, it is widely naturalised near habitation in hedgerows and thickets.

Honeysuckle 316 M
Lonicera periclymenum
A common climber in hedgerows and open scrub where it flowers abundantly. In woodland glades and margins, it twists its way up supporting trees to 7 metres high but flowers reluctantly in shade.

Twin Flower
Linnaea borealis
Although this plant, more typical of Scotland, flourished some time ago in a wood behind Levisham station, it has not been seen for many years and is believed to have died out.

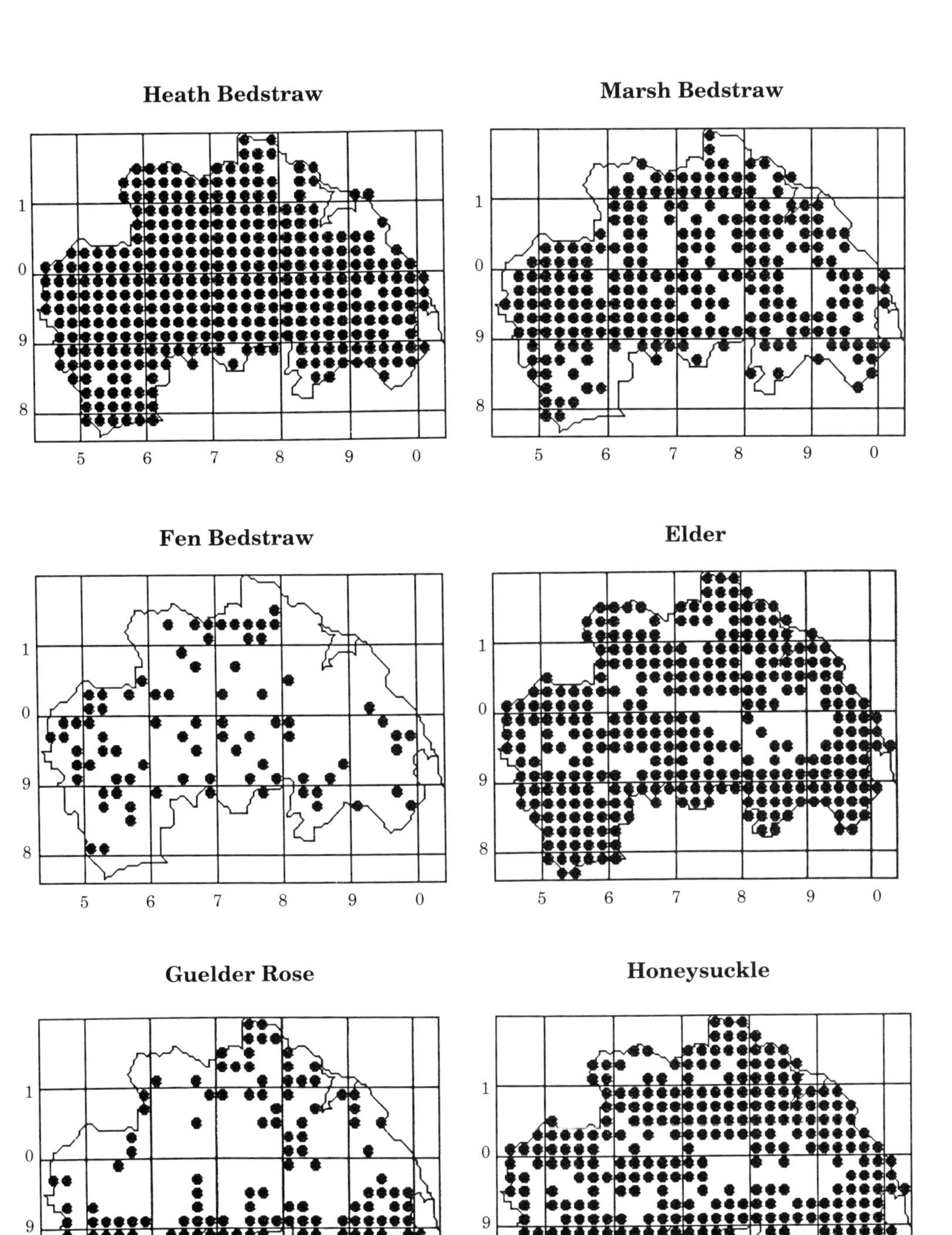
Heath Bedstraw
Marsh Bedstraw
Fen Bedstraw
Elder
Guelder Rose
Honeysuckle

MOSCHATEL FAMILY
ADOXACEAE

Townhall Clock or **Moschatel** 139 M
Adoxa moschatellina
This secretive small plant grows in damp fertile soils on shady hedgebanks, open woods and streamsides, often forming extensive ground cover amongst grasses and leaf litter. It indicates undisturbed land.

VALERIAN FAMILY
VALERIANACEAE

Corn Salad 7
Valerianella locusta
Formerly a common cornfield plant on light land, now almost eliminated by herbicides. A few surviving plants have been found in field corners and on set-aside land.

Valerianella carinata 1
This rare corn salad was found growing in paving cracks on Ruswarp station platform.

Common Valerian 239 M
Valeriana officinalis
Widespread in tall marsh vegetation, wet woods and poorly-drained grassland on less acidic soils.

Marsh Valerian 147 M
Valeriana dioica
This is the smaller of the two wetland valerians to be found in the Park. Its habitats include alder carr, marshes, streamsides and damp pastures. Avoiding very acid peat, it flourishes in seepage zones with nutrient enrichment and prefers sheltered sites.

Red Valerian 14
Centranthus ruber
Introduced as a garden plant from southern Europe, it has become well established in the wild on rocky outcrops and retaining walls. Most frequent near habitation on the coast. Lythe Bank, Robin Hood's Bay and Port Mulgrave.

TEASEL FAMILY
DIPSACACEAE

Teasel 19
Dipsacus fullonum
As a native plant, teasel has been found only rarely in rough grassland often near water. A few colonies established on verges are likely to have originated from garden outcasts.

Field Scabious 117 M
Knautia arvensis
A common roadside plant away from acid soils and too rigorous verge cutting. It is widely distributed along most lanes and rough grassland on the limestone belt but infrequent elsewhere.

Small Scabious 26 M
Scabiosa columbaria
Not a common plant in this area where it is more or less confined to disused quarries and short grassy outcrops on thin calcareous soils.

Devilsbit Scabious 242 M
Succisa pratensis
This attractive scabious, whose strange name refers to the "bitten-off" appearance of its roots, is widespread on all but most acid soils. It thrives in wet unimproved grassland, along forest rides, damp woodland edges and waysides.

Townhall Clock or Moschatel

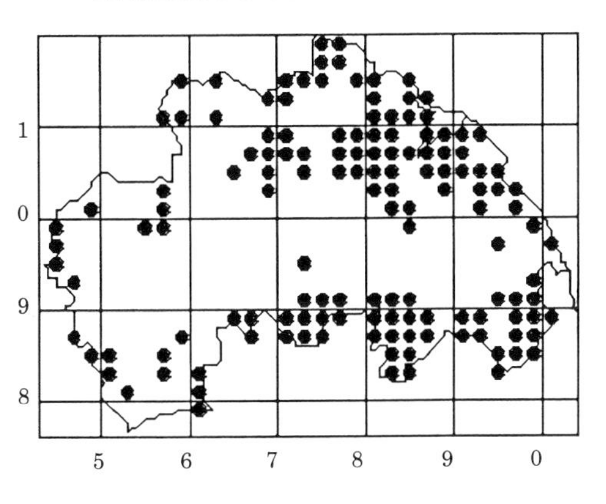

Common Valerian

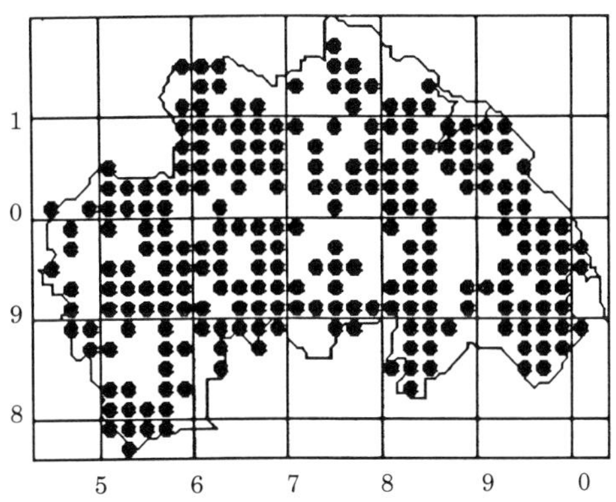

Marsh Valerian

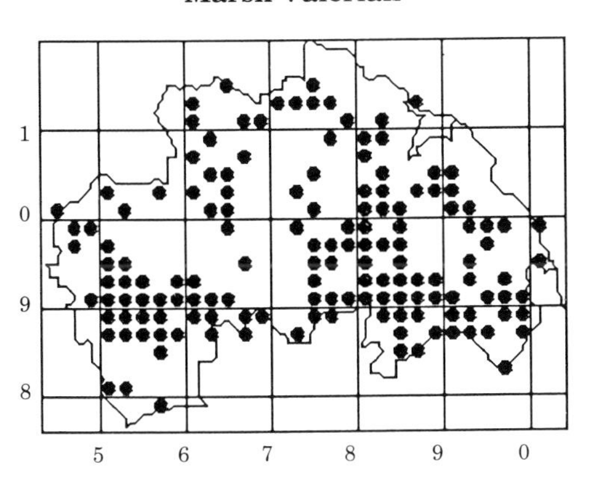

Field Scabious

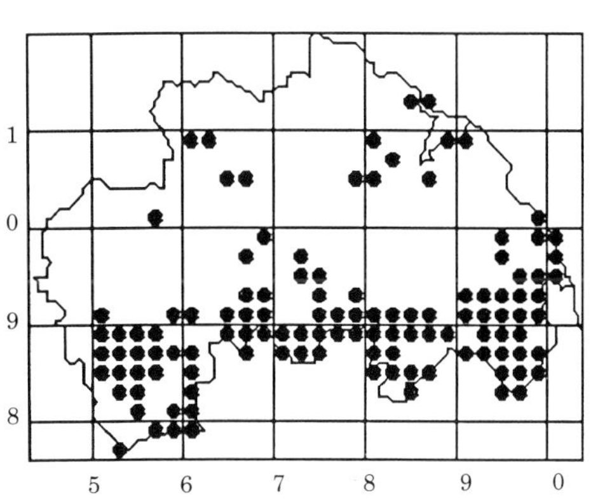

Small Scabious

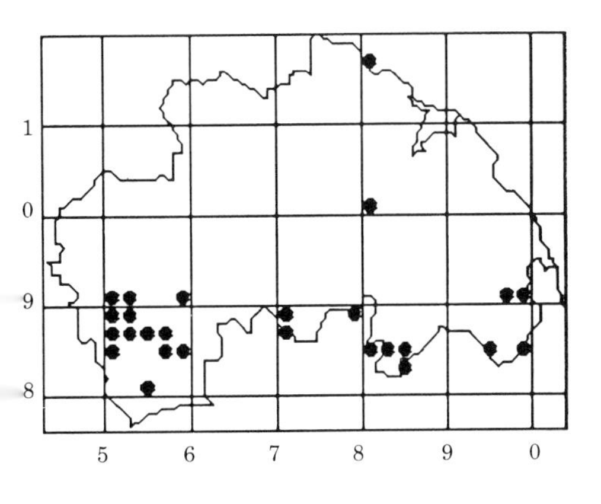

Devilsbit Scabious

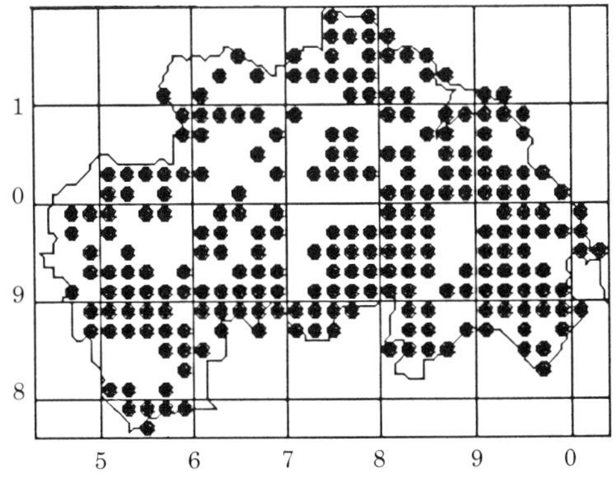

DAISY FAMILY
COMPOSITAE [ASTERACEAE]

Shaggy Soldier 1
Galinsoga ciliata
[Galinsoga quadriradiata]
This South American plant, only known in this country since 1925, was first recorded in this area on disturbed ground near Whitby in 1987.

Ragwort 344
Senecio jacobaea
This familiar weed is very common on poor light soils, road and rail verges and wayside grassland. Poisonous to stock, it indicates overgrazed or worn-out pastures.

Marsh Ragwort 75 M
Senecio aquaticus
Occurs in large numbers in damp grassland on heavy and alluvial soils. It is frequent in watery meadows beside the Murk Esk and feeder streams of the Rye, Esk and Seph. Often grows in wet hollows poached by grazing stock.

Hoary Ragwort 14 M
Senecio erucifolius
Occurs infrequently on hedgebanks and rough grassland on base-rich soils, mostly near the coast.

Oxford Ragwort 27 M
Senecio squalidus
A native of Sicily which has spread throughout this country since the 1950s. It flourishes on disturbed ground and, from a stronghold around Whitby harbour, its local distribution closely follows the main road west from Whitby and along Bilsdale. It is becoming established on unstable rocky exposures at the former whinstone quarry at Cliff Rigg.

Wood Groundsel 46 M
Senecio sylvaticus
After forest felling and brash burning, this plant covers the ground for a year or two. Elsewhere it is found infrequently on disturbed ground in scrub or open woodland.

A hybrid *S. squalidus* x *viscosus* grows on the railside at Battersby.

Stinking Groundsel 29 M
Senecio viscosus
This well-named plant occurs on waste ground and hedgebanks in a few localities.

Groundsel 314 M
Senecio vulgaris
Very common on fertile disturbed or cultivated ground.

Leopardsbane 13
Doronicum pardalianches
Believed to have originated from garden throwouts, a few clumps flourish on roadsides, in woodland clearings and plantation fringes.

Coltsfoot 331
Tussilago farfara
An early-flowering wayside plant, coltsfoot covers extensive patches on disturbed wet clay soils. It is also widespread on rail ballast, bare road verges and grit piles. A real colonist, it survives in pavement cracks, in car parks and damp quarry bottoms while it can be abundant on spring lines on coastal cliffs.

Butterbur 66 M
Petasites hybridus
A vigorous plant which spreads vegetatively to cover large areas of damp roadside or waste ground. Large colonies of male plants are abundant in Forge

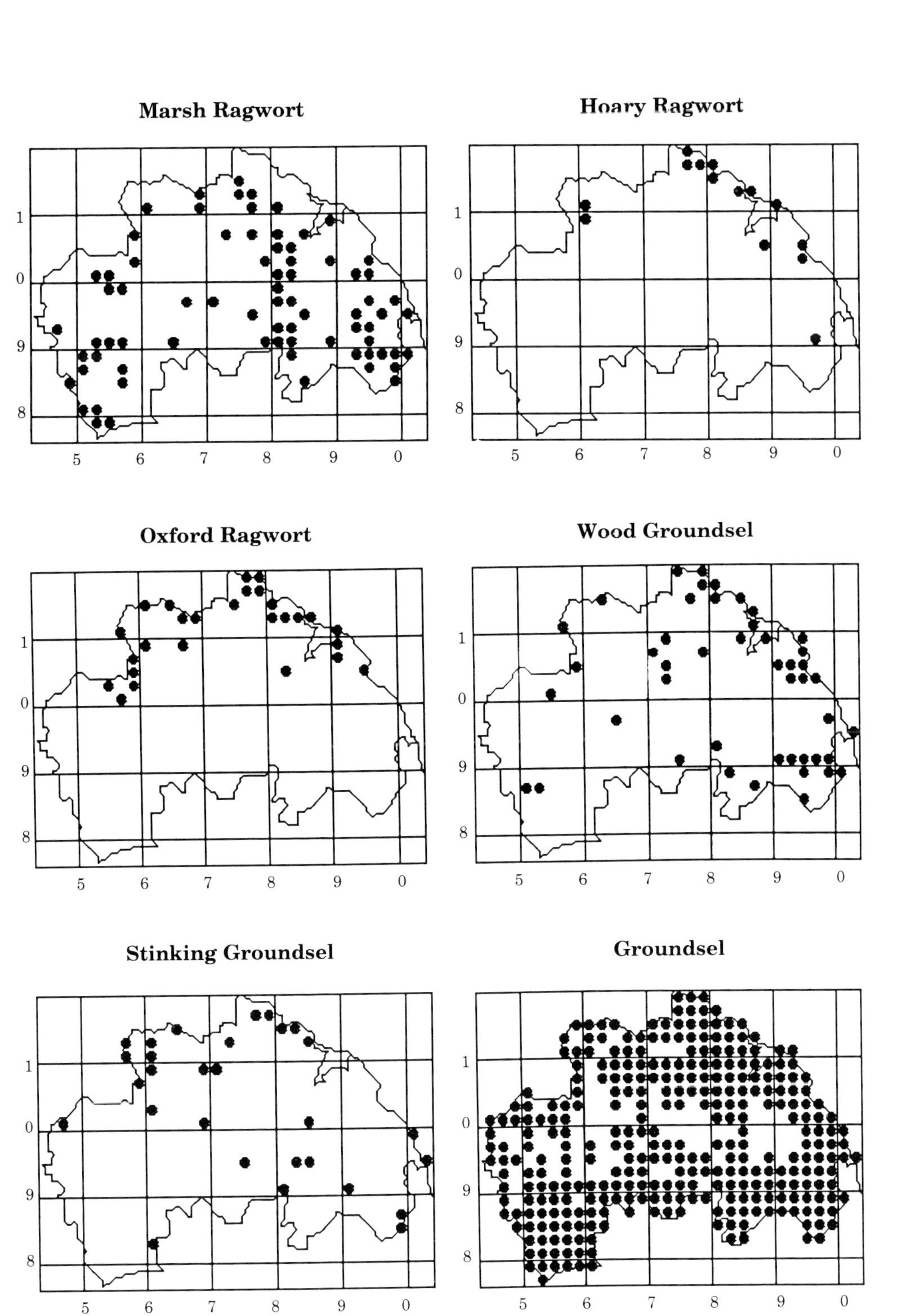
Marsh Ragwort
Hoary Ragwort
Oxford Ragwort
Wood Groundsel
Stinking Groundsel
Groundsel
1
0
9
8
5
6
7
8
9
0

Valley and similar habitats. A rare stand of female plants was discovered in 1991 just outside the Park boundary near Kirkbymoorside.

Winter Heliotrope 27 M
Petasites fragrans
Although only brought to this country from the Mediterranean in the early 19th century, it has become an established roadside plant. Its fragrant flowers appear and wither early in the year, thus the circular leaves are more familiar, creating extensive ground cover on many grassy verges, especially within a mile or two of the sea.

Elecampane 4
Inula helenium
Once cultivated for medicinal and culinary use, a few relics have naturalised at Hayburn Wyke, Kirkdale and Sutton Bank.

Ploughman's Spikenard 16 M
Inula conyza [Inula conyzae]
Found infrequently in old quarries, on rough grassy banks and a few roadsides with well-drained calcareous soil. Murton, Appleton-le-Moors, Newbridge, Yoadwath, Grosmont, Raincliffe and West Ayton.

Fleabane 100 M
Pulicaria dysenterica
The prominent yellow flowerheads of this plant can be seen in large colonies on rail and road verges, in ditches, cattle-trodden wetland and spring lines on coastal cliffs. Most plentiful on boulder clay.

Common Cudweed 11 M
Filago vulgaris
Despite the name, it is far from common in these parts. A few plants are dotted around on sheep-grazed turf on Egton High, Glaisdale, Wheeldale and Rosedale Moors and in Cliff Rigg quarry.

Wood Cudweed 4
Gnaphalium sylvaticum
This unobtrusive cudweed is rare locally, found only on a Wykeham Forest ride, in heathy grassland in Lonsdale, in Tup Hag Wood and on Poverty Hill near Danby. Its short-lived, inconspicuous shoots may have been overlooked elsewhere.

Marsh Cudweed 113 M
Gnaphalium uliginosum
By contrast to the previous species, this unprepossessing little cudweed is widespread and common. An annual plant, it springs up in damp or trampled mud in gateways, wheel ruts, pathways and disturbed acid ground where water stands for long periods.

Mountain Everlasting or **Catsfoot** 5
Antennaria dioica
An uncommon low-growing plant of dry grassy banks on calcareous or base-rich soil with surface acidification. Easily mistaken for mouse-ear hawkweed, with which it often grows, it can be found in Caydale, Sanddale, lower Farndale and on Poverty Hill, Danby.

Golden Rod 86
Solidago virgaurea
On undisturbed dry grassland, in quarries, rocky outcrops and woodland edges, a few plants occur in scattered locations. It is nowhere plentiful.

Solidago canadensis
This popular garden version of golden rod is quite often naturalised on verges and in rough grassland well away from its garden of origin.

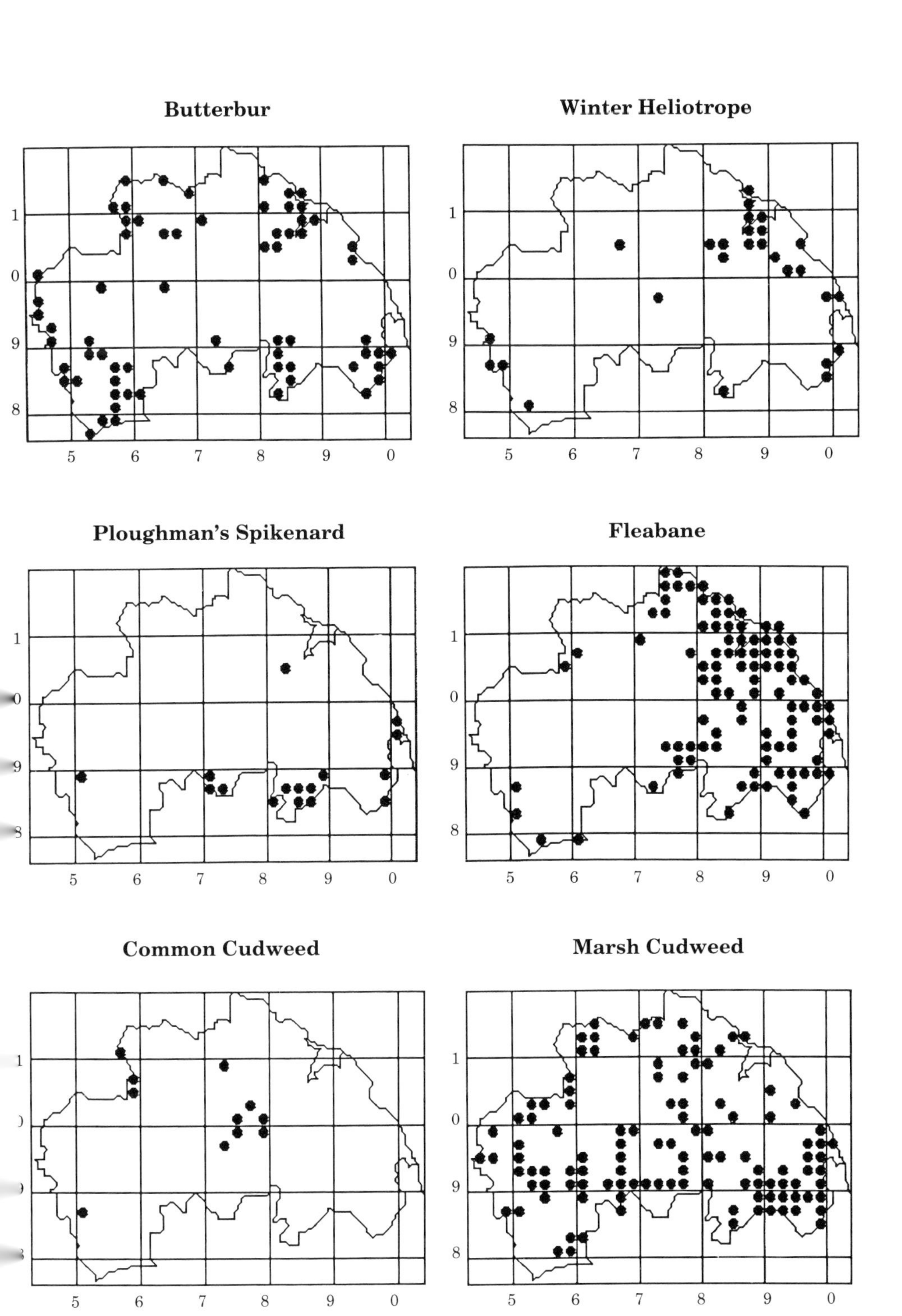
Butterbur
Winter Heliotrope
Ploughman's Spikenard
Fleabane
Common Cudweed
Marsh Cudweed

Sea Aster 2
Aster tripolium
A saltmarsh plant, restricted by lack of suitable habitat, but grows abundantly on tidal mudflats beside the Esk from Ruswarp to Whitby.

Michaelmas Daisy
Aster novi-belgii
A garden escape naturalised on the railside at Battersby Junction.

Blue Fleabane 2
Erigeron acer
A plant of well-drained calcareous soils, blue fleabane is locally rare and has been found only on Ellerburn Bank and in ballast at Grosmont rail sidings. Liberal weed spraying at the latter site is jeopardising the continuity of the species in this area.

Daisy 390
Bellis perennis
Recorded almost everywhere except on very wet acid peat. This familiar determined little plant thrives despite incessant sheep nibbling, regular lawn mowing and constant trampling.

Hemp Agrimony 98 M
Eupatorium cannabinum
A continental plant reaching the northern edge of its range in this area is increasingly confined to a climate tempered by proximity to the sea. Large populations occur on wet grassland and verges, by ditches and streamsides along the coastal plain and in seepage zones on the cliffs. Inland it is local in sheltered valleys and forest ride margins.

Stinking Mayweed 10
Anthemis cotula
An uncommon arable weed which occurs on boulder clay fields around Staithes and on base-rich loams further west.

Corn Chamomile
Anthemis arvensis
This southern annual of arable land was discovered on disturbed ground at Battersby Junction, probably introduced with hardcore.

Scentless Mayweed 193 M
Tripleurospermum inodorum
This common mayweed is widely dispersed across farmland. Somewhat resistant to herbicides, it flourishes on arable and disturbed ground, in stackyards and on waysides.

Wild Chamomile 41 M
Matricaria recutita
An aromatic mayweed, far less common than scentless mayweed, it grows on much lighter sandy ground, in arable fields and on disturbed wasteland.

Pineapple Weed 353 M
Matricaria matricarioides
[Matricaria discoidea]
This persistent carpeting plant was unknown in this country until a century ago. Now it is abundant in gateways, on field tracks, pathways and waste ground, resisting any amount of trampling to which it responds by releasing a strong pineapple aroma.

Yarrow 372 M
Achillea millefolium
A former medicinal herb, now a very common plant of neutral grassland. Its prominent flowering heads are a familiar sight on many road and rail verges. Its feathery leaves can be seen in mown lawns and grazed swards.

Sneezewort 154 M
Achillea ptarmica
Grows extensively in poorly drained acid pasture, in roadside ditches, wet scrubland and forest margins away from limestone.

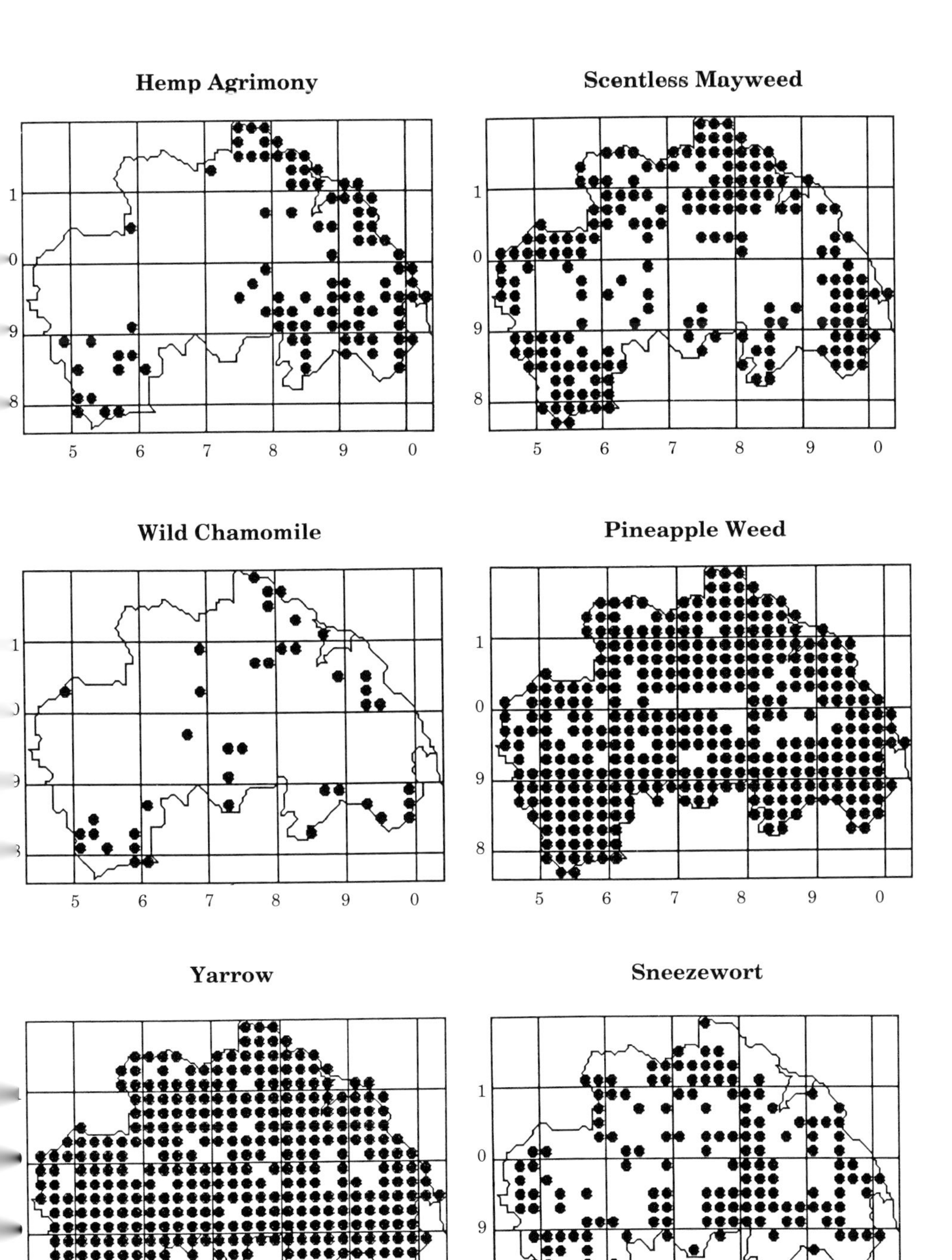
Hemp Agrimony
Scentless Mayweed
Wild Chamomile
Pineapple Weed
Yarrow
Sneezewort
1
0
9
8
5
6
7
8
9
0

Corn Marigold 6
Chrysanthemum segetum
Formerly a common sight in cornfields on lighter land, this plant is now a local rarity, known only from field edges at Thornton-le-Dale, Lastingham and Whitby. Its last known roadside locations between Thornton-le-Dale and Snainton were destroyed by roadworks in the 1980s despite a conservationist's plea for topsoil to be retained.

Ox-eye Daisy 240 M
Leucanthemum vulgare
A showy plant, familiar amidst the taller vegetation on most lowland roadsides and grassy wasteland and in remaining traditional hay-meadows.

Shasta Daisy
Leucanthemum maximum
[Leucanthemum x *superbum]*
A garden plant found naturalised on a road verge near Fylingthorpe and at Turkey Carpet.

Blue Sowthistle 20 M
Cicerbita macrophylla
This handsome blue-flowered plant was brought to this country for use in gardens, whence its feathered seeds have spread far and wide to establish it as a roadside plant.

Daisy Bush
Olearia sp.
Widely planted and naturalised as a coastal hedging shrub, this garden evergreen withstands forceful salt-laden winds, especially around Ravenscar.

Feverfew 84 M
Tanacetum parthenium
Once widely grown for medicinal use, its yellow-green leaves and white flowers are prominent on walls and banks in and around villages.

Tansy 26 M
Tanacetum vulgare
Formerly cultivated both as a culinary and a medicinal herb, the prevalence of tansy on verges of roads radiating from Whitby Abbey may indicate its local origin. Found inland infrequently on base-rich stony soils.

Mugwort 66 M
Artemisia vulgaris
Away from higher exposed ground, this tall plant grows widely amongst rank roadside vegetation on fertile soils, particularly alongside main roads. Occasional in nutrient-rich pockets in stackyards and on wasteland.

Wormwood 2
Artemisia absinthium
A rare coastal plant to be found in ones and twos on cliff grassland between Kettleness and Runswick.

Sea Wormwood 1
Artemisia maritima
A plant of upper saltmarshes, sea wormwood survives in tidal sands on the riverside at Ruswarp.

Carline Thistle 54 M
Carlina vulgaris
A warmth-seeking plant which grows abundantly on dry short calcareous grassland, especially in sheltered hollows, old limestone quarries and on south-facing grazed slopes.

Burdock 275
Arctium agg.
Widespread on roadsides and in rough grassland throughout the Park except on high moorland.

Slender Thistle 2
Carduus tenuiflorus
A wasteland plant, only recorded between Staithes and Boulby.

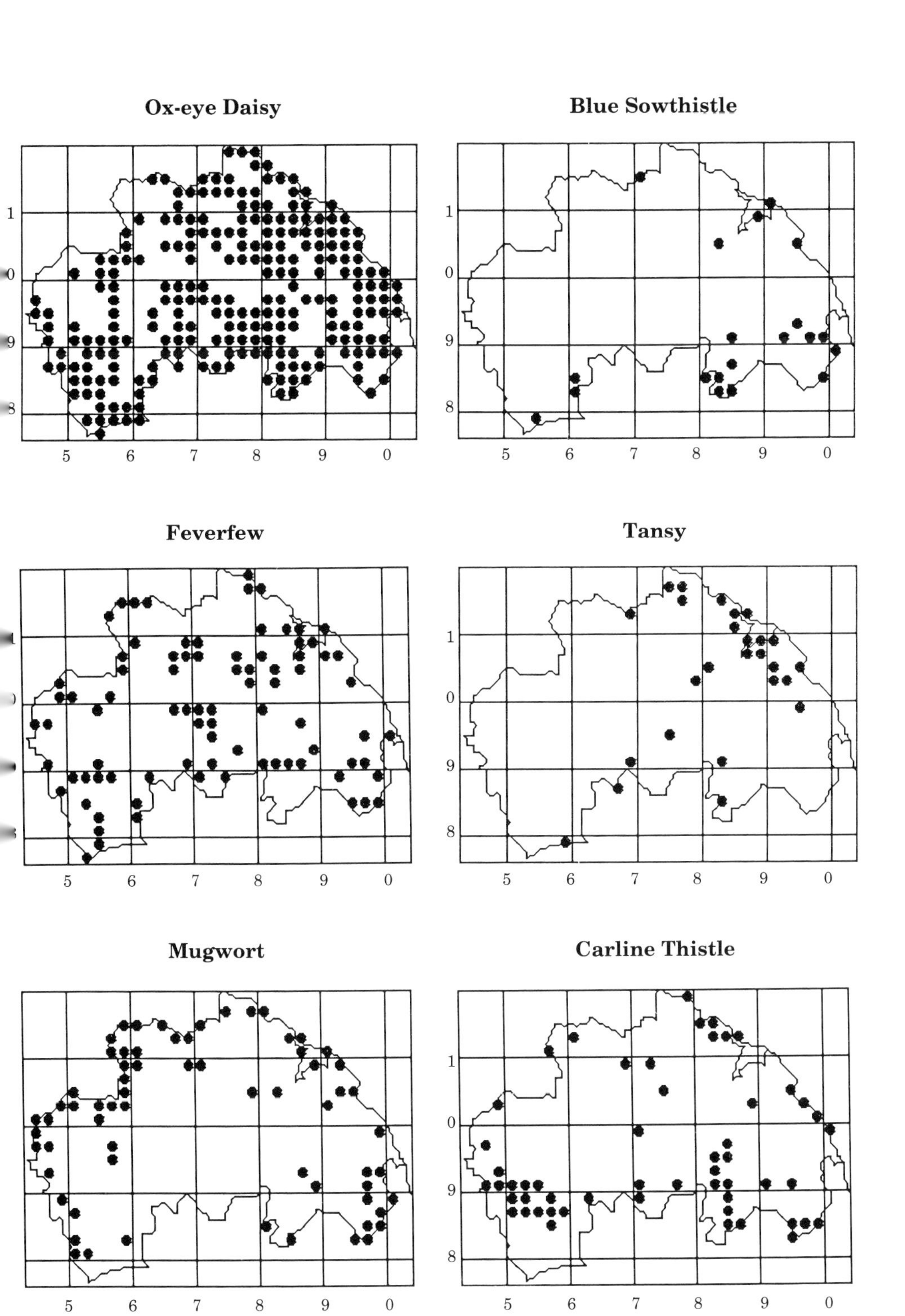

Ox-eye Daisy
Blue Sowthistle
Feverfew
Tansy
Mugwort
Carline Thistle
1
0
9
8
5
6
7
8
9
0

Musk Thistle 87 M
Carduus nutans
On free-draining calcareous soils, this plant is prominent during the summer when sheep reduce all surrounding vegetation to a tight green sward. Tall spikes of its purple nodding flowers are plentiful on the Hambleton Hills and around Levisham.

Welted Thistle 23 M
Carduus acanthoides
Often the only plant to be seen on spoil from recent roadworks, this thistle thrives on disturbance and appears spasmodically.

Woolly Thistle 15
Cirsium eriophorum
Reaching its northern limit in Britain, this is a rare plant here, confined to old quarries and scrub on the southern limestone fringe. Hutton Buscel to Hackness, Ellerburn, Yoadwath and Rievaulx to Gowerdale.

Spear Thistle 385
Cirsium vulgare
A common grassland thistle on drier soils away from the high moors.

Marsh Thistle 385 M
Cirsium palustre
By no means confined to marshes, this deep purple-flowered thistle grows in pasture and wasteland from the lower farmed land almost up to the moorland ridge. Absent only from very calcareous soils.

Field Thistle 389
Cirsium arvense
An aggressive and troublesome weed of both pasture and arable land, its deep rooting system ensures long term survival. Propagating from broken rootlets, it can rapidly infest a field, and grows in a range of soils and altitudes.

Stemless Thistle 1
Cirsium acaule
At the northern end of its range, this attractive low-growing thistle was known for many years on a site near Helmsley until it was dug up and planted in a local garden, needless to say not surviving. Another site succumbed to roadworks, and it was feared that the plant had been lost to this area until a new colony was found north of Hackness in 1991. The plants in this location are a short-stemmed variety of the "stemless" thistle. A record for this plant in Raindale needs confirmation.

Melancholy Thistle 2
Cirsium helenioides
[Cirsium heterophyllum]
More common further west and north in Britain, this thistle has rare outposts here in Newtondale and Raisdale.

Meadow Thistle 20 M
Cirsium dissectum
Grows only in non-acid peaty pasture and fen or wet heath with calcareous seepage. A southern plant, in this area it begins to replace the more northerly melancholy thistle, and can be found in a few widely distributed marshy sites.

Greater Knapweed 41 M
Centaurea scabiosa
The shaggy purple flowers of this plant are seen infrequently on rough grassland, verges and in old quarries on calcareous or base-rich soils. Mostly on the southern limestone, also in Kildale, Lealholm and Mulgrave.

Hardheads or **Lesser Knapweed** 342 M
Centaurea nigra
A very common plant on nutrient-poor rough grassland, road and rail verges, hedgebanks and field margins, away from the high moors.

Musk Thistle

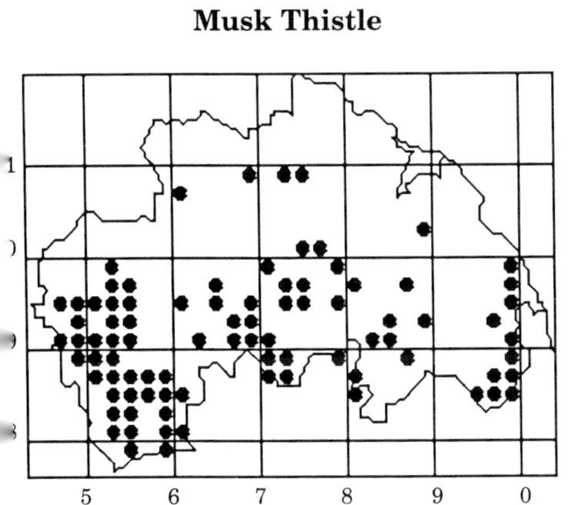

Welted Thistle

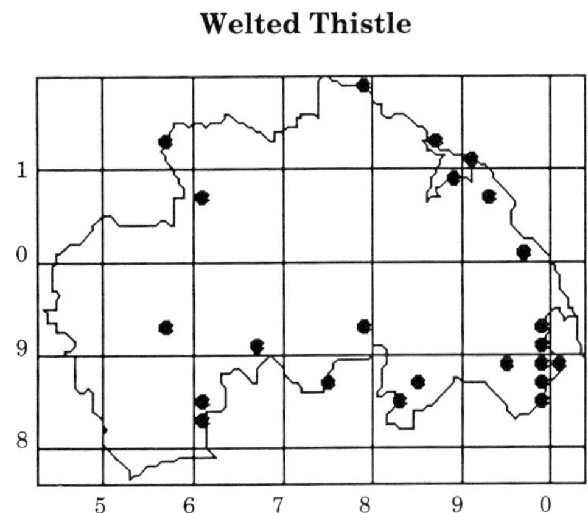

Marsh Thistle

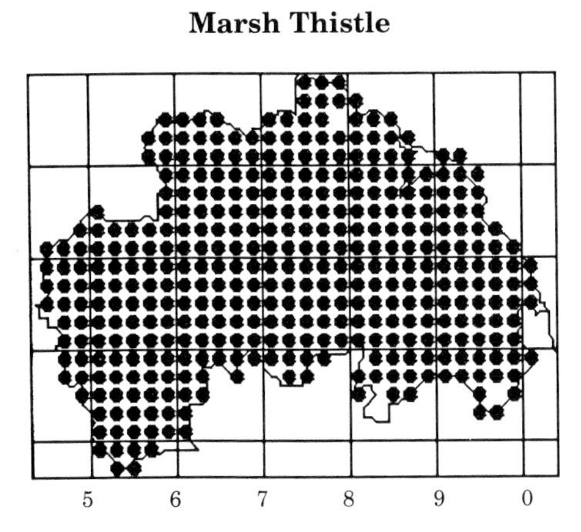

Meadow Thistle

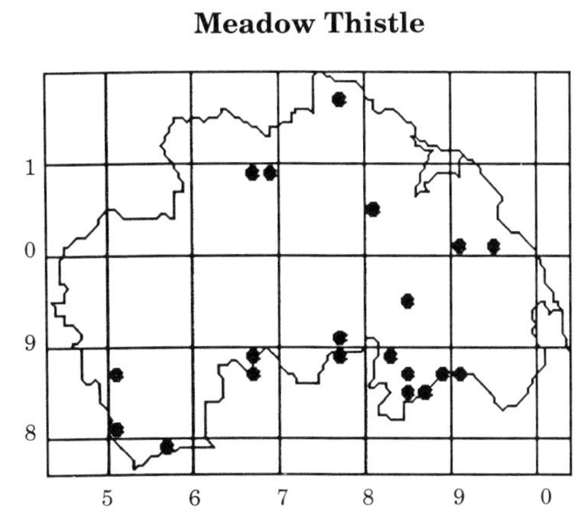

Greater Knapweed

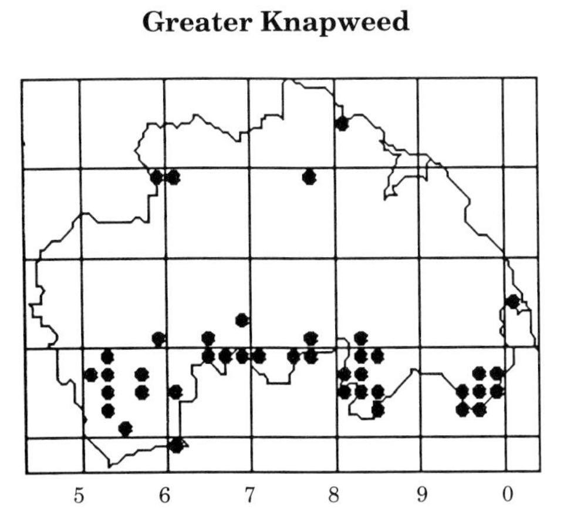

Hardheads or **Lesser Knapweed**

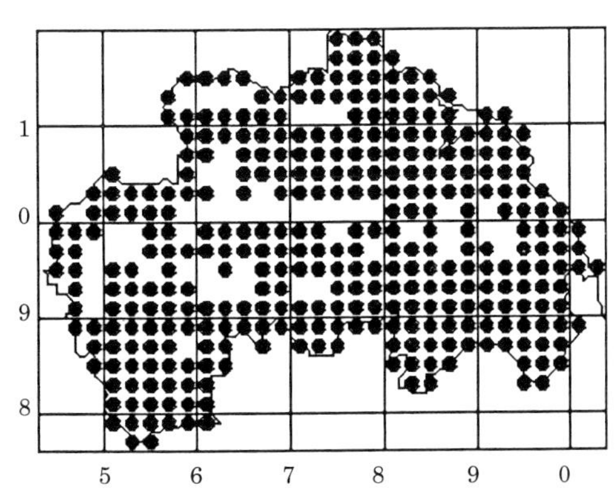

Sawwort 12 M
Serratula tinctoria
Calcareous scrub and rough grassy verges or pastures are the habitats for this uncommon species. It has been found at Murton, Raindale, Ellerburn, Ruston, Suffield, Sandsend and Waupley.

Chicory 6
Cichorium intybus
This plant is making a come-back on organic farms, where it is sown in seed mixtures, and occasionally escapes to a nearby roadside. Recorded in Harwood Dale and Danby Dale.

Nipplewort 274
Lapsana communis
Formerly used as a salad plant, nipplewort is now commonly found in gardens, on wasteland and verges. It thrives in the half-shade of walls and hedges and away from very acid soils.

Catsear 335
Hypochaeris radicata
One of the commonest "yellow daisies" in this area. It inhabits most short grassland on slightly acid soils, avoiding only the high moorland.

Autumn Hawkbit 233 M
Leontodon autumnalis
This more delicate member of the "yellow daisy" tribe occupies short turf on calcareous soils where it grows abundantly on verges and in open scrubland.

Rough Hawkbit 213 M
Leontodon hispidus
In similar habitats to autumn hawkbit, it is plentiful on hedgebanks, waysides and rough grassland away from acid soils.

Lesser Hawkbit 49 M
Leontodon taraxacoides
[Leontodon saxatilis]
With so little of its preferred habitat, calcareous grassland, remaining, this hawkbit survives only in sparse populations on a few road and forest verges and dalesides.

Bristly Oxtongue 8 M
Picris echioides
This plant, which takes its name from the resemblance of its prickly leaf to an ox tongue, thrives on coastal boulder clay. It grows in limited numbers on waysides and woodland fringes from Staintondale to Boulby but is plentiful around Boulby mine where it is likely to have been introduced with hardcore.

Hawkweed Oxtongue 2
Picris hieracioides
A plant which is believed to be spreading northwards, it has been found on calcareous wasteland in a quarry near Ruston and on cliff scrub at Runswick.

Goatsbeard 98 M
Tragopogon pratensis
Although widespread in distribution, it rarely exceeds more than a handful of plants in any one location. An occupant of rank grassy banksides, rail cuttings and verges, it is well camouflaged after midday when its yellow petals close behind long green sepals. Hence its alternative name of Jack-go-to-bed-at-noon.

Salsify
Tragopogon porrifolius
An introduced plant, formerly grown as a vegetable, it has naturalised on wasteland in the Whitby area.

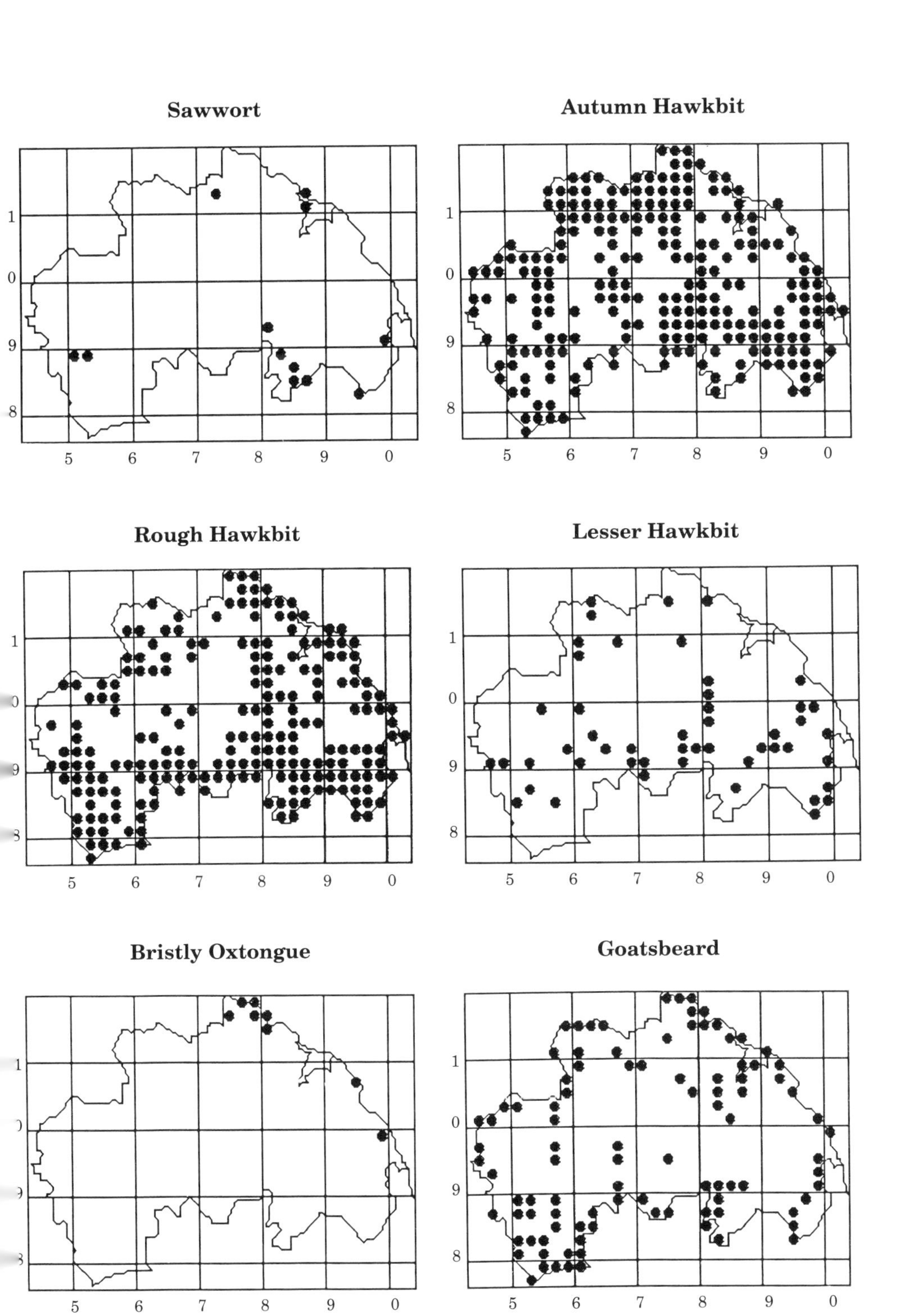
Sawwort
Autumn Hawkbit
Rough Hawkbit
Lesser Hawkbit
Bristly Oxtongue
Goatsbeard
1
0
9
8
5
6
7
8
9
0

Wall Lettuce 124 M
Mycelis muralis
Scattered plants grow from crevices in alkaline rocks, old walls and stony woodsides. It likes to be in a shady gill or under tree canopy.

Corn or **Perennial Sowthistle** 193 M
Sonchus arvensis
The deep yellow glandular flowers of this plant are abundant on many a roadside, field edge and ditchbank in late summer.

Smooth Sowthistle 242 M
Sonchus oleraceus
This thistle-like plant with its yellow flowers and soft prickles is a frequent weed on cultivated fertile soil. Often to be seen on pathsides, in gardens and waysides as well as on cultivated land.

Prickly Sowthistle 290 M
Sonchus asper
Occupying much the same habitats as smooth sowthistle, this plant is similar in appearance but has stronger prickles and is more abundant. It has been found on a range of disturbed soils including car parks and at the bottom of a well.

Hawkweeds 211
Hieracium agg.
Sub-division of this extensive group of plants has not been possible from the data available. Further work is needed in this area. Hawkweeds have been recorded in a range of grassy or rocky habitats away from very acid soils and the high moors.

Mouse-ear Hawkweed 288 M
Hieracium pilosella
[Pilosella officinarum]
On dry slopes, grazed heath, walls and in old quarries, this vigorous small plant forms extensive ground cover. On sunny banks its tangled mat of leaves and runners, intertwined with yellow flowers, often smothers other vegetation.

Orange Hawkweed 25
Hieracium brunneocroceum
[Pilosella aurantiaca]
Introduced from central Europe as a garden plant, it has taken to the open countryside in a big way and has naturalised on many road verges. Its brick-red flowers contrast sharply with a background of sombre conifers in Dalby Forest. It is particularly numerous in railside ballast along Eskdale.

Beaked Hawksbeard 9 M
Crepis vesicaria
First recorded in Britain in 1843, when plants were found in Essex, it quickly spread north and was recorded in Hutton Buscel quarry in 1906. The recent survey revealed nine locations including the walls of Rievaulx Abbey, the same Hutton Buscel quarry and the old rail tracks at Robin Hood's Bay and Runswick.

Rough Hawksbeard 5
Crepis biennis
This European plant of dry alkaline soils here approaches the northern limit of its range. Not surprisingly, it is locally rare. It was discovered in disused quarries and on the old rail track by the coast. Ruston, Ruswarp, Lythe, Charltons and Robin Hood's Bay.

Wall Lettuce

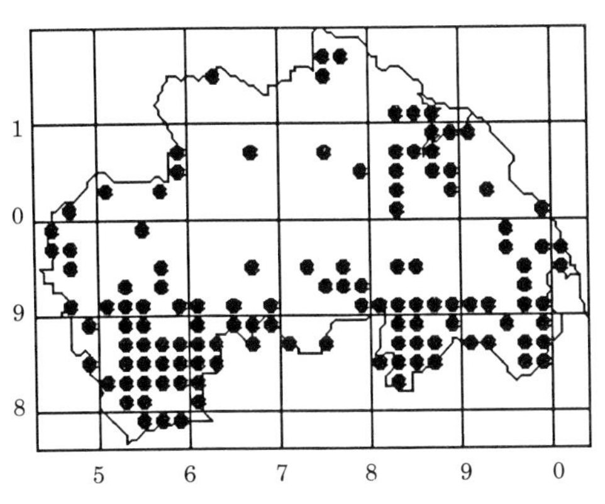

Corn or **Perennial Sowthistle**

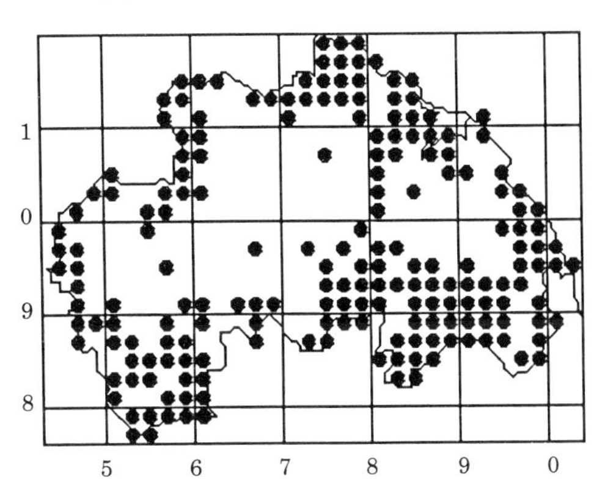

Smooth Sowthistle

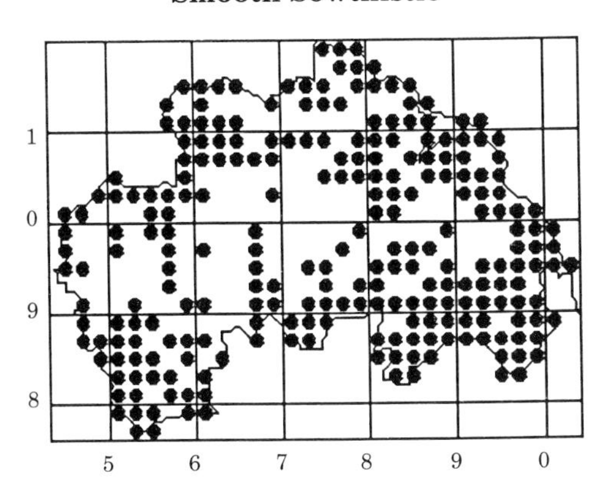

Prickly Sowthistle

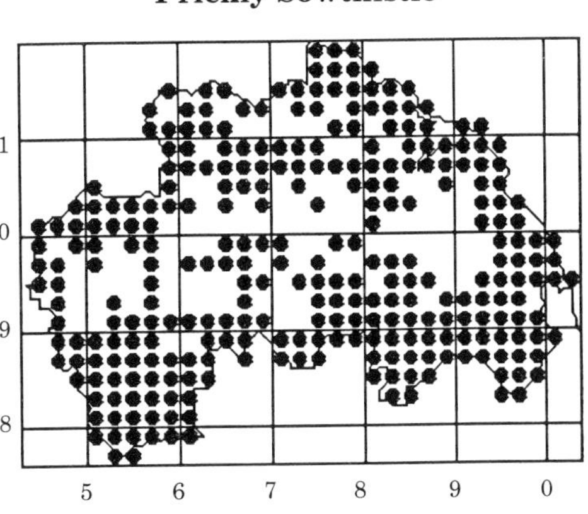

Mouse-ear Hawkweed

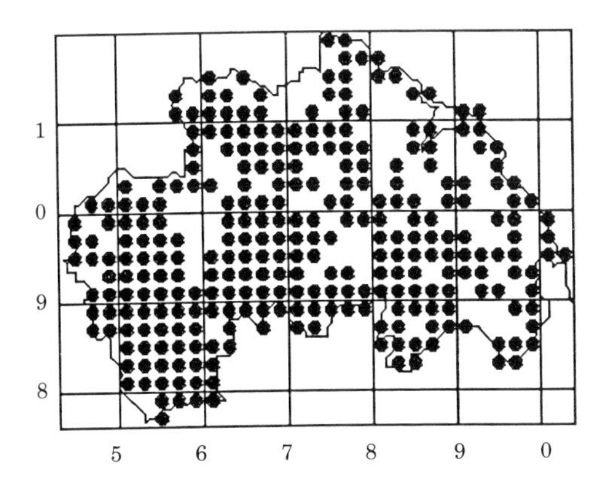

Beaked Hawksbeard

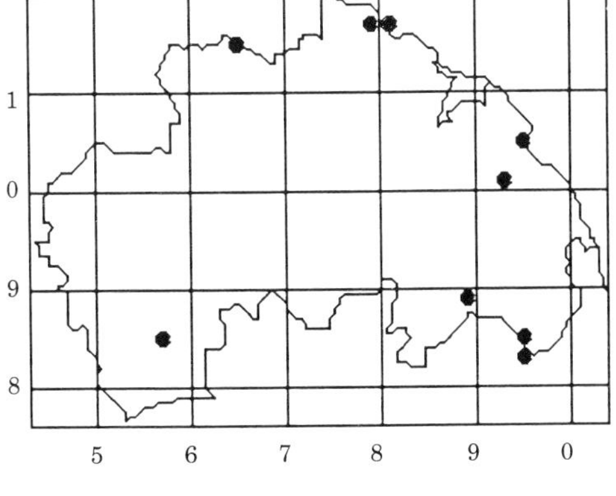

Smooth Hawksbeard 175 M
Crepis capillaris
This is a common plant on dry grassy banks, in short grassland and on walls.

Marsh Hawksbeard 153 M
Crepis paludosa
In partial shade of wet woodland, alder carr and swampy streamsides, this sturdy marshland plant grows in large populations.

Dandelion 378 M
Taraxacum agg.
Dandelions are one of the most numerous and familiar plants in the countryside. Widely distributed and abundant in most grassland, their flowers provide a spectacular splash of gold on many verges. Marsh dandelions *(T. palustria* group) have not been mapped separately but have been noted in wetland at Raisdale, Kildale, Sleddale, Castlebeck and Goathland amongst other places. Once common in water meadows, this is now a rare habitat and it could be that further study would reveal that the Park retains a nationally significant population of marsh dandelion.

WATER PLANTAIN FAMILY
ALISMATACEAE

Lesser Water Plantain 2
Baldellia ranunculoides
An uncommon plant throughout Britain, this species is locally very rare. It requires shallow enriched slightly moving water and has been found only in drainage ditches at Mowthorpe and on the shore of Lake Gormire.

Water Plantain 28 M
Alisma plantago-aquatica
Prominent in the lakeside vegetation at Gormire, Throxenby, Elleron and Crosscliff, it also grows as a riverside plant along the Rivers Esk and Derwent, Scalby Sea Cut and Rigg Mill Beck. Quite often planted around new ponds.

FLOWERING RUSH FAMILY
BUTOMACEAE

Flowering Rush
Butomus umbellatus
The remarkable pink flowers of this tall water plant appear in a few places in the lower Derwent just outside the Park. It has been planted and appears to be established further up river north of West Ayton and in a nearby pond.

FROGBIT FAMILY
HYDROCHARITACEAE

Canadian Pondweed 31 M
Elodea canadensis
A native of North America introduced as an aquarium plant in the mid 19th century, it soon appeared in waterways up and down the country and threatened to become a serious pest until populations stabilised. In the lower reaches of local waterways it is a common submerged plant but is not known to cause a problem anywhere.

ARROWGRASS FAMILY
JUNCAGINACEAE

Marsh Arrowgrass 107 M
Triglochin palustris
[Triglochin palustre]
Frequent in seepage areas at the side of forest rides, in moorland bogs and flushes, marshy slacks and nutrient-poor wet grassland.

Smooth Hawksbeard

Marsh Hawksbeard

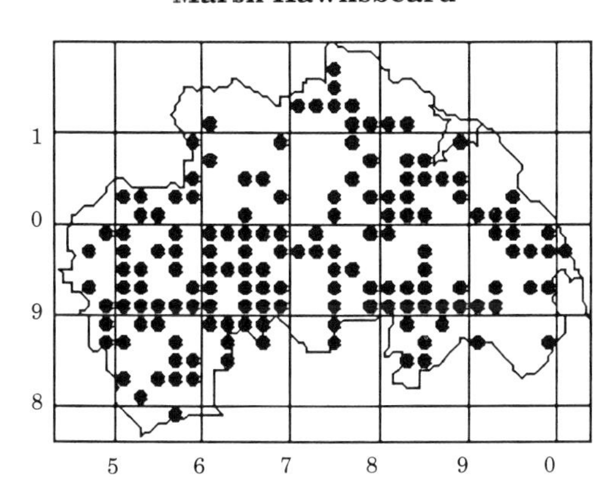

Dandelion

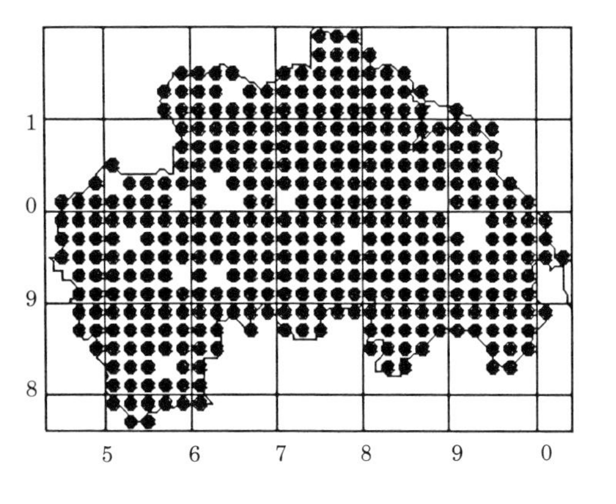

Water Plantain

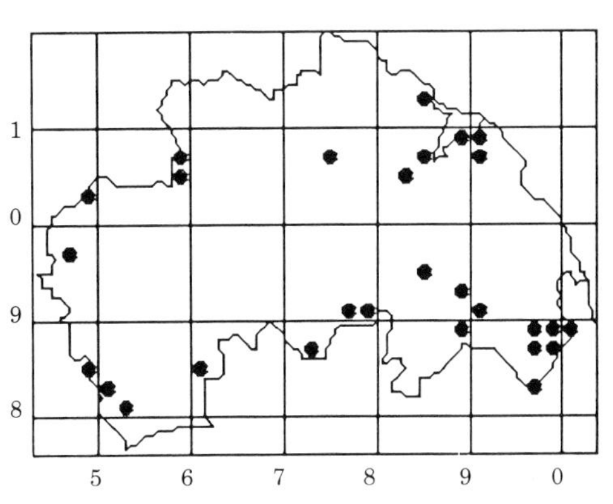

Canadian Pondweed

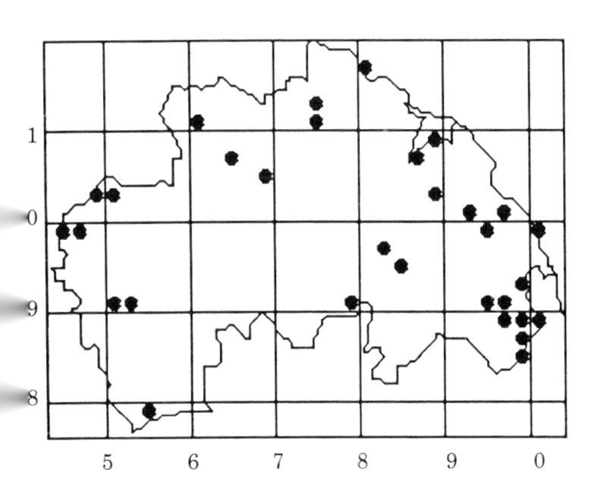

Marsh Arrowgrass

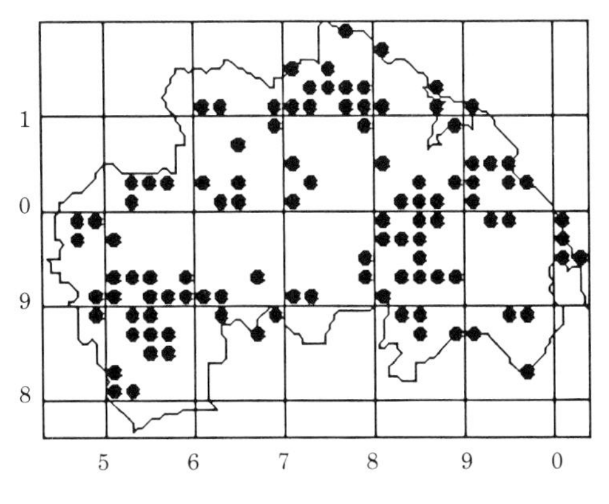

Sea Arrowgrass 6 M
Triglochin maritima
[Triglochin maritimum]
Its typical saltmarsh habitat is rare on this coast but plants have been found in saline mud at Boggle Hole, Ruswarp Batts and in a brackish pool at Roger Trod.

PONDWEED FAMILY
POTAMOGETONACEAE

Opposite-leaved Pondweed 2
Groenlandia densa
A pondweed more common further south, it has been found rarely in local streams at Newbridge, Pickering, in Scalby Sea Cut and the River Derwent in Forge Valley.

Broad-leaved Pondweed 53 M
Potamogeton natans
The oval floating leaves of this pondweed are frequently seen in clear standing or sluggish water on organic soils. The plant grows extensively in the feeder streams of the lower Derwent, Rivers Leven and Esk, and waterways beneath the northern escarpment.

Bog Pondweed 143 M
Potamogeton polygonifolius
More of an upland plant than the previous species, this pondweed is widespread in the moorland area. In shallow pools with acid peaty water, and in sphagnum bogs, acid flushes and runnels, large rafts are formed by its mass of floating leaves.

Reddish Pondweed 3
Potamogeton alpinus
This plant is rare in the area generally but plentiful in parts of Pickering Beck in Newtondale and in a pond on Blakey Rigg.

Small Pondweed 4 M
Potamogeton berchtoldii
Recorded rarely, in ponds at Raincliffe, Hagg Wood near Farwath and at Arden.

Curled Pondweed 13 M
Potamogeton crispus
Fragments have been found drifting in Scalby Sea Cut, lower reaches of the Esk and Derwent, at Scaling, Newgate and Lockwood Beck reservoirs and in Hackness Lake. Other sites may have been overlooked due to the difficulty of locating this plant in deep water.

Various-leaved Pondweed 1
Potamogeton gramineus
Found only in Crabdale Beck.

Perfoliate Pondweed 2
Potamogeton perfoliatus
Found only in Scaling and Lockwood Beck reservoirs.

Lesser Pondweed 1
Potamogeton pusillus
Found only in Cropton Castle pond.

HORNED PONDWEED FAMILY
ZANNICHELLIACEAE

Horned Pondweed 1
Zannichellia palustris
Known only from a pond near Hob Hole ford on Hograh moor.

LILY FAMILY
LILIACEAE

May Lily 2
Maianthemum bifolium
An eastern European perennial, very rare in Britain. It is known on sites in Durham and Lincolnshire and is surviving precariously on a hillside north of Forge Valley, where it was discovered in 1857.

Sea Arrowgrass

Broad-leaved Pondweed

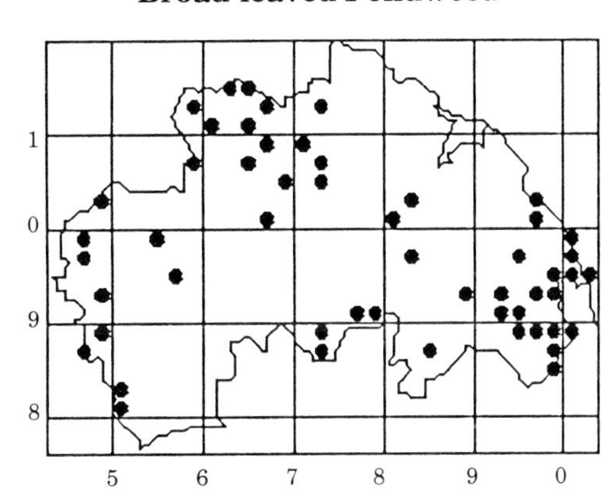

Bog Pondweed

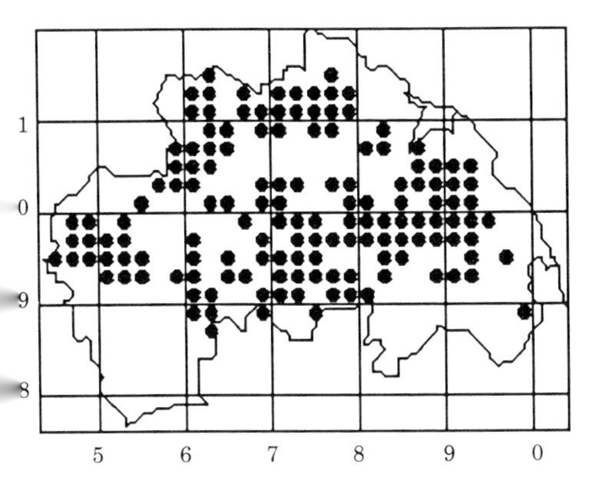

Small Pondweed

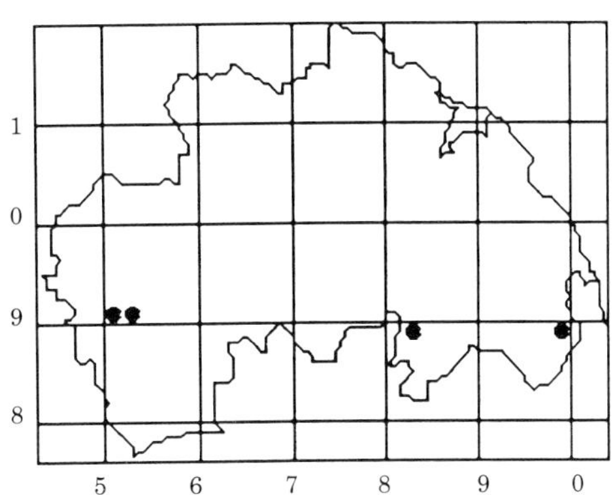

Curled Pondweed

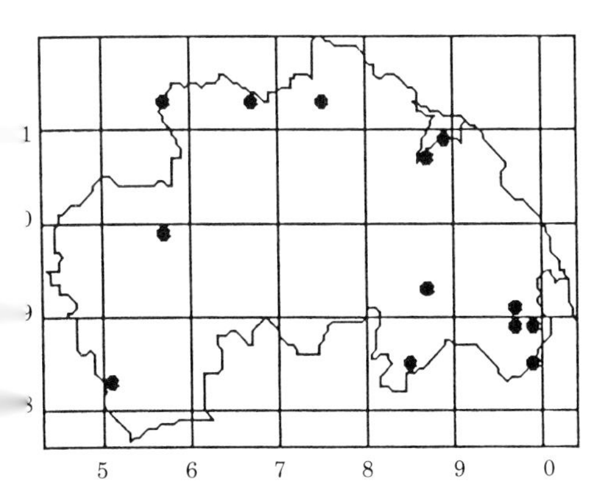

Bog Asphodel 126 M
Narthecium ossifragum
In acid flushes and valley mires on the moorland fringe and spring lines in upper dales, this yellow-flowered plant grows in large masses. In optimum conditions around some forest ponds, it out-competes all other vegetation. Not found on high ground.

Lily of the Valley 22 M
Convallaria majalis
As a wild plant this is now rare occurring only in undisturbed ash and oak woods, where it spreads over glades and rocky banks. It was formerly abundant in the Helmsley area but coniferisation and collecting have all but eliminated it there. Less accessible woods along the southern fringe and by the coast retain scattered populations.

Solomon's Seal 11
Polygonatum x *hybridum*
(P. multiflorum x *odoratum)*
This garden plant has naturalised in a few out of the way places such as the midst of a conifer plantation at Bakers Warren in Wykeham Forest, beside Hartoft Beck and at Duncombe Park.

Martagon Lily
Lilium martagon
Introduced from southern Europe in the 16th century, it has escaped to the wild along becks and ditches, producing new plants far from habitation.

Yellow Star of Bethlehem 4
Gagea lutea
This eastern European plant grows sparingly in Britain and locally is confined to the southern edge of the Park. It grows on alkaline loamy soils and has been found in damp woodland near Thirlby, Yedmandale, Welburn and Hutton Buscel.

White Star of Bethlehem
Ornithogalum umbellatum
A garden plant which has naturalised on grassy verges at Newby, Thirlby and Boltby.

Bluebell 336 M
Hyacinthoides non-scripta
In ungrazed deciduous woods, this plant creates an almost magical blue spring-time carpet. The numerous bluebell woods of the Park are a valuable botanical resource, becoming less common in other parts of Britain and almost unknown in such profusion overseas.

Few-flowered Garlic
Allium paradoxum
Naturalised in a wood near Duncombe Park, presumably having originated from nearby ornamental gardens.

Three-cornered Garlic
Allium triquetrum
This is a garden plant found naturalised in a copse near Boltby.

Ramsons 239 M
Allium ursinum
An abundant ground cover plant in nutrient-rich moist woodland away from the hills. Its presence is indicated in spring by a strong smell of garlic. It also flourishes in hedge bottoms and copses with sufficient damp humus and light shade.

Herb Paris 12 M
Paris quadrifolia
A poisonous plant once used to dispel witchcraft, herb Paris is confined to undisturbed ancient woodland. Large colonies grow in damp shade on calcareous nutrient-rich loam. It has been found in woods at Hawnby, Sleightholmedale, Sinnington, Ellerburn,

Bog Asphodel

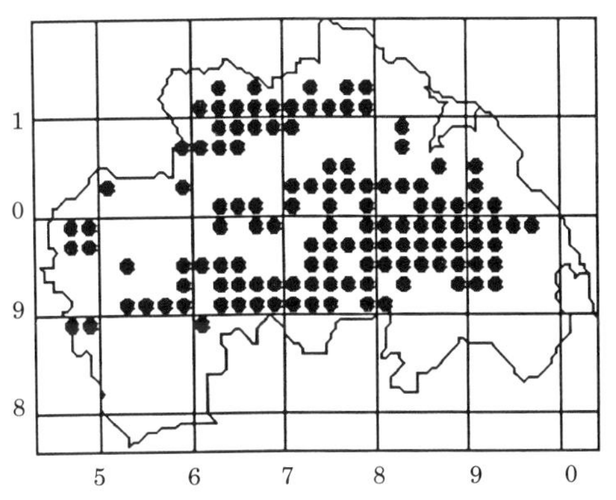

Lily of the Valley

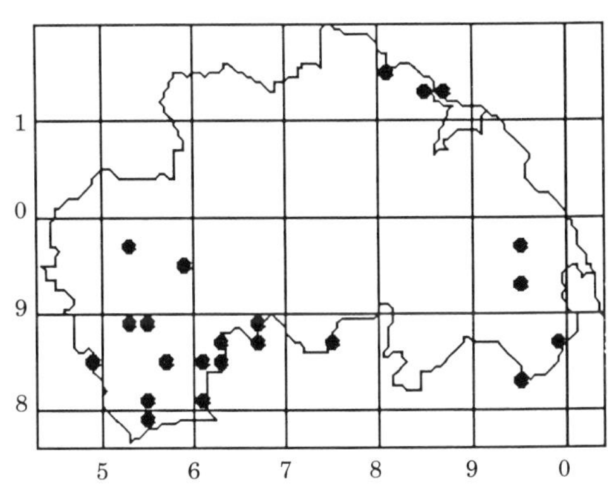

Bluebell

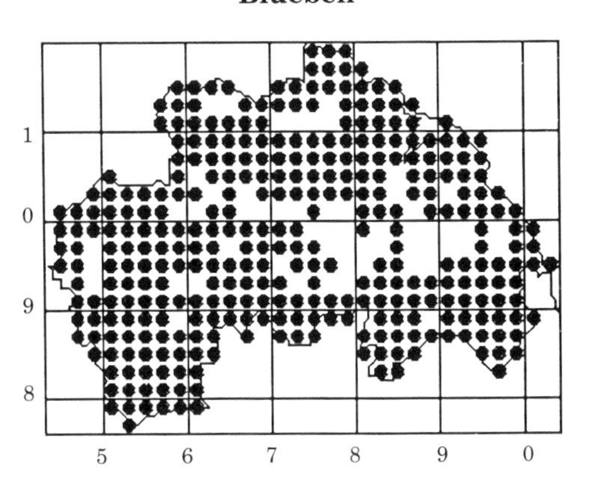

Ramsons

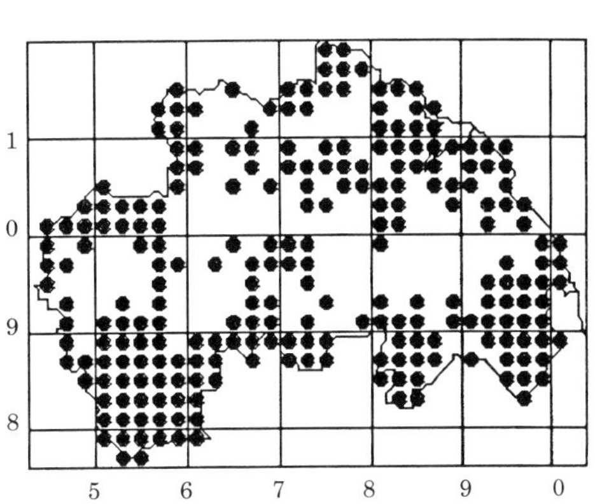

Herb Paris

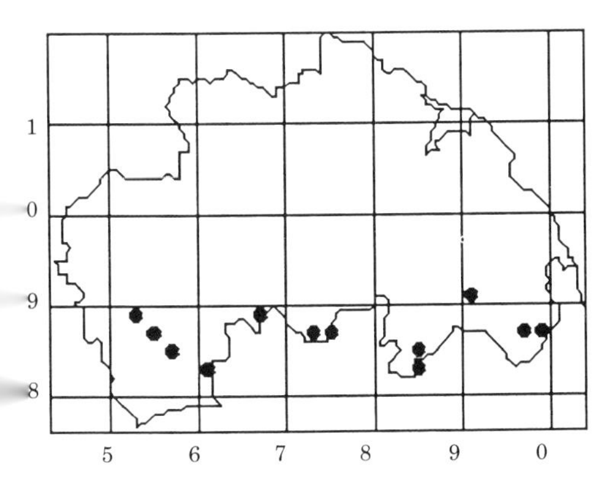

Yedmandale, Forge Valley and Deepdale.

Butcher's Broom
Ruscus aculeatus
Not a native shrub this far north but occasionally planted in gardens, whence small colonies have naturalised in Riccaldale, Forge Valley and Duncombe Park woodlands.

RUSH FAMILY
JUNCACEAE

Heath Rush 265 M
Juncus squarrosus
Tufts of this wiry perennial are common on the higher damp acid moors and wet peaty tracks throughout the uplands.

Mud Rush 4
Juncus gerardii
Plentiful in tidal mud on Ruswarp Batts and less common in the shallow muddy fringe of Scalby Sea Cut.

Toad Rush 243 M
Juncus bufonius
This little green creeping rush is found on moist grassy forest rides, in trampled gateways, ditchsides and wheel ruts on nutrient-poor ground.

Hard Rush 232 M
Juncus inflexus
The tough glaucous stems of this tall rush indicate a somewhat alkaline soil. It is widespread in waterlogged pastures, ditches and on verges, especially on base-rich boulder clay.

Soft Rush 388 M
Juncus effusus
Found in a range of conditions from damp ground to swamps, this is the commonest rush of the area. Its local name of "seaves" is echoed in the many wet slacks and fields so called. Despite much time and money spent on drainage schemes in the hill pastures in recent decades, seaves can now be seen reappearing in many slacks such as at Evan Howe.

Conglomerate Rush 301
Juncus conglomeratus
Frequent on fertile acid soils in wet moorland, pasture and woodland edge, often with soft rush.

Blunt-flowered Rush 17 M
Juncus subnodulosus
Demanding marshy ground, with a constant supply of alkaline water, this uncommon rush occurs in fens such as at Farwath, Crosscliff, Hern Head, Breaday Gill and Caydale.

Sea Rush 1
Juncus maritimus
A saltmarsh plant growing in suitable habitats around Whitby.

Jointed Rush 322
Juncus articulatus
Abundant on wet grazed grassland and moor edge and often fringing upland streams, pools and waysides. Although more widespread than sharp-flowered rush, their habitats often overlap and hybridisation is evident.

Sharp-flowered Rush 224
Juncus acutiflorus
Forms large dominant stands in wet acid soils in the uplands.

Bulbous Rush 268 M
Juncus bulbosus
One of the smallest rushes but widespread and plentiful. Its tufts thrive in wet acid peaty soils, on tracksides, in ditches and bogs. In larger open water such as forest pools, an elongated aquatic form proliferates into a streaming mass of vegetation.

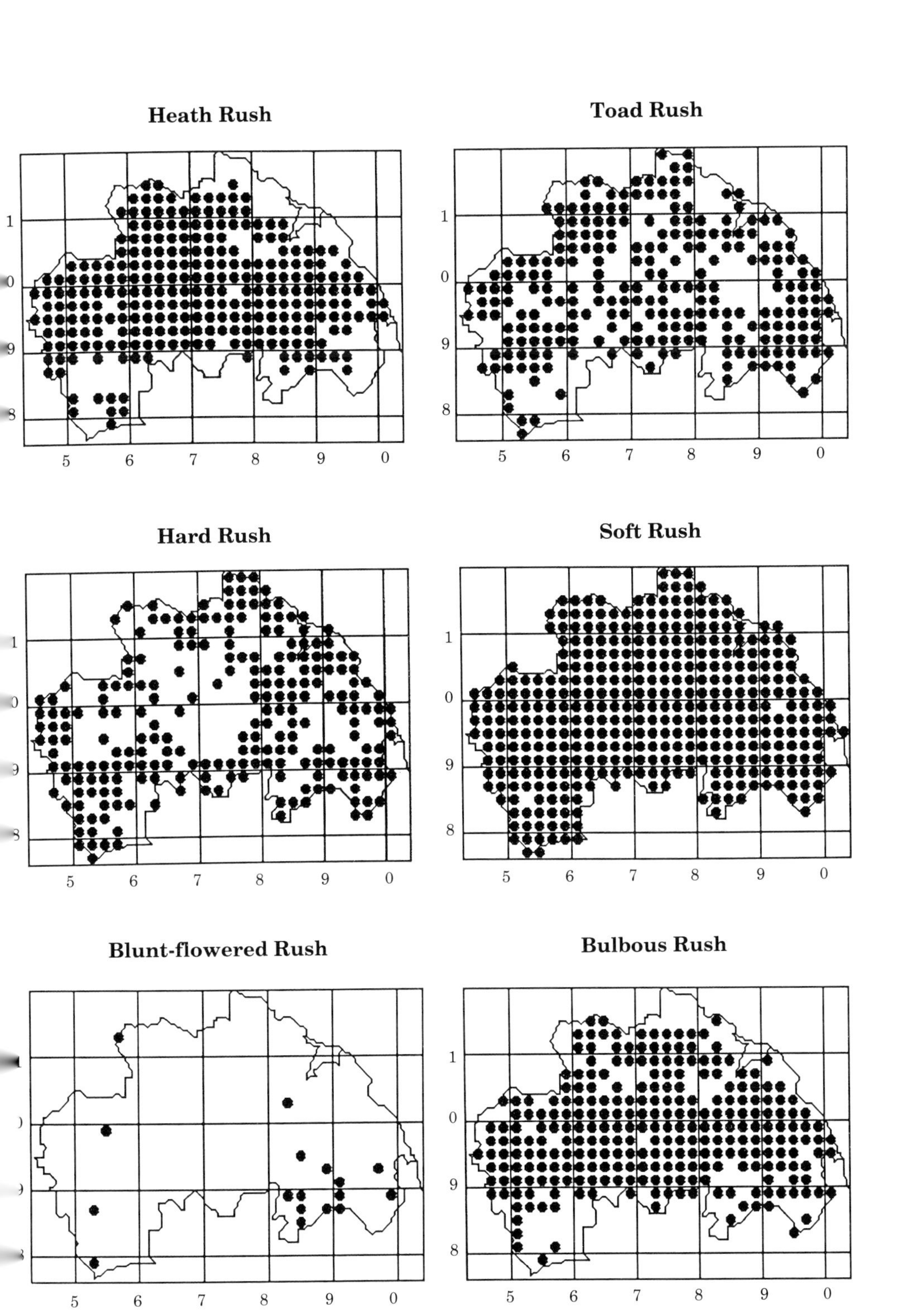
Heath Rush
Toad Rush
Hard Rush
Soft Rush
Blunt-flowered Rush
Bulbous Rush
5
6
7
8
9
0

Hairy Woodrush 203 M
Luzula pilosa
Most frequent on the steep cut side of a forest track, this dainty woodrush is to be found dispersed through woods and plantations on acid soils.

Great Woodrush 266 M
Luzula sylvatica
Large, lush and abundant, this woodrush is often the dominant plant alongside an acid moorland stream. It fringes upland river banks and dominates the vegetation in moist rocky gills.

Field Woodrush 326 M
Luzula campestris
In complete contrast to the above species, this little woodrush – often known as Good Friday grass as it flowers around Easter – never grows more than a few centimetres high and is scattered over less acid pasture and garden lawns.

Heath Woodrush 246 M
Luzula multiflora
Found chiefly on acidic grassland, the numerous single spikes of this widespread upland rush are common in old intakes and dalehead pastures.

DAFFODIL FAMILY
AMARYLLIDACEAE

Snowdrop 57
Galanthus nivalis [LILIACEAE]
A popular garden bulb, it is often deposited with rubbish on roadsides near habitation and attempts to naturalise. Occasionally it succeeds to become the dominant spring ground flora, such as in churchyards at Bransdale and Kirkdale, in woods at Littlebeck and Mulgrave Castle, on a hillside at Cropton and riverside at Sinnington.

Wild Daffodil 68 M
Narcissus pseudonarcissus
[LILIACEAE]
The spring display of wild daffodils in Farndale riverside meadows draws thousands of visitors to this Local Nature Reserve. The plant grows in many other valleys, both along the southern edge and on the coastal plain, though nowhere else in such profusion.

IRIS FAMILY
IRIDACEAE

Yellow Flag 70
Iris pseudacorus
A colony of these bold yellow-flowered irises gives a surprising splash of colour to many wetland areas. As a native plant it is frequent in marshy fields, ponds, carr woodland and riverside swamp. It is often planted and soon gets established in newly-made ponds.

Montbretia
Tritonia x *crocrosmiflora*
It seems strange to come across the vivid orange flowers of this popular garden plant far from cultivated ground but a few clumps are established in the wild, even on remote sea cliffs.

YAM FAMILY
DIOSCOREACEAE

Black Bryony 125 M
Tamus communis
Commonly found twining its way up hedges and scrubby banks, this plant with its distinctive shiny leaves and bright red berries is a familiar sight on many roadsides with moist fertile soils away from higher ground.

Hairy Woodrush

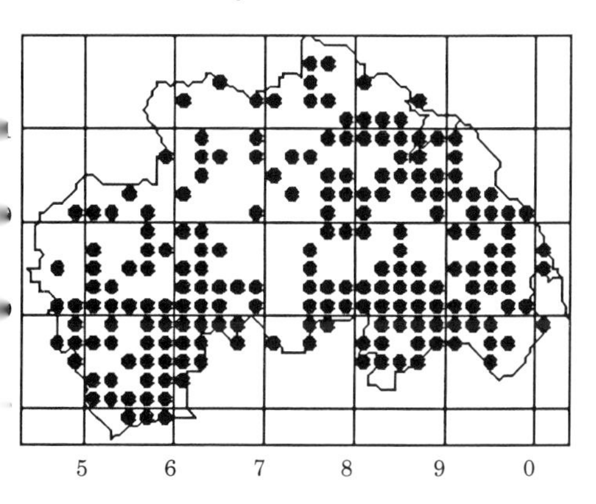

Great Woodrush

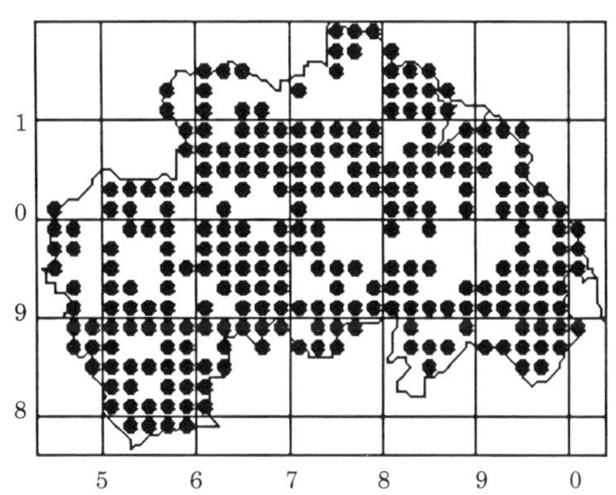

Field Woodrush

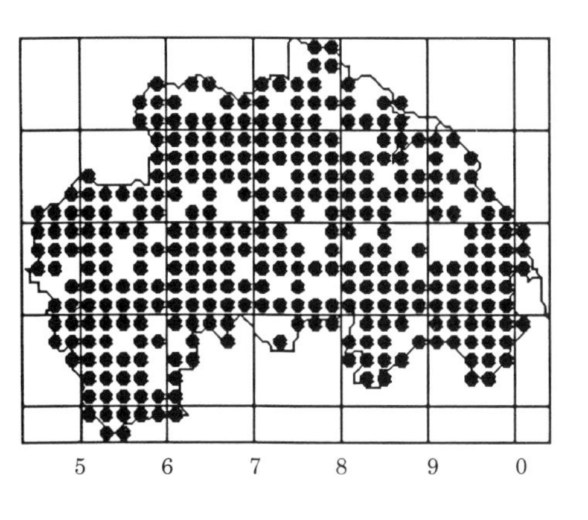

Heath Woodrush

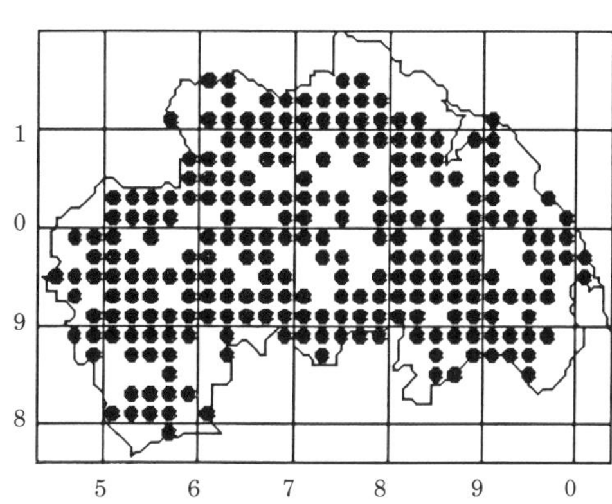

Wild Daffodil

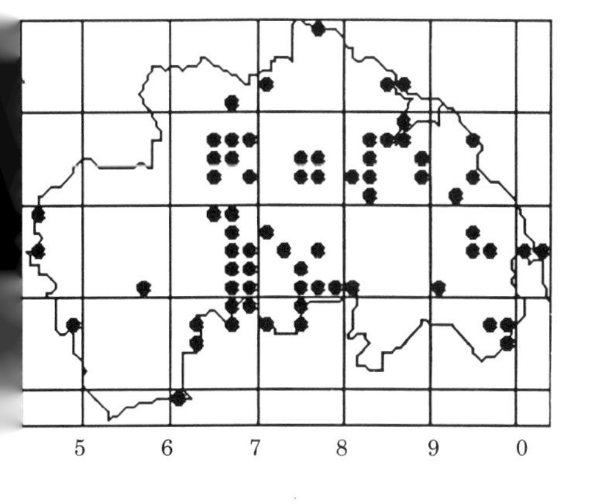

Black Bryony

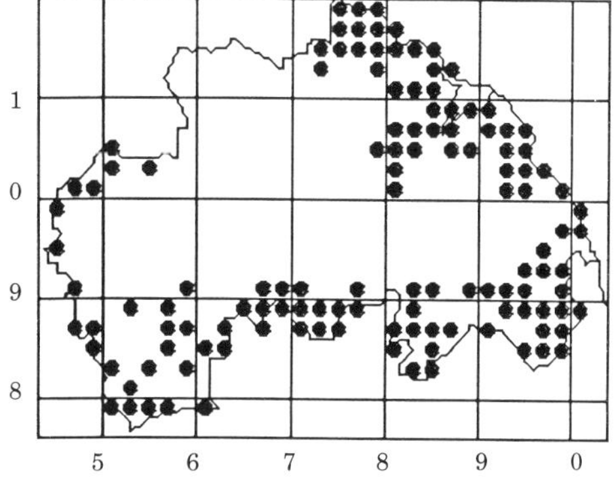

ORCHID FAMILY
ORCHIDACEAE

Lady's Slipper Orchid
Cypripedium calceolus
Once widespread in the wooded gills of the Rye valley, this remarkable flower was picked and uprooted for gardens and its woodland habitats turned into conifer plantations until the plant became locally extinct earlier this century. Survival at its only other site in Britain hangs in the balance.

Marsh Helleborine 11 M
Epipactis palustris
This attractive wetland orchid has decreased countrywide owing to habitat loss. In the Park it is rare, secreted amongst rich calcareous fen vegetation in a few undrained valley pastures.

Broad Helleborine 34 M
Epipactis helleborine
A plant of ancient woodland, it has adapted to a new niche in gravelly railway ballast and can be found in shady parts of the coastal disused railtrack. It still grows in a number of older woods though it is nowhere numerous.

Autumn Lady's Tresses
Spiranthes spiralis
Formerly recorded at Ruston and elsewhere, it has not been seen for many years and is now considered extinct in this area.

Twayblade 105 M
Listera ovata
This robust and well-named orchid with its two prominent leaves is widespread and occasionally abundant in alkaline soils on woodland edges, banks and rough grassland. A tolerant plant found in a range of habitats from an exposed rocky outcrop at Saltergate to forest clearings in Sanddale and a grassy verge at Keldy.

Lesser Twayblade 8
Listera cordata
An orchid of Caledonian pinewoods, here approaching its southern limit, it is found rarely on acid moorland or in peaty gills. Its tiny flowering spike hides beneath bracken or heather and may be much overlooked, but it has been recorded at Keysbeck, Kildale, Darnholm, Gerrick, Biller Howe Dale and Moorsholm.

Birdsnest Orchid 6
Neottia nidus-avis
A rare saprophytic orchid, its buff-coloured spikes may be found after much searching amongst the deep humus of old beech plantations.

Frog Orchid 7 M
Coeloglossum viride
Formerly widespread in dry hilly pasture, this plant has suffered a severe decline in recent years due to loss of habitat and changes in farming methods. Since discovered in 1988 one of its few remaining sites has been lost to grassland improvement.

Fragrant Orchid 38 M
Gymnadenia conopsea
Seacliff grassland provides a stronghold for this perfumed orchid which has suffered a decline inland as its habitat has diminished. Essentially a plant of base-rich grassland, especially on limestone, it retains a tenuous hold on a few steep valleysides which have escaped reseeding.

Greater Butterfly Orchid 17 M
Platanthera chlorantha
An inaccessible railway cutting in Eskdale provides a northerly safe haven for this orchid. Elsewhere it is now rare in a few undisturbed ancient woods and unimproved grassland.

Marsh Helleborine

Broad Helleborine

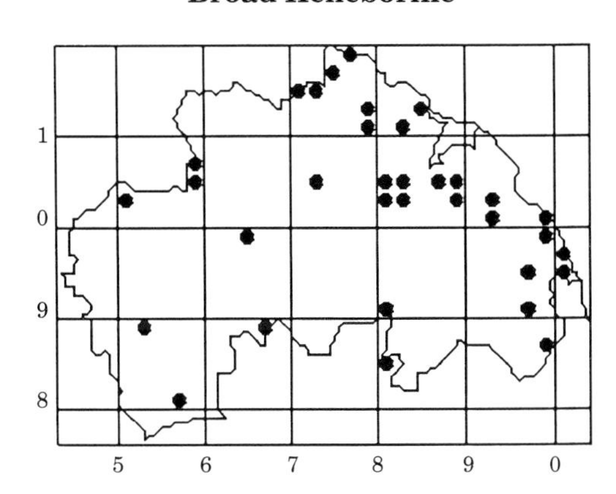

Twayblade

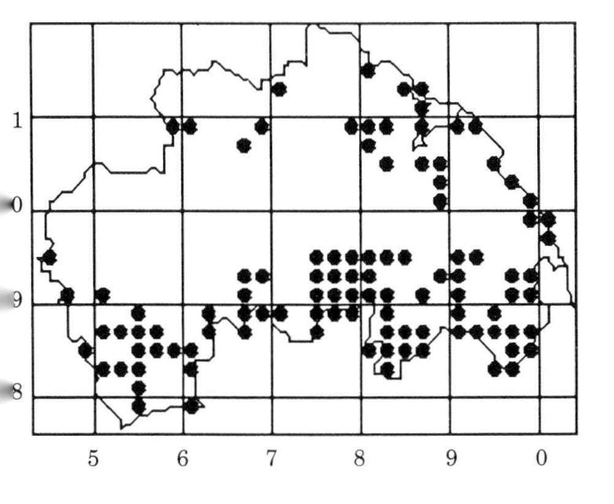

Frog Orchid

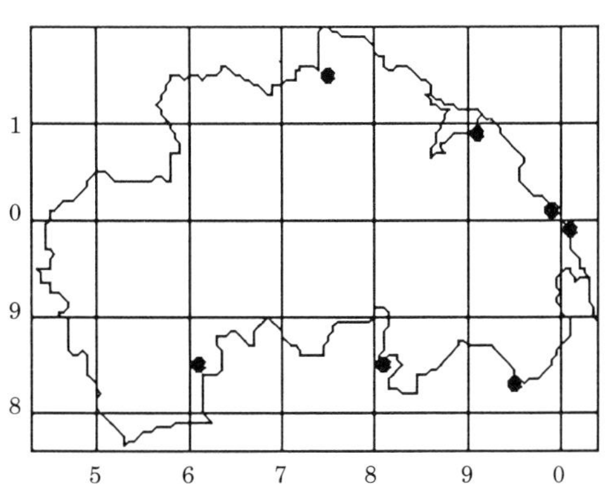

Fragrant Orchid

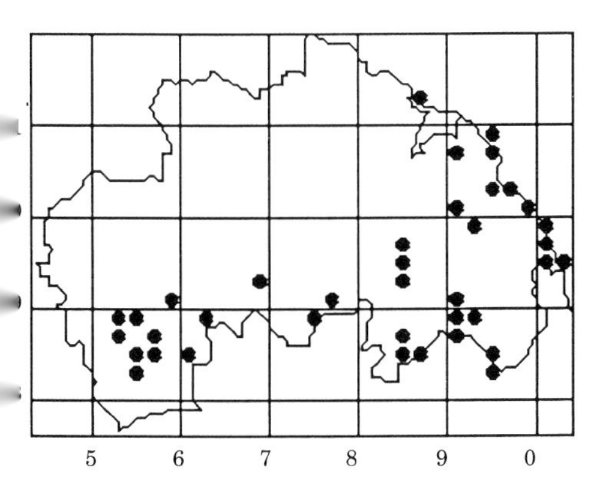

Greater Butterfly Orchid

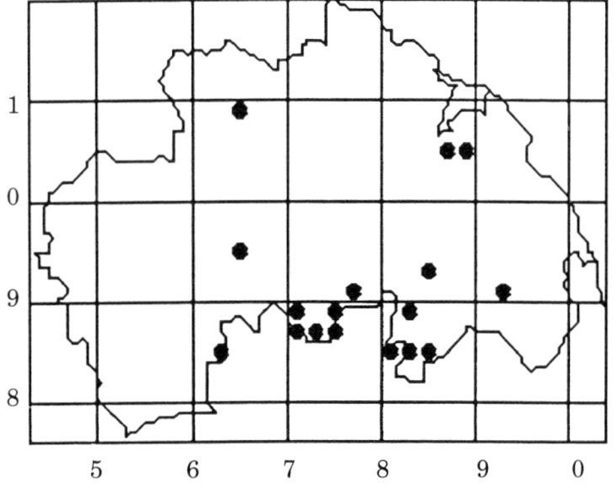

Lesser Butterfly Orchid 6
Platanthera bifolia
Only six sites are now known for this once common grassland orchid. Like most orchids, it quickly succumbs to herbicides and fertilisers and survives in only a few unimproved pastures.

Bee Orchid 7 M
Ophrys apifera
This orchid, so called because its bee-like flowers rely upon bees for pollination, is another plant to have declined severely in recent decades. Much of its preferred habitat of lime-rich pasture has disappeared under agricultural improvement.

Fly Orchid 13 M
Ophrys insectifera
Once described as "numerous" in this area, this is another orchid which has declined dramatically in recent decades due to habitat loss. Like the above species it requires unimproved calcareous grassland or scree.

Green-winged Orchid 5
Orchis morio
Perhaps this is the most depleted orchid species. In *The Natural History of the Scarborough District* published in 1953, it was described as "common in meadows" – today only five fields are known to have a few plants.

Burnt-tip Orchid 2
Orchis ustulata
An uncommon orchid nationally, it is rarely seen in the National Park. One or two spikes have appeared erratically on a site near West Ayton, and a single plant was found in 1990 in Dalbydale. This is another orchid with a preference for unimproved base-rich pasture.

Early Purple Orchid 136 M
Orchis mascula
This robust orchid is still present in considerable numbers in ancient woodlands and on hedgebanks with base or neutral soils. Its sturdy spikes covered with deep purple flowers provide an impressive springtime display.

Heath Spotted Orchid 96 M
Dactylorhiza maculata ssp. *ericetorum*
Small populations are scattered over unimproved hill grazings on more acid soil, often near the moorland edge.

Common Spotted Orchid 262 M
Dactylorhiza fuchsii
Widespread and common in many grassy habitats, this orchid has established extensively on road, rail and forest verges. It appears to thrive on a limited amount of disturbance, although it cannot tolerate herbicides.

Early Marsh Orchid 9
Dactylorhiza incarnata
This is an uncommon orchid in this area. It grows in a few fens and marshes in undisturbed valleys.

Northern Marsh Orchid 23 M
Dactylorhiza purpurella
This late-flowering orchid occurs infrequently in damp, unimproved grassland with some soil enrichment. It grows giant-sized flowering spikes on some of its coastal sites and maintains a few sizeable populations of smaller plants inland, though it has a strong easterly preference.

Narrow-leaved Marsh Orchid 7
Dactylorhiza traunsteineri
A rare plant countrywide, it flourishes on a few base-rich fens in undrained moorland slacks and valleys.

A range of hybridisation occurs in *Dactylorhiza* species.

Bee Orchid

Fly Orchid

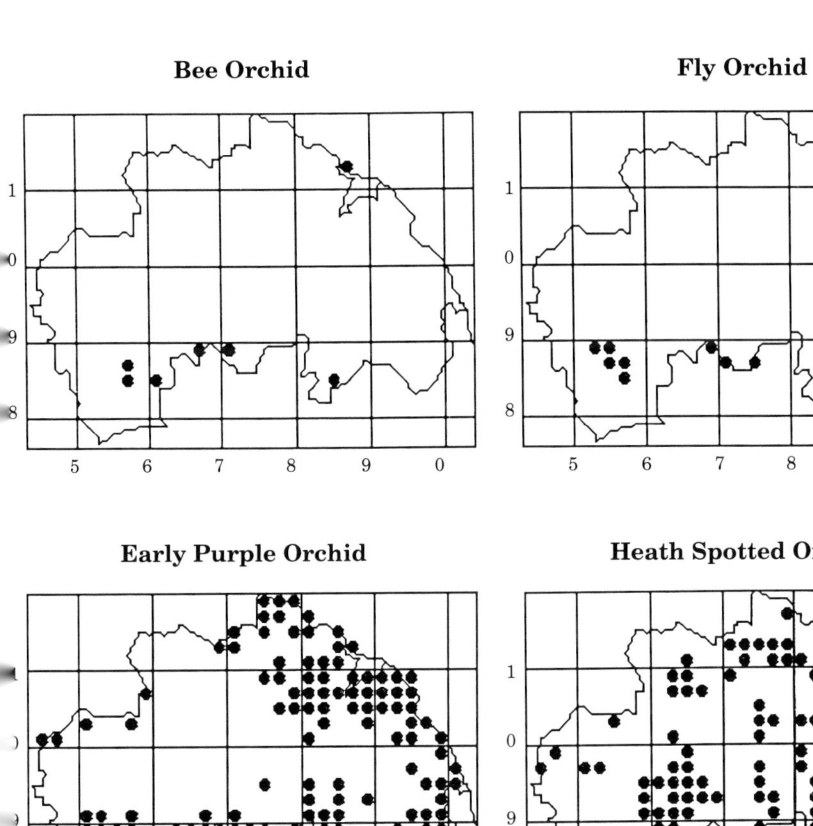

Early Purple Orchid

Heath Spotted Orchid

Common Spotted Orchid

Northern Marsh Orchid

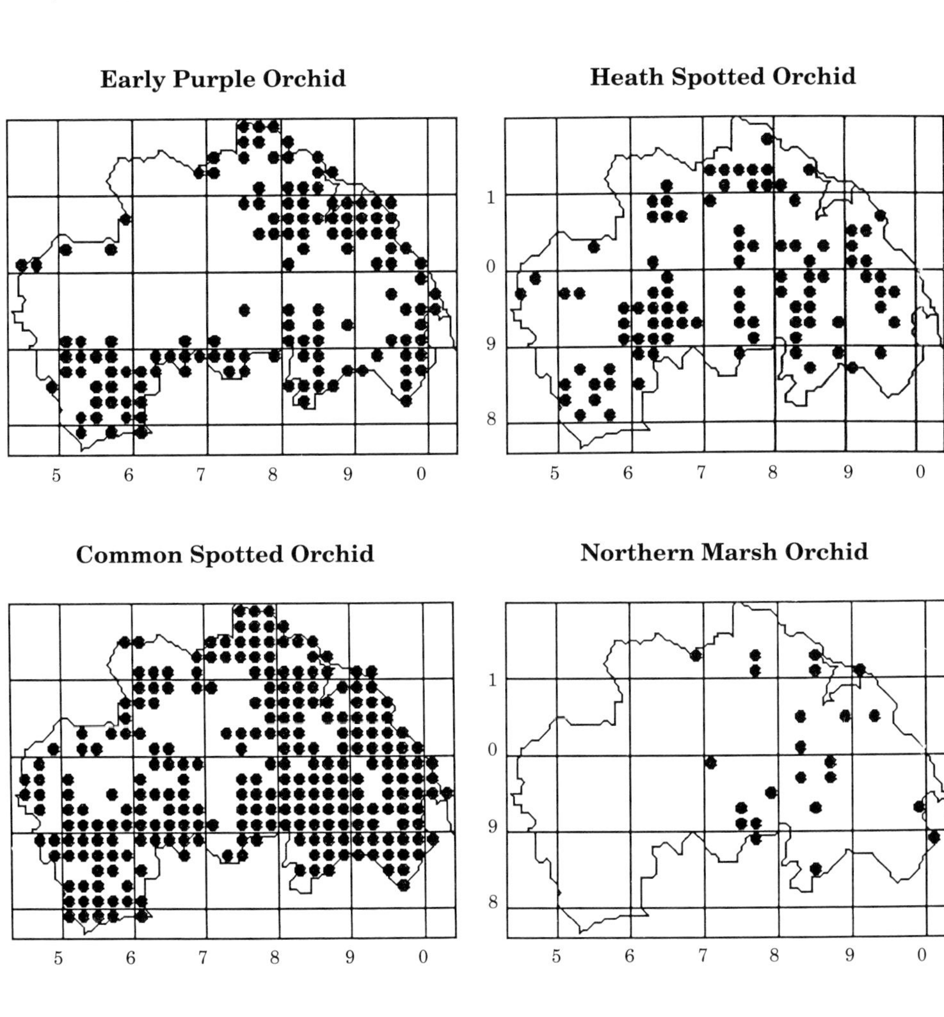

Pyramidal Orchid 15 M
Anacamptis pyramidalis
This plant survives on alkaline rocky outcrops on coastal cliffs and inland in a few disused limestone quarries. It is nowhere plentiful but small populations continue in a few unimproved pastures.

Small White Orchid 1
Pseudorchis albida
A small colony flowers erratically on a damp heathy hillside on Fylingdales Moor. Previously known to occur in Newtondale and in the Hole of Horcum, it has not been seen in these locations for many years. This is one of several species on the verge of extinction locally.

ARUM FAMILY
ARACEAE

Lords and Ladies or **Cuckoo Pint**
229 M
Arum maculatum
Along the base of hedgerows with an accumulation of moist humus, the prominent scarlet fruiting spikes of this plant are a familiar feature in late summer. It grows also in damp open woods on base-rich soils. Both leaf forms – plain green and green with black blotches – have been noted.

DUCKWEED FAMILY
LEMNACEAE

Ivy Duckweed 2
Lemna trisulca
Locally very rare, being more of a lowland plant. Recorded only in an old quarry pond at Kildale and in a farm pond near Raincliffe.

Common Duckweed 78 M
Lemna minor
Each year this tiny bright green water plant, with its rapid vegetative reproduction, covers shallow water standing in puddles, track ruts, drinking troughs and small pools.

BUR-REED FAMILY
SPARGANIACEAE

Common Bur-reed 54 M
Sparganium erectum
In many marshes, pond edges and streams, the prickly round fruits of this robust plant are noticeable amongst tall rush and sedge vegetation. It is plentiful on alluvial soils in fairly shallow water, especially where there is some enrichment from cattle.

Unbranched Bur-reed 5
Sparganium emersum
This locally uncommon Baltic plant has been recorded in Scalby Sea Cut, Forge Valley, Biller Howe Dale and Newtondale.

REEDMACE FAMILY
TYPHACEAE

Greater Reedmace 57 M
Typha latifolia
The large brown fruiting spikes of this robust plant form impressive stands in marshes and slow running streams. It is often planted in new ponds.

Lesser Reedmace 3 M
Typha angustifolia
This smaller version of the above species is a rare plant this far north. It has been found in Newtondale marshes and Beast Cliff ponds.

Pyramidal Orchid

Lords and Ladies or Cuckoo Pint

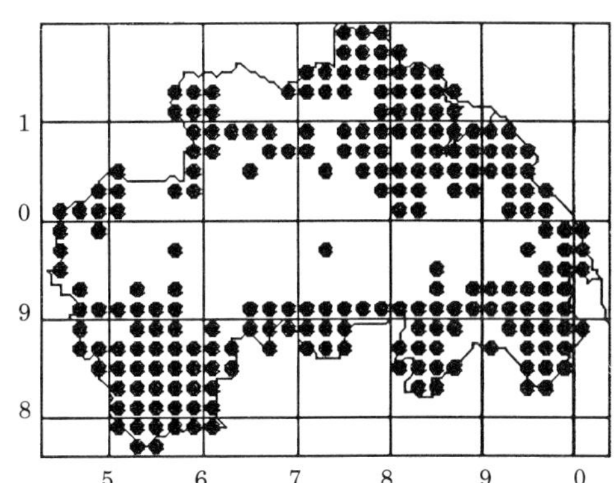

Common Duckweed

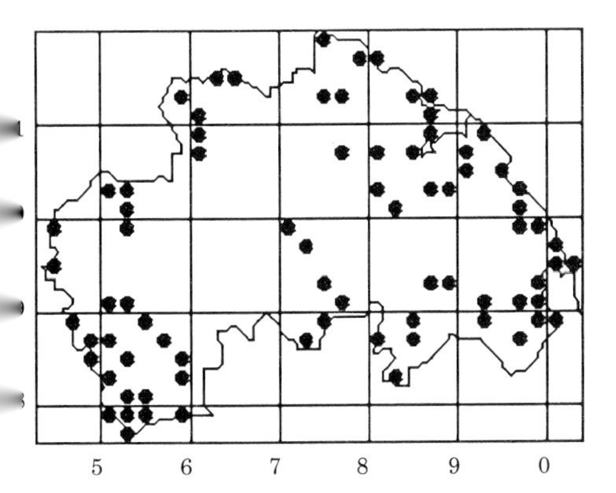

Common Bur-reed

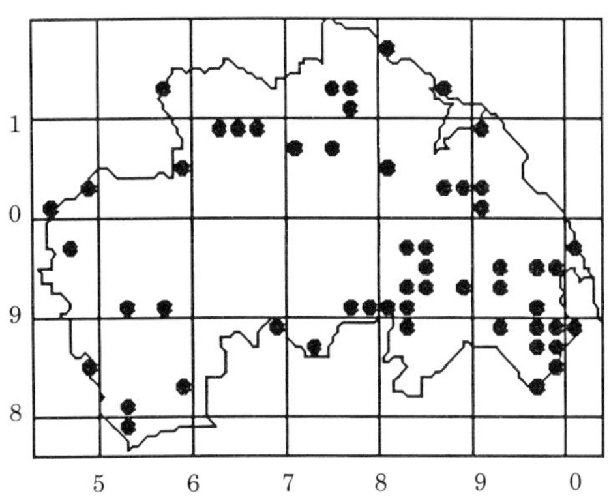

Greater Reedmace

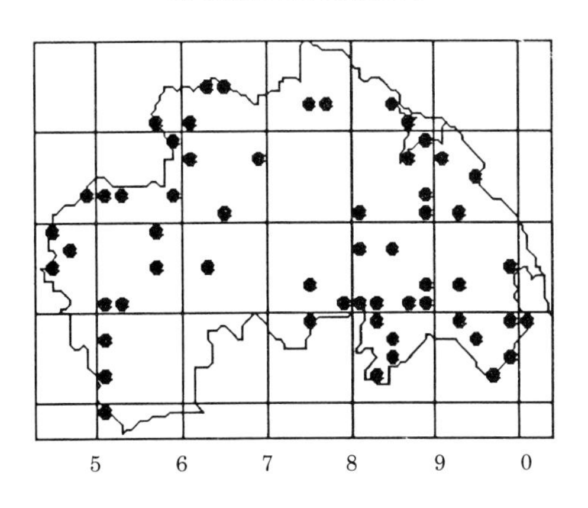

Lesser Reedmace

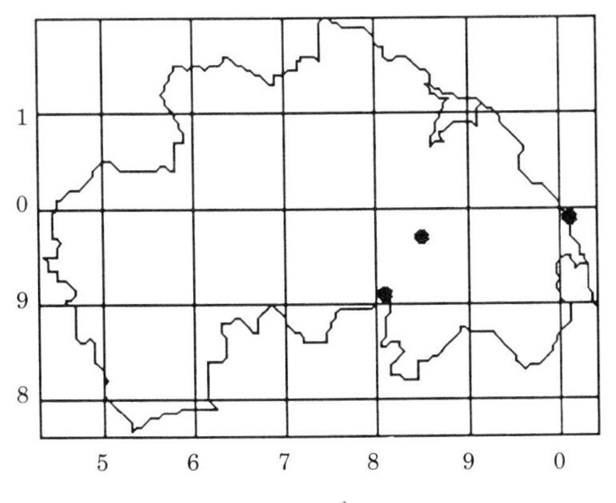

SEDGE FAMILY
CYPERACEAE

Common Cottongrass 237 M
Eriophorum angustifolium
Over wide stretches of the wetter moorland, this plant often dominates the vegetation. In early summer, its profusion of soft white flowering heads gives a distant illusion of snowcover. In saturated peat and in some slacks its red-tinted foliage stands in almost permanent water. Many upland pools are fringed with cottongrass.

Broad-leaved Cottongrass 23 M
Eriophorum latifolium
Much less frequent than the other cottongrasses, this species is mostly confined to flushes, fens and marshes on base-rich soils. Not uncommon on Newtondale and Pamperdale moors and riversides in lower Bilsdale but rare elsewhere.

Harestail Cottongrass 144 M
Eriophorum vaginatum
The distinctive tussocks of this plant often flower amidst late winter snow on the moors. Widespread and occasionally abundant on wet acid peat.

Deergrass 101 M
Trichophorum cespitosum
A widely dispersed plant of the uplands, especially on areas of wet acid peat. Sparse on drier moors in the west, it is plentiful in track ruts and seepage lines. It also occurs round the edge of sphagnum bogs and moorland pools, where the ground is permanently saturated but not actually standing in water. Never the dominant plant, its wiry shoots are nevertheless a distinctive component in wet heath vegetation.

Needle Spike Rush
Eleocharis acicularis
Recorded on the shores of Lake Gormire, where it formed a bright green "lawn" by the water's edge but has not been seen in recent years. Its only other known site in this vicinity is near Rievaulx.

Few-flowered Spike Rush 38
Eleocharis quinqueflora
Uncommon on the moors on damp peat and bare marshy soils with nutrient-enriched ground water.

Many-stemmed Spike Rush 34
Eleocharis multicaulis
Uncommon in acidic flushes, margins of sphagnum bogs and spring lines on the moors.

Slender Spike Rush
Eleocharis uniglumis
Rare in base-rich moorland flushes and marshy ground, usually with dioecious sedge.

Common Spike Rush 68 M
Eleocharis palustris
Widely dispersed in moorland slacks, shallow upland pools and sluggish water in ditches and marsh. Feeder streams to Scaling Dam, Scalby Sea Cut, Fen Bog, Fryupdale and Wheeldale are typical locations.

Sea Club Rush 6 M
Scirpus maritimus
[Bolboschoenus maritimus]
A rare plant on this coast due to lack of suitable habitat. It grows sparsely on the shore at Sandsend and is more plentiful on tidal mudflats up the Esk. A little way inland it has established in an old farm pond on Kirk Moor.

Common Cottongrass

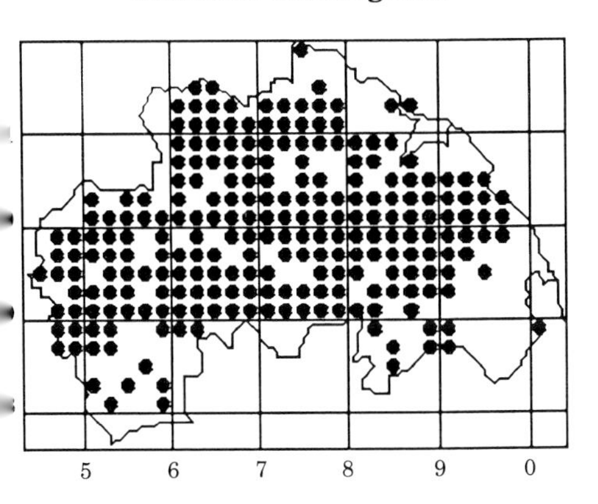

Broad-leaved Cottongrass

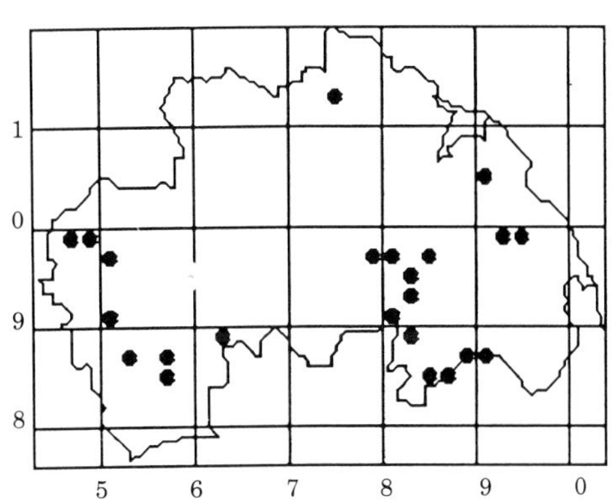

Harestail Cottongrass

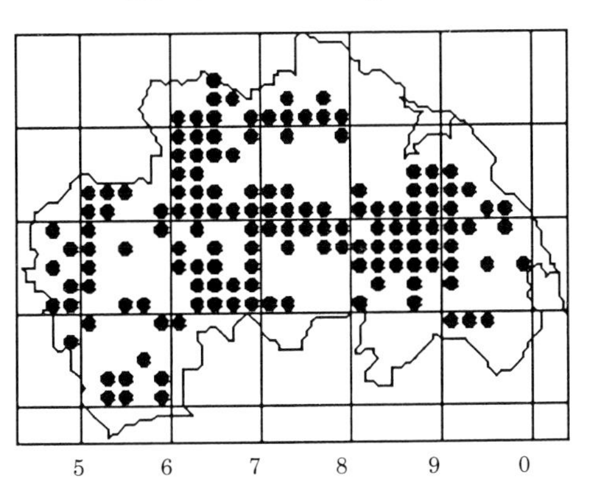

Deergrass

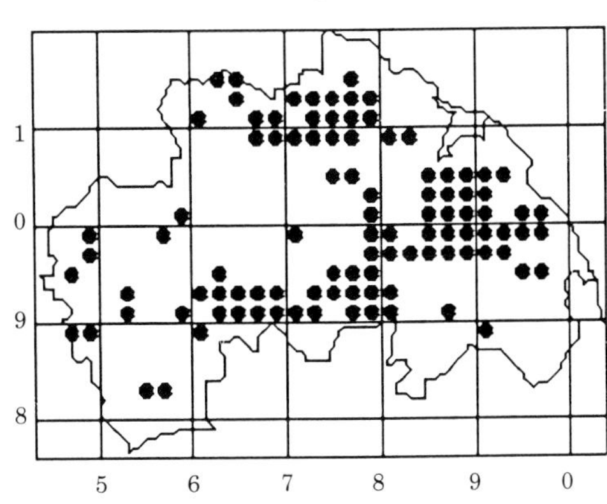

Common Spike Rush

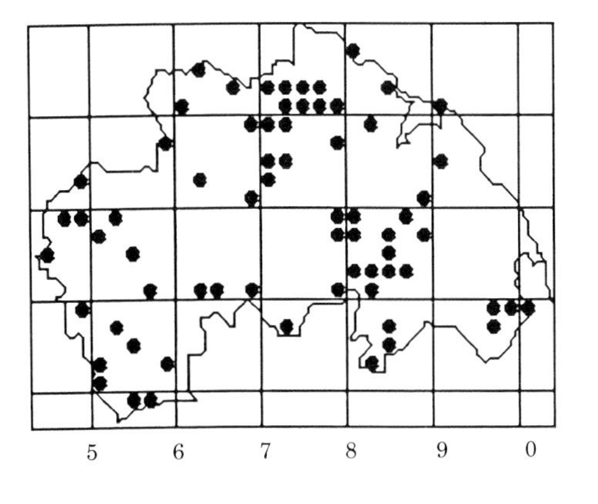

Sea Club Rush

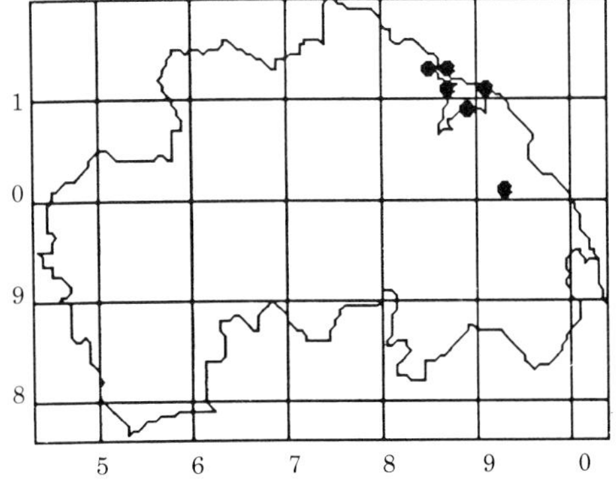

Wood Club Rush 23 M
Scirpus sylvaticus
Only in a few undisturbed upland riversides can this handsome plant be found. It flourishes in quite deep shade on swampy ground in alder carr or wet woodland beside the Seph, upper Derwent, Hodge Beck and other rivers.

Flat-headed Sedge 7 M
Blysmus compressus
This uncommon plant flourishes in damp grassland fed by calcareous springs in Caydale, Old Byland, Sanddale, Riccaldale and a few small fens elsewhere.

Bulrush 6
Schoenoplectus lacustris
A rare plant in the Park, it grows in deep water on the edge of lakes. Believed to be native in ponds at Beast Cliff and Roger Trod and likely to have been planted at Whorlton, Elleron and Appleton.

Grey Bulrush 2
Schoenoplectus tabernaemontani
Very rare in this area, it has been found only in Atkinson Wood, Guisborough and in a pond near Lockton.

Bristle Scirpus 65 M
Isolepis setacea
This secretive small plant is not uncommon on damp streamsides and in moorland bogs and flushes on lower land.

Floating Scirpus 6
Eleogiton fluitans
This grass-like rush is very infrequent. It forms a floating mass in a few rivulets with flowing acid water and has been found in Leach Bog slack, Keysbeck ponds, Kirkmoor slack, at Wardle Green and on Mickleby Moor.

Black Bog Rush 20 M
Schoenus nigricans
Restricted to fens and flushes on base-rich soil, this plant grows sparsely in slacks, mainly on Fylingdales and Cawthorn Moors, in Troutsdale and Dalbydale and around Rievaulx.

White Beak-sedge 6
Rhynchospora alba
A plant of southern Scandinavia and the western Highlands, its local occurrence has been diminished by moorland drainage. Now known from only six sites in Bloody Beck, Biller Howe Dale, Fen Bog, Troutsdale and on Hawnby Moor.

Tufted Sedge 3
Carex acuta
Rare in lowland marshes with standing water in Newtondale, Fen Bog and Ashberry.

Lesser Pond Sedge 46 M
Carex acutiformis
The most widespread of the larger pond sedges in this area, it forms extensive stands on base-rich soils in lowland marshes, ponds and along streamsides. Where it grows in alder and willow carr it indicates an early stage in natural transition from swamp to wet woodland.

Sand Sedge 2
Carex arenaria
A creeping root system enables this sedge to spread extensively in sandy pockets along the coast above the strandline. Sandsend and Runswick Bay.

Ribbed Sedge 195 M
Carex binervis
Essentially an upland plant of acidic soils, its bold clumps are frequent on rough hill grazing, forest rides and

Wood Club Rush

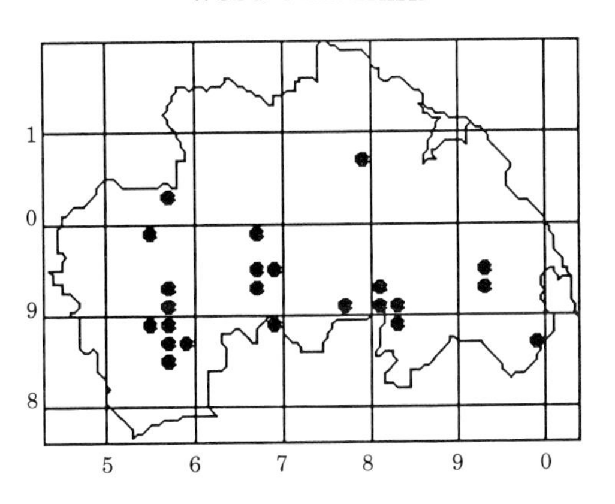

Flat-headed Sedge

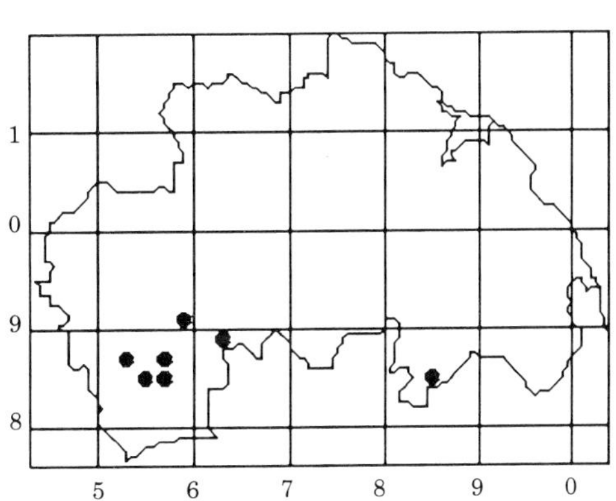

Bristle Scirpus

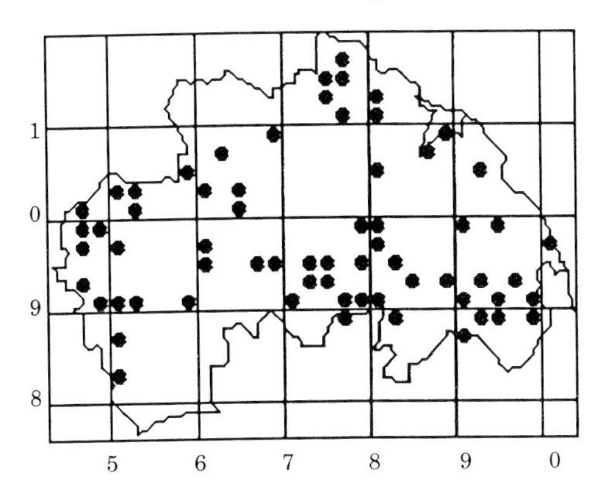

Black Bog Rush

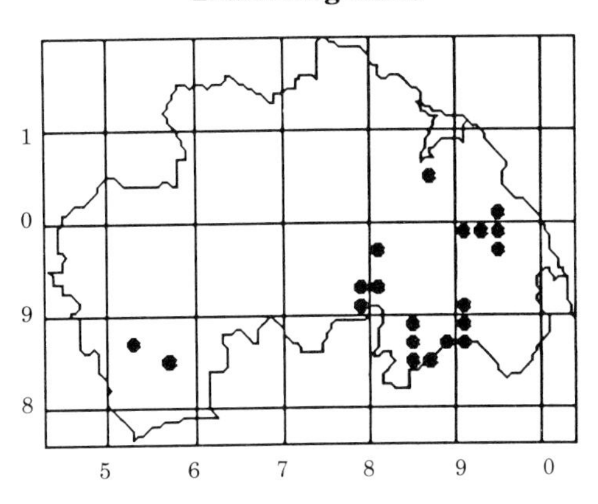

Lesser Pond Sedge

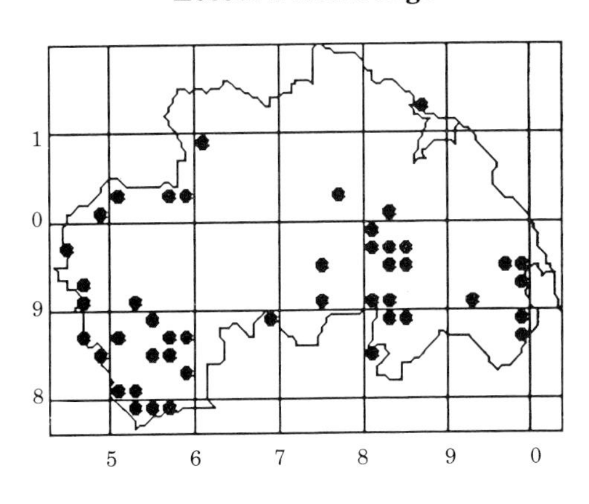

Ribbed Sedge

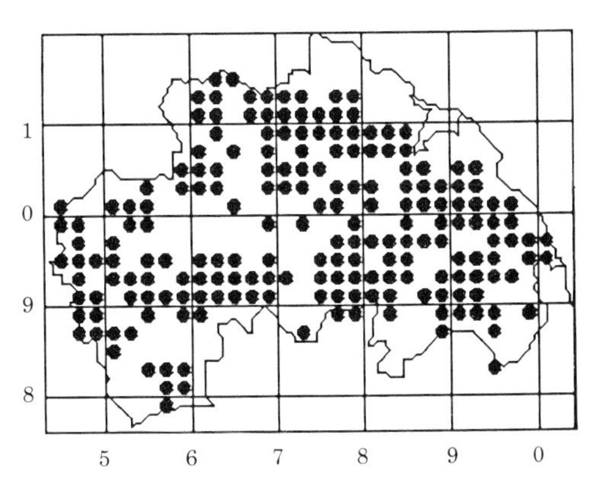

glades and old intakes. Its wintergreen leaves stand out amongst decaying vegetation on the moors.

Spring Sedge 82 M
Carex caryophyllea
Frequent on dry unimproved limestone pasture in the Hambleton Hills. Occasional on more acidic hill pasture where its early yellow-green leaves show brightly against the sombre turf.

White Sedge 20 M
Carex curta
This locally rare sedge grows in wet acid moorland vegetation and nutrient-poor sphagnum bogs. Its flattened grass-like tussocks are most often found in drying-out peaty pools.

Common Yellow Sedge 205
Carex demissa
[*Carex viridula* ssp. *oedocarpa*]
A common sedge in sandy ditchsides, on forest ride edges and in nutrient-poor moorland flushes. (See also *C. lepidocarpa*).

Fingered Sedge 7
Carex digitata
Very rare on calcareous rocky outcrops at Murton, Kirkdale, Sleightholmedale, Forge Valley and in dales of the upper Rye. A plant which is rare throughout Britain, these local populations form a major portion of its national distribution.

Dioecious Sedge 47
Carex dioica
Uncommon in nutrient-rich moorland flushes and calcareous seepage zones. It is often found amongst flea sedge and sundew.

Brown Sedge 26
Carex disticha
Mainly in lowland marshes, this is a sedge of unimproved rough grassland on more alkaline soils with plenty of humus and where water stands for many months. Its gingery brown spikes spread over a wide area in suitable habitats such as occur in Nettledale, Beckhole, Oldstead and lower Eskdale.

Star Sedge 232 M
Carex echinata
A common sedge in acid soils on waterlogged slopes and bogs on moorland and dalesides, often intermingled with soft rush or cottongrass.

Glaucous Sedge 294 M
Carex flacca
In short grassland on limestone or alkaline boulder clay, it may be abundant on verges, waste ground, moorland flushes and grassy areas. It has a wide habitat range from dry turf to spring line pools and is absent only from very acid moorland.

Hairy Sedge 115 M
Carex hirta
This is a vigorous plant of damp grassland, hedgebanks and woodland fringe. Common in railway ballast along lower Eskdale, it grows beside most of the southern rivers, in coastal valleys and in rough ground below the western escarpment.

Tawny Sedge 69 M
Carex hostiana
In marshy grassland and enriched flushes away from the moor tops, it often grows with bog pimpernel. Widespread in Bilsdale, Hole of Horcum to Goathland, Jugger Howe and Tranmire but only found in small numbers.

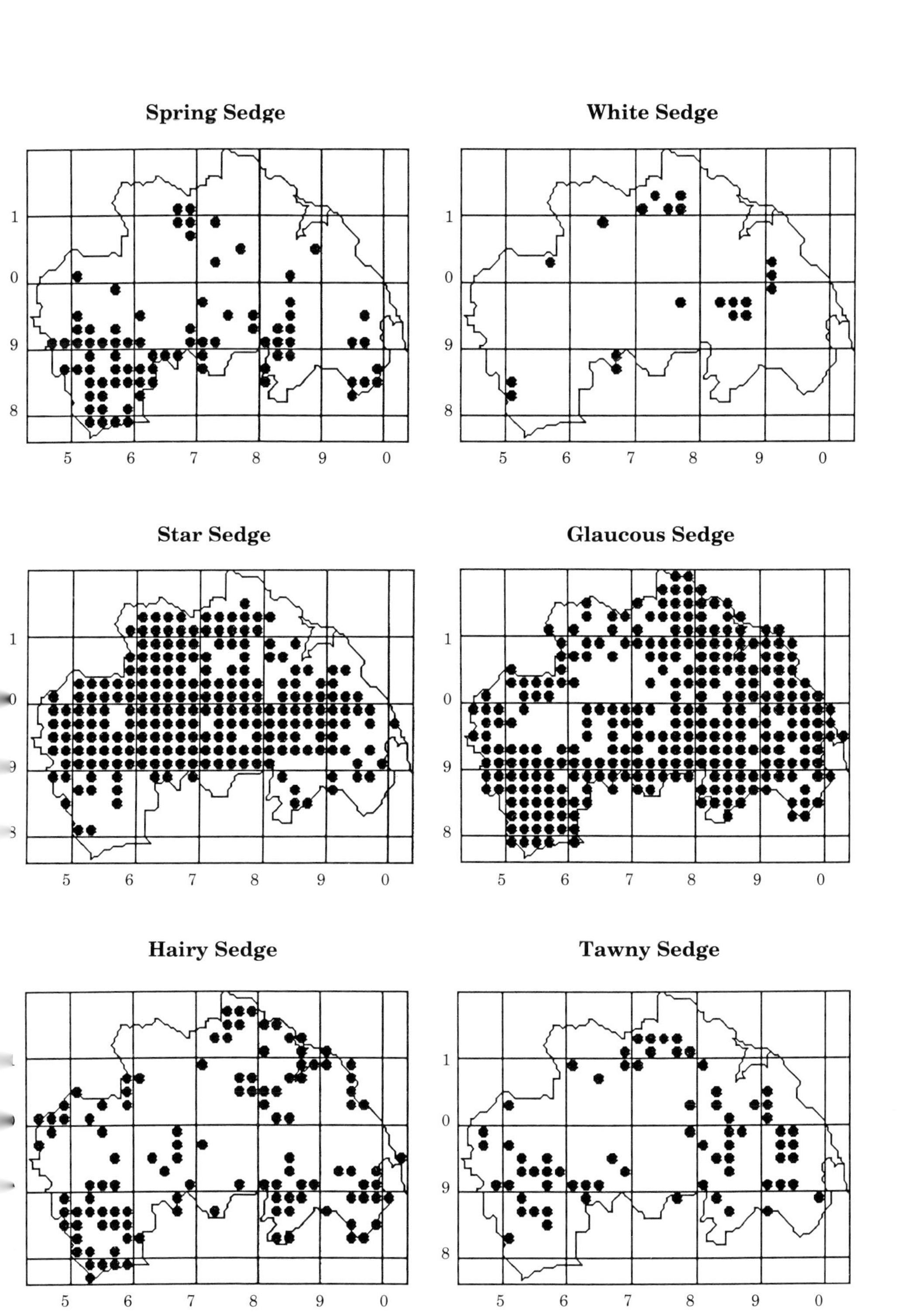
Spring Sedge
White Sedge
Star Sedge
Glaucous Sedge
Hairy Sedge
Tawny Sedge
1
0
9
8
5
6
7
8
9
0

Smooth Sedge 32 M
Carex laevigata
This tall imposing sedge is invariably found in remnants of undisturbed ancient woodland on heavy acidic soils, often growing with globeflower. Its limited distribution reflects the shortage of suitable habitat.

Slender Sedge
Carex lasiocarpa
Formerly recorded at Fen Bog, where further searching is required to ascertain its continued existence there.

Long-stalked Yellow Sedge 110
Carex lepidocarpa
[Carex viridula ssp. *brachyrrhyncha]*
Quite frequent in base-rich flushes on the moor and alongside forest rides.

[C. lepidocarpa and *C. demissa* show much similarity in distribution and growth forms and are now regarded as sub-species of *Carex viridula].*

Mud Sedge 2
Carex limosa
Known only at Fen Bog where it grows on shallow pool fringes.

Prickly Sedge 1
Carex muricata ssp. *lamprocarpa*
Recorded once at Goathland on the old rail incline.

Common Sedge 267
Carex nigra
Widespread in a range of habitats such as damp nutrient-poor grassland on verges and ditchsides. It is also found in upland bogs, pastures and on pool margins. This sedge shows a wide diversity of growth form from a few diminutive plants in impoverished grazing to tall lush stands on water's edge.

False Fox Sedge 18 M
Carex otrubae
An infrequent sedge, growing mainly on heavy soils in damp lowland ditches, by roadsides and in poorly-drained pastures. It is absent from the uplands.

Oval Sedge 179 M
Carex ovalis
This is quite a common plant, occurring in damp acidic rough grassland, on the edge of forest rides and farm tracks and in neglected intakes. It is not found on the high moors.

Pale Sedge 57 M
Carex pallescens
Sparse, mainly in poorly-drained permanent grassland and woodland fringe.

Carnation Sedge 259 M
Carex panicea
A widespread and plentiful sedge on much of the moorland. It has been found in a range of situations from acid sphagnum bogs to calcareous flushes, on open moor to forest rides.

Greater Tussock Sedge 47 M
Carex paniculata
Where water stands for much of the year and there is some water movement, impressive tussocks, a metre or more high, can be found in fens, carr woodland and old wet riverside scrub, indicating gradual reversion from swamp to woodland. Large stands grow in Hagg Wood marsh, Bilsdale, Kildale Woods, Eskdaleside and Douthwaite Dale. Unmanaged alder coppice in Lonsdale has exceptional old tussocks which form micro-habitats for other plants such as wood sorrel and herb robert.

Smooth Sedge

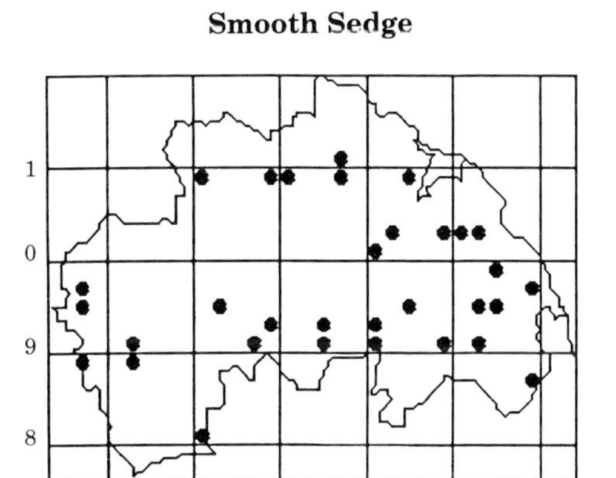

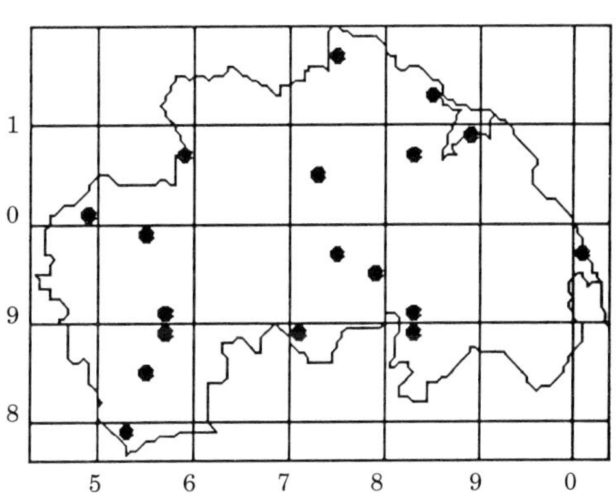

Oval Sedge

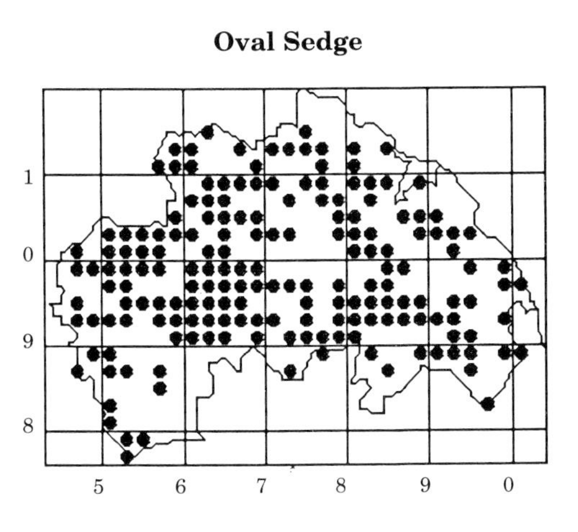

Pale Sedge

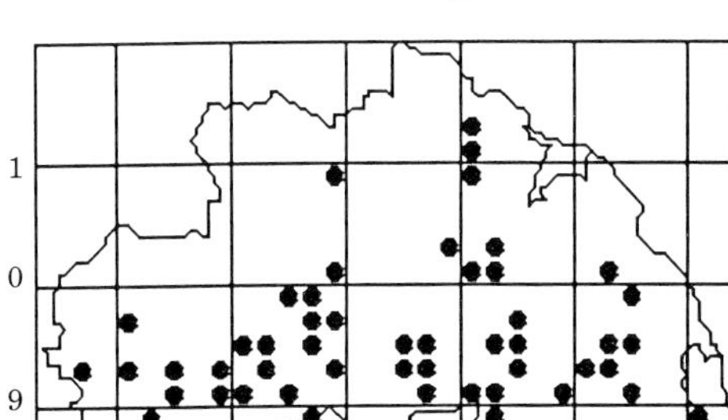

Carnation Sedge

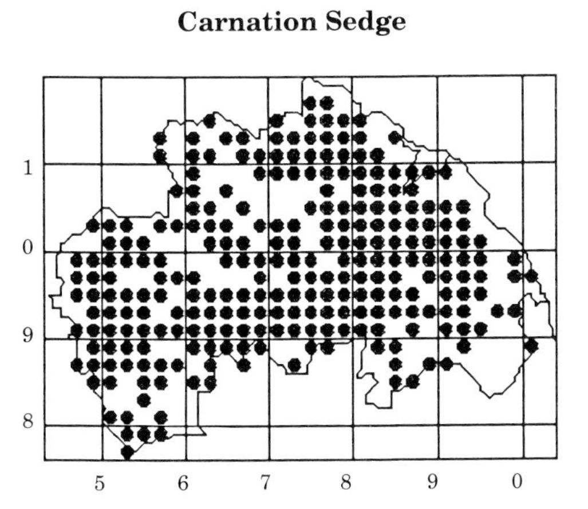

Greater Tussock Sedge

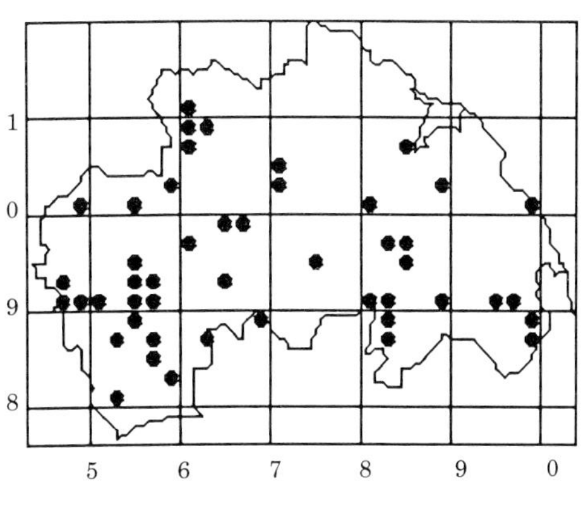

Few-flowered Sedge 1
Carex pauciflora
A sedge of the western Highlands which has its most southerly British site on the North York Moors. Early records for this rarity at Lilla Howe and Fen Bog were not refound but a few plants were discovered amongst cross-leaved heath and sphagnum in the vicinity of Derwent Head on Fylingdales Moor.

Pendulous Sedge 87 M
Carex pendula
Most abundant in old deciduous woods on alkaline boulder clay in the north-east where this sedge grows to enormous size. Fine specimens can be seen in woods at Mulgrave Castle, Glaisdale and Roxby.

Pill Sedge 185 M
Carex pilulifera
Grows on dry acidic soils and peat in the upper dales and moorland fringe, although infrequent on the high moors. It occupies grassy patches in heather mosaic vegetation, especially after fire.

Flea Sedge 84 M
Carex pulicaris
A sedge to be found in moorland flushes, poolsides and spring seepage with some nutrient enrichment. It often grows with dioecious sedge.

Remote Sedge 200
Carex remota
Tussocks of this grass-like sedge are plentiful in moist wooded streamsides in the dales, especially amidst alder and birch carr on saturated peat.

Greater Pond Sedge 18
Carex riparia
Covers extensive patches in marshes and alder carr in Newtondale, often with lesser pond sedge and yellow flag. It also grows in Harwood Dale Syme, Hackness Lake and Cams Head, Byland but is not a common pond sedge in this area.

Bottle Sedge 51 M
Carex rostrata
This is a common plant around lochs in Scotland but its local stands are small by comparison. It fringes open water at Boltby, Scarth Wood and Scaling reservoirs and Lake Gormire and grows in acid peaty slacks on Rosedale, Commondale, Kildale and Wheeldale Moors.

Spiked Sedge 5
Carex spicata
Rare this far north. Isolated plants have been recorded at Goathland, Hawnby, Ellerburn and Byland.

Thin Spiked Wood Sedge 1
Carex strigosa
This uncommon sedge flourishes in wet woodland in Forge Valley where it survives annual cutting to clear a boardwalk. Old records for Yedmandale, Newbiggin in Eskdale, Ravenscar Undercliff and Castlebeck wood have yet to be confirmed.

Wood Sedge 195 M
Carex sylvatica
A common plant in damp deciduous woodland and along rides where plantations have replaced older woods. It often grows in light shade of trackways and glades.

Bladder Sedge 30 M
Carex vesicaria
Stands are occasionally found in lowland streams and ponds on base-rich peat. Most frequent, however, in wet areas below Greenhow plantation, in Langdale and lower Eskdale.

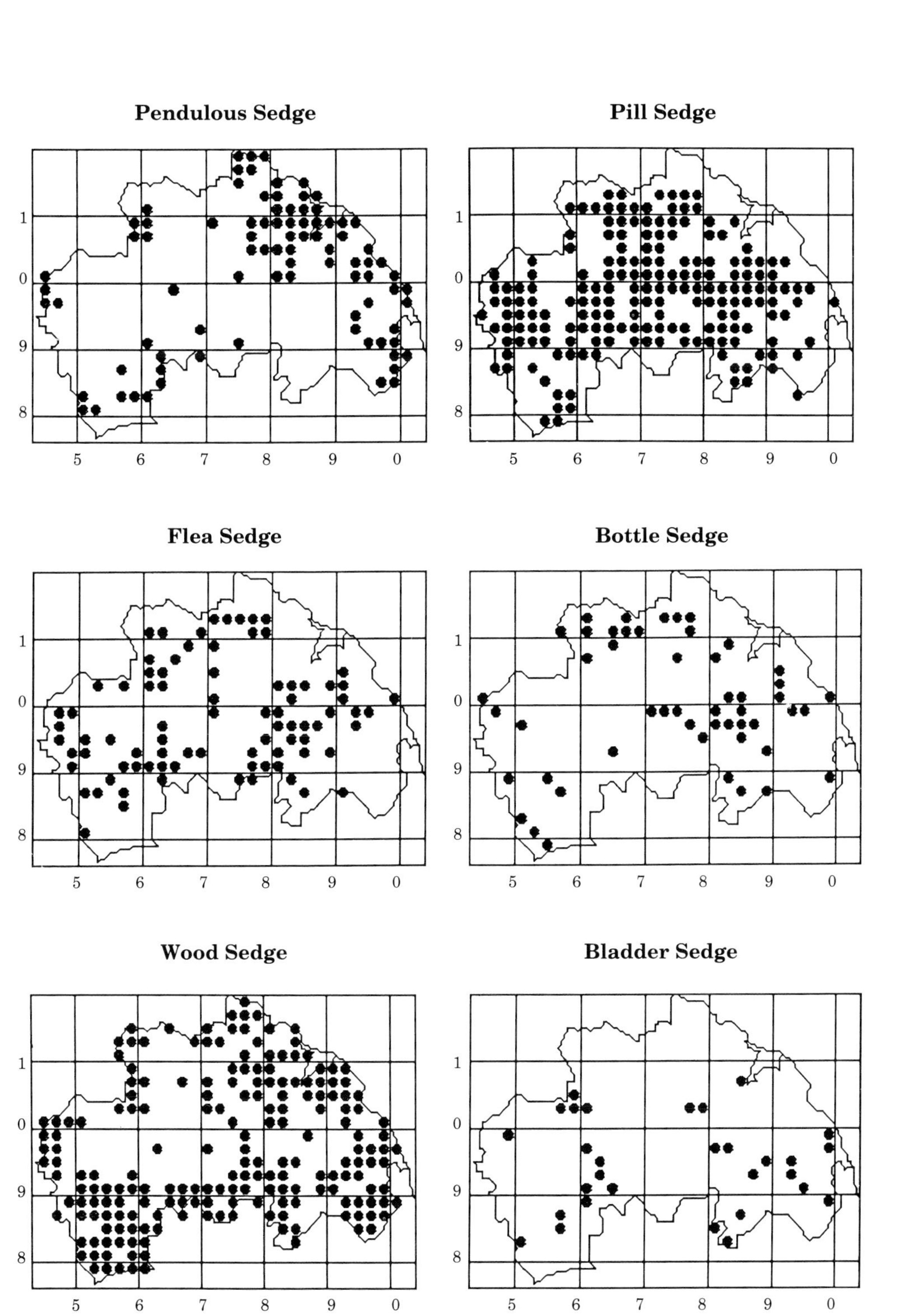
Pendulous Sedge
Pill Sedge
Flea Sedge
Bottle Sedge
Wood Sedge
Bladder Sedge

GRASS FAMILY
GRAMINEAE [POACEAE]

Brown Bent 229
Agrostis canina
Patch forming on damp acid heath, in shallow upland pools and trackways, mainly on the moors.

Common Bent 390
Agrostis capillaris
Very common throughout in grassland, epecially in rough hill grazing.

Black Bent 157 M
Agrostis gigantea
A frequent field edge weed, occasionally in large quantity in cereal crops.

Creeping Bent 388
Agrostis stolonifera
Very common in damp grassy places, in shallow streamsides and pools, on wasteland, roadside and in gardens.

Silvery Hairgrass
Aira caryophyllea
Infrequent on dry exposed soils but occasionally covers old shale heaps and dry sandy areas such as wall tops, gravelly rail ballast and exposed rock faces.

Early Hairgrass 183 M
Aira praecox
Widespread on bare ground on the moors where it may be an early coloniser after fire. It also grows on acidic sandy thin soils in old quarries and paths.

Marsh Foxtail 213 M
Alopecurus geniculatus
Often abundant in poorly-drained pastures and in trackways with standing water.

Blackgrass 12 M
Alopecurus myosuroides
An uncommon weed in cereal fields on heavy soils. It appeared in disturbed ground near Ruswarp Mill during building works in 1990.

Orange Foxtail 1
Alopecurus aequalis
Known only on the shores of Scaling Dam.

Meadow Foxtail 314 M
Alopecurus pratensis
Common in meadows, pastures and coarse grassy roadside banks on rich loamy soils. It is today less often included in reseeding mixtures than formerly but is still a common field edge grass.

Marram Grass 2
Ammophila arenaria
A coloniser of coastal sand dunes so, not surprisingly, rare on this coast. Small colonies are established at Sandsend and on shale at Saltwick.

Sweet Vernal Grass 380
Anthoxanthum odoratum
Abundant in old pastures and can be found in undisturbed swards from lowland verges and woodsides, through the dales and up to the moor tops in heather/grass mosaic vegetation.

False Oat Grass 329 M
Arrhenatherum elatius
This is a traditional hay meadow grass of fertile soils. It flourishes nowadays on road verges fed by nutrient run-off from adjacent fields. It may dominate the rank vegetation further back from the road where cutting is absent or less frequent. It avoids the higher land and is soon out-competed under grazing pressure.

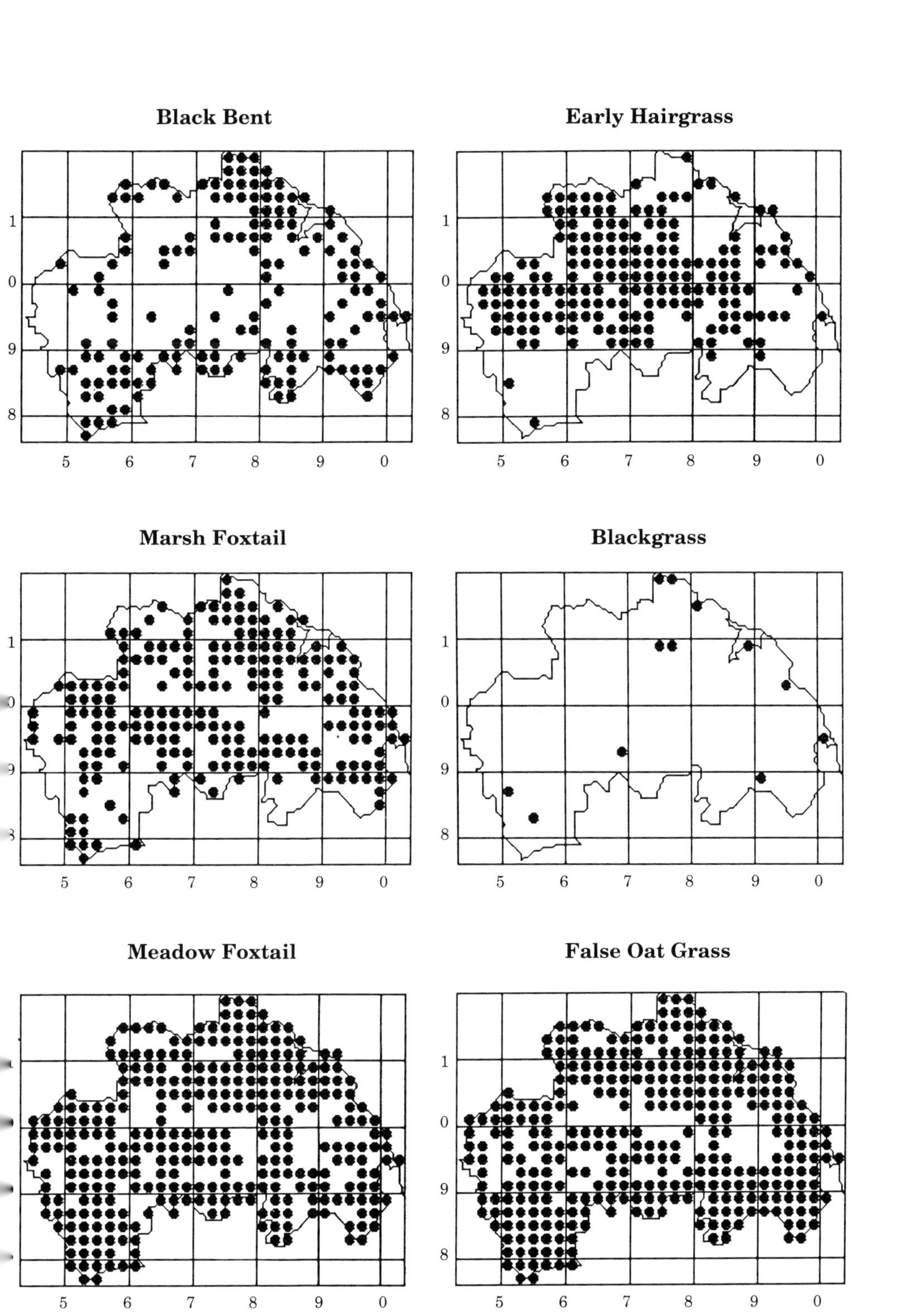
Black Bent
Early Hairgrass
Marsh Foxtail
Blackgrass
Meadow Foxtail
False Oat Grass

Wild Oat 190 M
Avena fatua
Wild oat is still a very common cornfield weed and may actually have increased since the practice of "roguing" or hand-pulling this persistent grass has declined. Also plentiful in nearby hedgerows.

Cultivated Oat
Avena sativa
A few survivors from fields of oats persist for a while in the vicinity but as a crop, oats are rarely grown in this area.

Meadow Oat Grass 19
Avenula pratensis
[Helichtotrichon pratense]
Found infrequently on old limestone grassland which remains on some steeper south-facing dalesides.

Hairy Oat Grass 57 M
Avenula pubescens
[Helichtotrichon pubescens]
This oat grass is also confined to calcareous soils but appears in a wider range of habitats, including disused quarries and verges.

Tor Grass 8
Brachypodium pinnatum
A few patches occur in rough, calcareous grassland and scrub on dalesides such as Gowerdale, Caydale, Ashberry and near Runswick Bay.

Slender False Brome 209 M
Brachypodium sylvaticum
Abundant in shady deciduous woodland and forest edges on base-rich soils. Unpalatable to stock, it survives in grazed woods and seems to persist on field edges and waysides after removal of trees.

Quaking Grass 229 M
Briza media
This attractive grass grows in a range of habitats where there is some alkalinity in the soil. It is abundant on the edge of forest rides made from limestone chippings; in disused limestone quarries; in bare thin soils on verge and wayside; and scattered liberally on unimproved hillsides in the southern dales.

Upright Brome 22
Bromus erectus [Bromopsis erecta]
Small populations grow on sheltered dalesides, verges and in quarries in the Hambleton Hills, around Hackness and a few other locations on the limestone belt.

Lop Grass 187
Bromus hordeaceus ssp. *hordeaceus*
Known also as soft brome this grass grows in hay meadows, pastures, rough grazings and in cereal crops, particularly in exposed farmland in the northeast.

Hairy Brome 180 M
Bromus ramosus [Bromopsis ramosa]
Widespread in open woodland, shady hedgebanks and rough grassland on damp fertile soils.

Sterile Brome 103 M
Bromus sterilis [Anisantha sterilis]
This is a common grass on well-drained wasteland, waysides and field edges. It may dominate the ground flora of hedgerows which have been sprayed with herbicide.

Bush Grass 21 M
Calamagrostis epigejos
An uncommon reed-like plant which grows in small colonies in damp wood edges, thickets, ditches and fens and

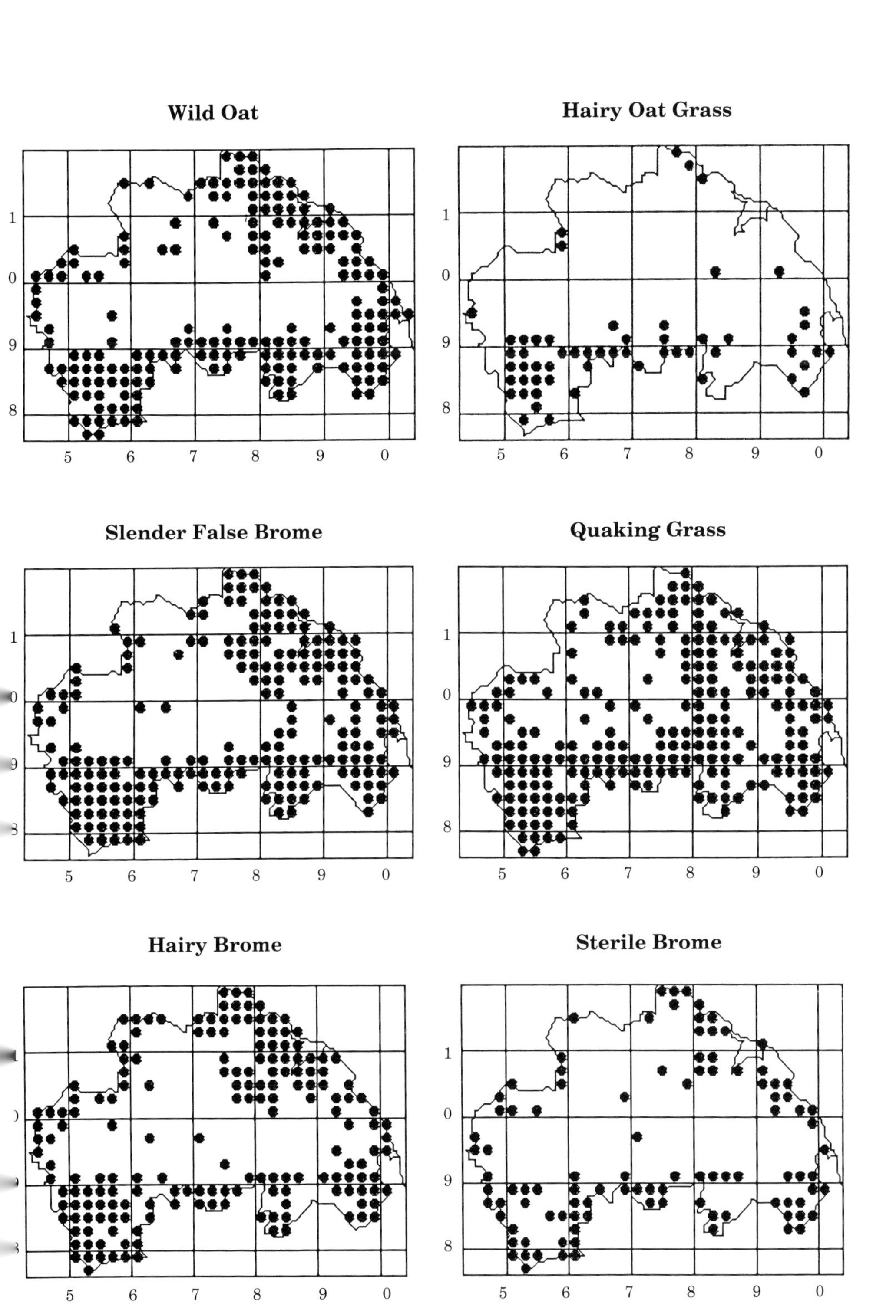
Wild Oat
Hairy Oat Grass
Slender False Brome
Quaking Grass
Hairy Brome
Sterile Brome

especially on the margins of forest plantations. It occurs in Newtondale, Borrowbydale, Appleton-le-Moors, Cropton and Allerston Forests and on land at Fylingdales Early Warning Station.

Purple Small Reed 1
Calamagrostis canescens
A rare grass throughout the country, it has been found once locally – in a wet alder wood in Dorman's Belt.

Water Whorl Grass 5
Catabrosa aquatica
A rare grass, only recorded in slow-moving water or muddy pools at Saltwick Nab, Throxenby Mere, Forge Valley and Raincliffe wood.

Crested Dogstail 363 M
Cynosurus cristatus
A common grass of upland pasture where it remains winter-green and provides useful sheep grazing throughout the year.

Cocksfoot 373
Dactylis glomerata
Abundant in a range of habitats from open woodland and waysides, to pastures and meadows, where its leafy tussocks provide useful grazing during a dry spell.

Heath Grass 147 M
Danthonia decumbens
Scattered in peaty or sandy soils on nutrient-poor hill grassland and open moorland. Its distinctive flowering spikes are prominent in sheep grazed turf.

Tufted Hairgrass 372 M
Deschampsia cespitosa
This is a common grass in damp rough grassland and moor edge. Its large tussocks of coarse, sharp-edged, leaves are avoided by stock and can dominate an unmanaged wet pasture.

Wavy Hairgrass 342 M
Deschampsia flexuosa
The beautiful mauve-tinted flowers of this upland grass are a common feature of the moorland scene in summer. Confined to acid peat or sandy soils, it is abundant after forest felling and is widely interspersed with mosaic moorland vegetation on drier heath.

Fern Grass 21 M
Desmazeria rigida
[Catapodium rigidum]
This small tough fern-like grass is uncommon on dry sandy calcareous soils.

Bearded Couch Grass 93
Elymus caninus
Occasional in small numbers in undisturbed woodland edge on fertile soil.

Sand Couch 4
Elymus farctus [Elymus juncea]
A lower sand-dune grass, able to withstand sea spray, occurs spasmodically in the few suitable habitats at Saltwick Bay, Sandsend and Hayburn Wyke.

Common Couch 286
Elymus repens
A very common plant in cultivated areas where it can be a persistent weed in farm and garden.

Wood Fescue 7
Festuca altissima
A rare grass countrywide, it survives in moist ancient woodland. It has been found locally in woods at Beckhole, Kirkdale and Holey Gill, Eskdaleside and in some of the steep rocky gills of the upper Rye.

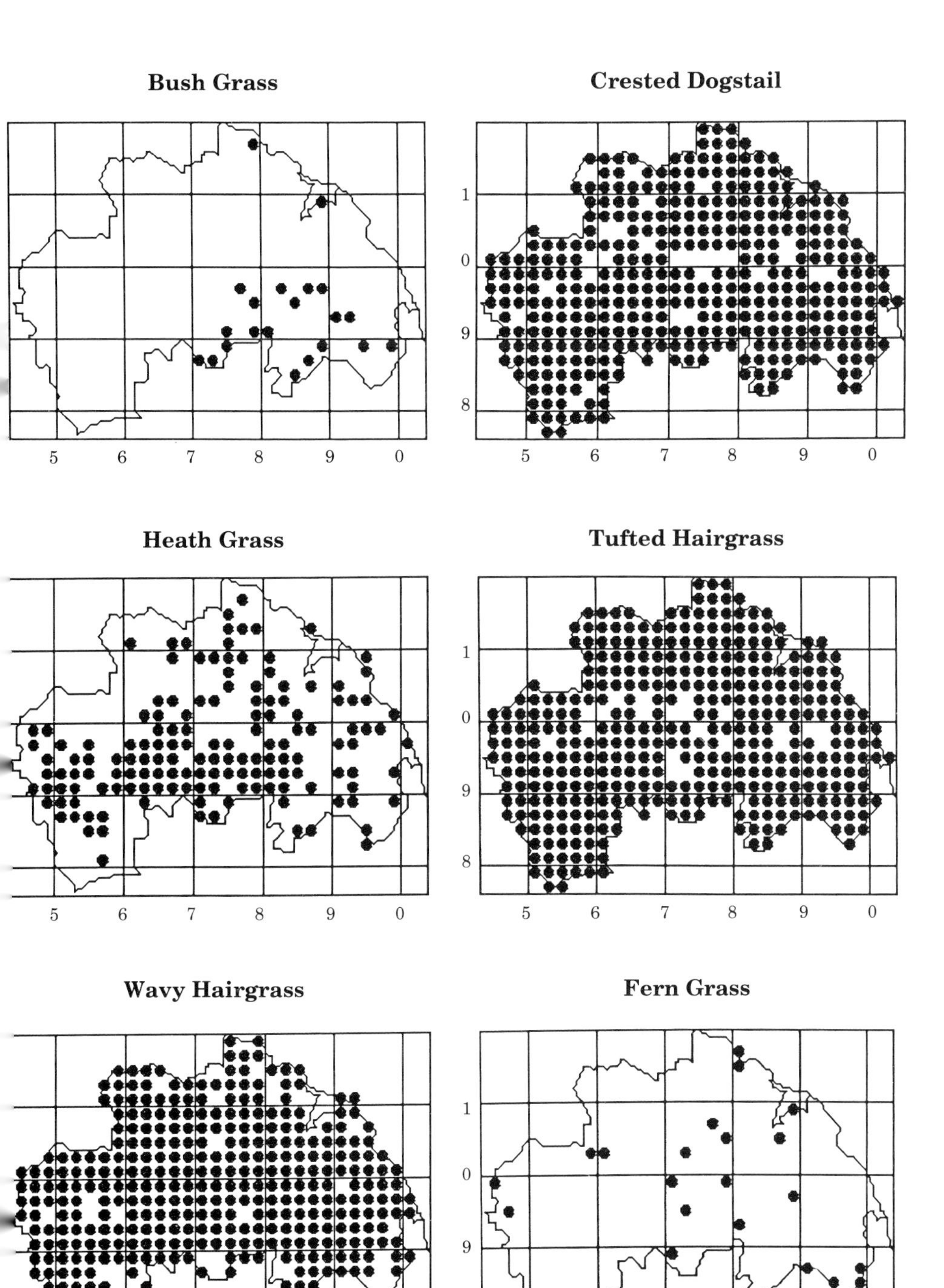
Bush Grass
Crested Dogstail
Heath Grass
Tufted Hairgrass
Wavy Hairgrass
Fern Grass
1
0
9
8
5
6
7
8
9
0

Tall Fescue 80 M
Festuca arundinacea
Frequent on lowland road verges, in rough grassland, on riversides and coastal cliffs.

Giant Fescue 151 M
Festuca gigantea
Grows on the fringes of damp deciduous woods, often with slender false brome and hairy brome.

Sheep's Fescue 307 M
Festuca ovina
This grass is an important component of the fescue/bent grassland community of plants which comprise most of the grazing sward in dalehead and moorland fringe.

Fine-leaved Sheep's Fescue 26 M
Festuca tenuifolia [Festuca filiformis]
Has been found in small scattered populations on acid peat on moor edge and dry heath.

Meadow Fescue 65 M
Festuca pratensis
Not a common grass in these parts but found occasionally in lowland meadows and on verges with moist loamy soil.

Red Fescue 381
Festuca rubra
Very common in pastures, verges, pathways and most permanent grassy places away from the higher moors. The glaucous form grows plentifully on the sea cliffs.

Small Sweet Grass 66
Glyceria declinata
Found in pools and rivulets on upland farmland, usually rooted in mud, its prostrate leaves lying in shallow gently-moving water.

Floating Sweet Grass 277
Glyceria fluitans
Abundant in most standing or slow-moving water and wet grassland away from the high moors, often in large quantity.

Plicate Sweet Grass 38
Glyceria plicata [Glyceria notata]
The least common sweet grass, it has been found in somewhat drier situations such as muddy track ruts, pool edges and puddled field corners.

Reed Sweet Grass 11
Glyceria maxima
Extensive riverside populations grow in Bilsdale, Troutsdale, Newtondale and Greenhow and on a few lakesides such as Elleron and Whorlton.

Yorkshire Fog 388
Holcus lanatus
A very common grass with little agricultural value on more productive land but providing a useful bite in the absence of better feed on nutrient-poor pasture. Quick to invade disturbed ground, it spreads aggressively over wasteland, meadows and waysides.

Creeping Soft Grass 317 M
Holcus mollis
Not as widespread as Yorkshire fog but, being a rhizomatous plant, it almost carpets the ground where it grows in grazed woodlands.

Wood Barley 11
Hordelymus europaeus
An attractive tall grass of shady woodland, rare in this area and confined to ancient woods on alkaline soils at Sinnington, Gerrick, Kirkdale, Riccaldale, Hackness, Grosmont, Rievaulx, Gowerdale and Ouldray.

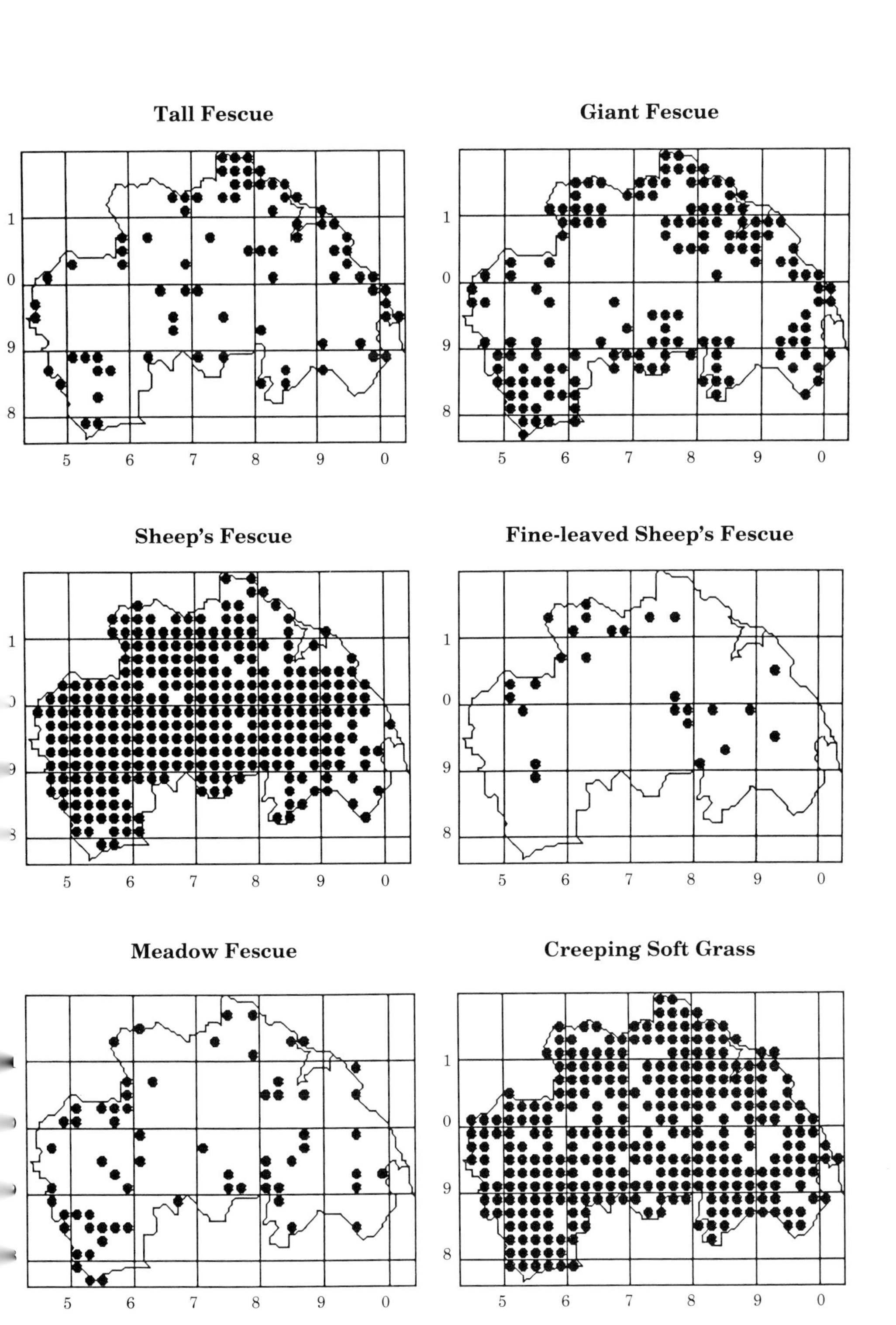
Tall Fescue
Giant Fescue
Sheep's Fescue
Fine-leaved Sheep's Fescue
Meadow Fescue
Creeping Soft Grass
1
0
9
8
5
6
7
8
9
0

Wall Barley 29 M
Hordeum murinum
A familiar urban grass to be found at the foot of buildings, kerbstones, car parks and footpaths in disturbed thin soils. Plentiful in such places along the northern coast but less frequent inland.

Crested Hairgrass 35 M
Koeleria macrantha
An attractive grass of dry alkaline soils, its silvery spikes are found on hill pastures and sunny dalesides in the limestone belt.

Lyme Grass 2
Leymus arenarius
Lack of sand-dune habitat restricts this plant to a few sandy shore locations at Sandsend and Runswick Bay.

Perennial Ryegrass 370
Lolium perenne ssp. *perenne*
Abundant throughout the farmed land where it is sown extensively for grazing and silage. Common in most lowland grassy areas such as verges, recreation fields, churchyards, gardens and village greens. *L. perenne* ssp. *multiflorum* has been found infrequently but is rarely included in seed mixtures nowadays.

Mountain Melick 17 M
Melica nutans
A rare grass found in ancient woodland and on shady limestone banks. Usually with wood melick but in less quantity.

Wood Melick 138 M
Melica uniflora
Widespread in undisturbed long-established woodland and roadside banks with some tree shading.

Wood Millet 24
Milium effusum
An attractive grass of streamside and wet woodland where it is locally plentiful, rooted in moist humus and overhanging the water's edge. Likely to be native in woods such as Tan Beck, Stonegate and Crunkly Gills and Harwood Dale. May have originated from pheasant feed in other locations.

Purple Moor Grass 242 M
Molinia caerulea
Widespread on wet peaty moors and mineral soils with some water movement. It can be the dominant plant on parts of the moor such as Saltergate and in alder carr and wet birch/willow woodland. Its rigid tussocks standing in water make a *Molinia* heath almost impassable for walkers.

Matgrass 277 M
Nardus stricta
An unpalatable wiry grass abundant on upland peat or acid mineral soils. It covers extensive parts of the moor north of Danby where its pale decaying foliage contrasts sharply with dark heather in a mosaic of vegetation. Where excessive sheep grazing follows moor burning, too much young heather growth may be removed, thus allowing matgrass to encroach and eventually become the dominant species.

Sea Hard Grass
Parapholis strigosa
Has been recorded in the Whitby area and may have been overlooked elsewhere in suitable habitats along the coast, its narrow erect spikes being difficult to detect in saltmarsh vegetation.

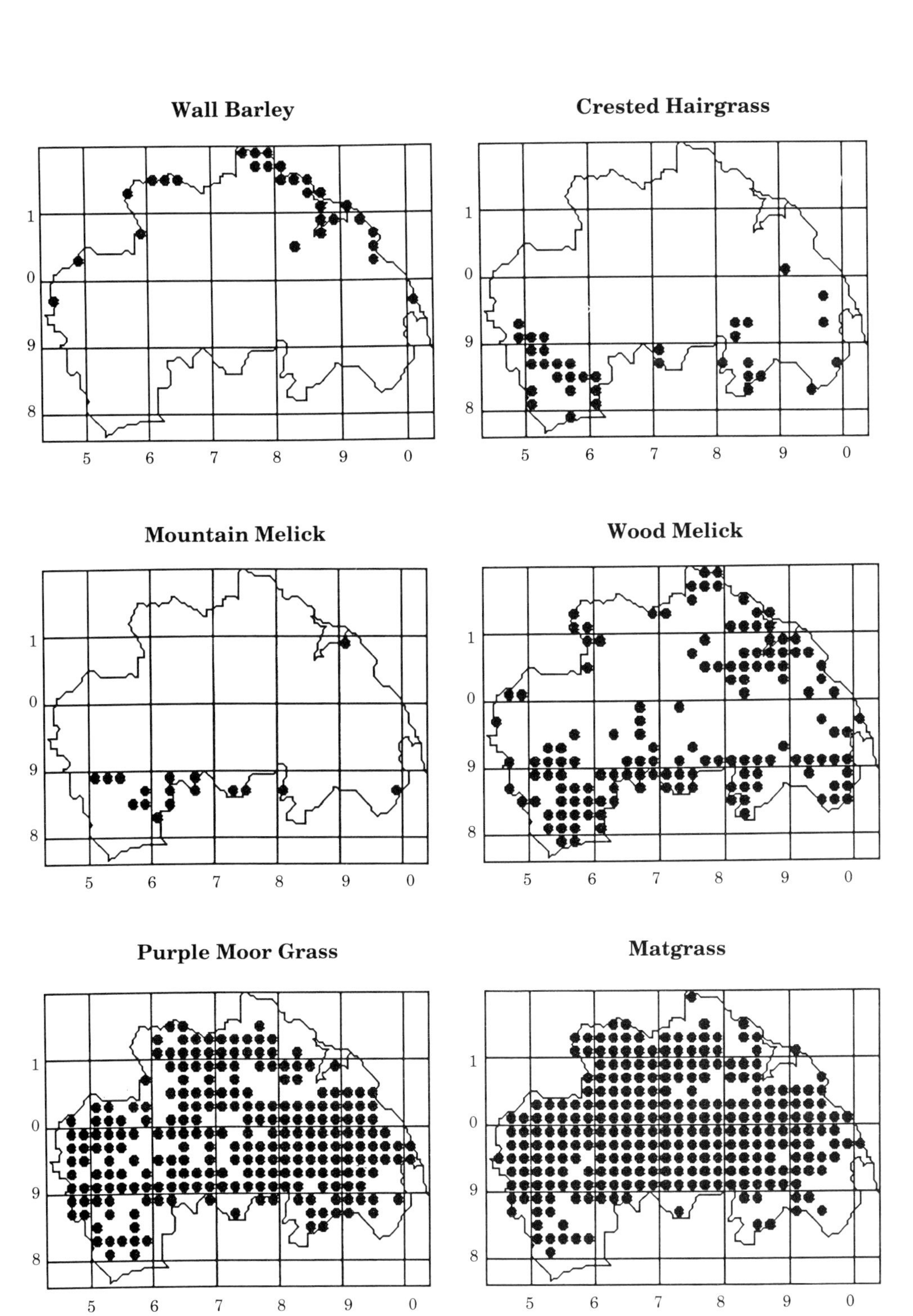
Wall Barley
1
0
9
8
5 6 7 8 9 0
Crested Hairgrass
1
0
9
8
5 6 7 8 9 0
Mountain Melick
1
0
9
8
5 6 7 8 9 0
Wood Melick
1
0
9
8
5 6 7 8 9 0
Purple Moor Grass
1
0
9
8
5 6 7 8 9 0
Matgrass
1
0
9
8
5 6 7 8 9 0

Reed Canary Grass 167 M
Phalaris arundinacea
Frequent clumps of this tall reedy grass grow alongside streams, ditches and pools on the edge of forest rides and in alder and willow carr.

Canary Grass
Phalaris canariensis
A bird seed relic, naturalised rarely on waste ground.

Timothy or **Catstail** 300
Phleum pratense ssp. *pratense*
A common nutritious grass found in abundance on farmland, especially in damper grassland. *P. pratense* ssp. *bertoloni* has been noted but not been recorded separately.

Common Reed 30 M
Phragmites australis
Grows in Throxenby Mere, Fen Bog and a few similar fens and swamps, especially in Newtondale, but is nowhere as extensive as stands of this plant are in the south of Britain.

Annual Meadow Grass 387
Poa annua
This ubiquitous grass is abundant on cultivated and disturbed ground, in short grassland and pathsides throughout the area.

Flattened Meadow Grass 7
Poa compressa
A rare grass, it grows on old walls at Ruswarp and Everley. It has also been found on old burial mounds on the moors and on coastal cliffs.

Wood Meadow Grass 73 M
Poa nemoralis
A delicate and distinctive grass with a localised distribution in shady woodland.

Smooth Meadow Grass 311
Poa pratensis
Very common on permanent grassland throughout the lowland, on roadsides and lanes up the dales.

Rough Meadow Grass 350
Poa trivialis
Very common on waysides and in permanent grassland.

Reflexed Poa or **Saltmarsh Grass** 29 M
Puccinellia distans
A saltmarsh grass invading inland with heavier use of salt on roads. Now common in the narrow splash zone fringing the A171, A169, A172 and A174 and has been found on a few nearby minor roads.

Sea Poa or **Common Saltmarsh Grass** 2
Puccinellia maritima
This saltmarsh plant remains strictly coastal. It has been found infrequently on the tidal riverside at Whitby and Ruswarp.

Yellow Oat Grass 110 M
Trisetum flavescens
When in flower this charming grass gives a golden sheen to fertile hill pastures and verges on calcareous soils.

Squirrel-tail Fescue 21 M
Vulpia bromoides
One of the few plants to colonise old shale heaps and roadside grit piles; it also thrives amongst disused sidings at Grosmont and Whitby stations, in sandy ground on the old coast railway and on the tops of dry stone walls.

Ratstail Fescue
Vulpia myuros
Rare, found on disturbed ground at Battersby Junction and around Whitby.

Reed Canary Grass

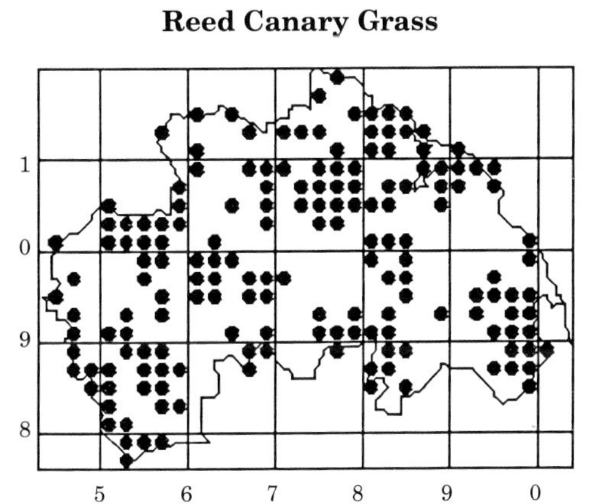

Common Reed

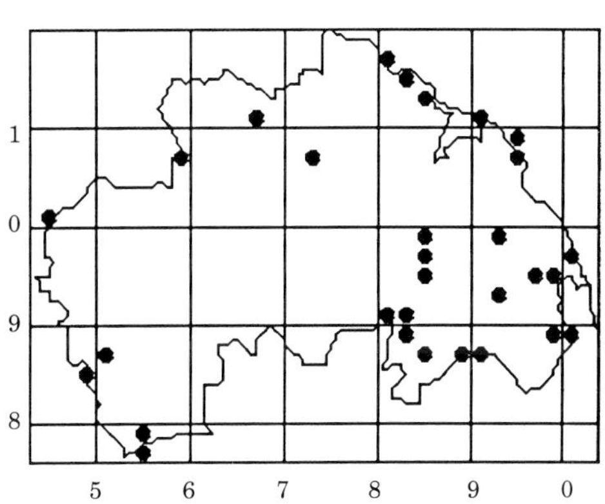

Wood Meadow Grass

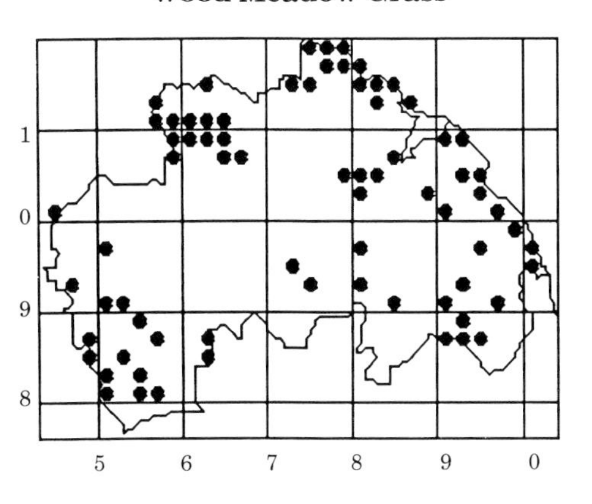

Reflexed Poa or **Saltmarsh Grass**

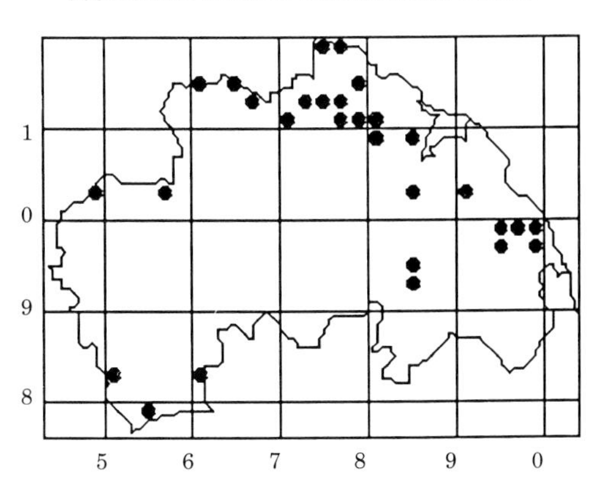

Yellow Oat Grass

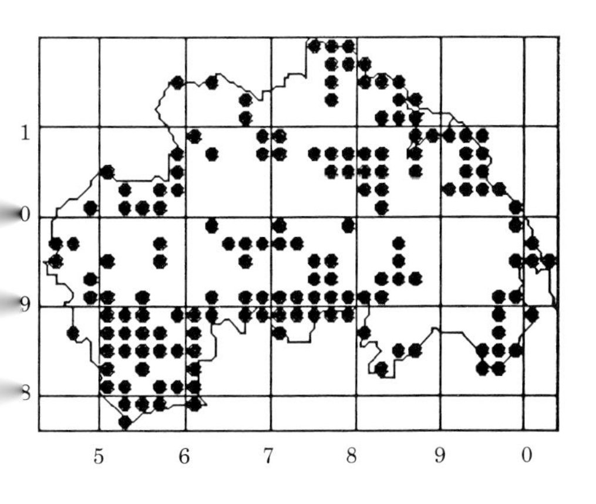

Squirrel-tail Fescue

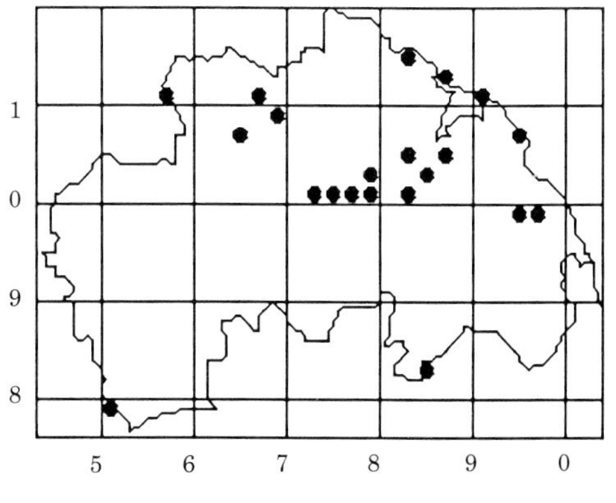

APPENDIX 1

Species at Risk

The following are those species considered at greatest risk of being lost to the local flora unless positive action is taken to rescue them. Those marked * are reduced to no more than two known populations:

Corn marigold
Venus' looking-glass
* Meadowrue
Common melilot
Sawwort
Bugloss
Dwarf spurge
Frog orchid
Lesser butterfly orchid
Greater butterfly orchid
Marsh St John's wort
Mountain St John's wort
* Purple milk vetch
* Stemless thistle
Blue fleabane
Marsh helleborine
Burnt-tip orchid
Corn mint
Barberry
Mountain everlasting
Adderstongue fern
* Basil thyme
Henbane
Flixweed
Night-flowering catchfly
* Corn buttercup
Purple loosestrife
Corn salad
Clustered bellflower
Field woundwort
Green-winged orchid
Water purslane
* Royal fern
Juniper
Houndstongue
Meadow thistle
* Small white orchid
Treacle mustard
Gypsywort
Flat-headed sedge
* Field gentian
Birdsnest orchid
Birdseye primrose
* Lesser water plantain
Long stalked cranesbill
* Intermediate wintergreen
Petty whin
Bee orchid
White-beak sedge
Wild pansy
* Hay-scented buckler fern

APPENDIX 2

Visiting Sites of Interest and Conservation Organisations

The National Park is mostly in private ownership, with some land being owned by the National Park Authority, other public bodies and conservation organisations. Within the North York Moors there are over 2000 km of public rights of way which provide access to many habitats previously described. All public rights of way are clearly shown on the Ordnance Survey 1:25,000 Outdoor Leisure Maps 26 and 27 which cover the Park area.

The following organisations own or lease land which is managed to protect and improve plant habitats.

NORTH YORK MOORS NATIONAL PARK
The Old Vicarage, Bondgate, Helmsley YO6 5BP

Land owned at Levisham and Lockton Moors, Cawthorn Camps and Beckhole, together with numerous car parks including Grosmont. Information and walks leaflets are available from National Park Information Centres at Danby, Sutton Bank and Helmsley or from the above address.

FOREST ENTERPRISE
42 Eastgate, Pickering YO18 7DS

Extensive areas of plantation woodland which include a range of unique wildlife habitats. A visitor centre at Dalby provides information on numerous trails and conservation areas.

ENGLISH NATURE
Institute of Applied Biology, University of York, York YO1 5DD

Forge Valley National Nature Reserve is managed by English Nature. Information boards at parking points show the extent of the reserve. Management guidance to landowners for nearly 60 Sites of Special Scientific Interest in the National Park is provided by English Nature.

YORKSHIRE WILDLIFE TRUST
10 Toft Green, York YO1 1JT

Manages reserves at:
Garbutt Wood, Ashberry, Littlebeck, Fen Bog, Ellerburn Bank
Haggwood, Newtondale }
Hayburn Wyke } managed jointly
Bridestones } with other agencies
For details of visiting and membership, contact YWT at the above address.
Volunteers to help manage reserves are always welcomed.

NATIONAL TRUST
Goddards, 27 Tadcaster Road, York

The National Trust owns about 1800 ha of land in the North York Moors National Park. This includes farmland, coast, moorland and woodland at:
Bridestones Moor, Hayburn Wyke, Mount Grace Priory, Beast and Common Cliffs, Robin Hood's Bay, Ravenscar, Bransdale, Saltwick Nab, Crosscliff, Blakey Topping, Rievaulx Terrace, Roseberry Topping, Scarthwood Moor, Newton Woods, Cliff Rigg Quarry, Boggle Hole, Sikehill, Sonley and Hall Woods, Farndale

Properties are shown on the Ordnance Survey maps. Further information is available from the above address.

WOODLAND TRUST
Autumn Park, Grantham, Lincs NG31 6LL

The following areas are owned and managed by the Woodland Trust, they are mostly ancient woodland sites:

Castlebeck and Scar End Wood
Cow Close Wood, Moorsholm
East Brow Wood, Newtondale
Church Plantation, Ingleby Greenhow

In addition to managing land holdings, the above organisations offer grants and/or advice on conservation management.

The following organisations are not landowners in the Park but offer financial incentives and/or guidance on conservation schemes.

CLEVELAND WILDLIFE TRUST
Unit 2A Brighouse Business Village, Brighouse Road, Middlesbrough
Cleveland TS2 1RT

About 4% of the National Park lies within the County of Cleveland and Cleveland Wildlife Trust aims to conserve locally valuable wildlife habitats in that area. Further information and membership details are available from the above address.

AGRICULTURAL DEVELOPMENT ADVISORY SERVICES (ADAS)
New Crown Building, Whitby Road, Pickering YO18 7HE

ADAS advises on Ministry of Agriculture grants and environmental conservation as well as on agricultural uses of land.

COUNTRYSIDE COMMISSION
Yorkshire & Humberside Regional Office, 2nd Floor, Victoria Wharf, Embankment IV, Sovereign Street, Leeds LS1 4BA

A number of incentive schemes available through the Countryside Commission are aimed at protection of wildlife habitats, hedges and footpaths.

APPENDIX 3

The rarest and commonest species

(Excluded from this list are transient plants such as garden throw-outs; plants which are inadequately recorded; and species likely to have been introduced or planted for amenity purposes.)

Rarest

The following species were found in only one tetrad:

Basil thyme
Sea wormwood
Sea bindweed
Few-flowered sedge
Orange foxtail
Rusty-back fern
Intermediate yellow rocket
Corn chamomile
Purple small reed
Ratstail fescue
Crown vetch
Fairy foxglove
Thin-spiked wood sedge
Danish scurvy grass
Dutch rush
Wood cranesbill
Dwarf mallow
Short-leaved crowfoot
Small white orchid
Spiked water milfoil
Lesser pondweed
Various-leaved pondweed
Horned pondweed
Tufted loosestrife
Tall broomrape
Sea hard grass
Royal fern
Yellow bird's nest
Upright yellow sorrel
Marsh rosemary
Hay-scented buckler fern
Dwarf furze
Golden dock
Strawberry clover
Cloudberry
Greater sea spurrey
Fine-leaved water dropwort
Narrow-leaved hemp nettle
Lesser swinecress
Bithynian vetch
Knotted hedge parsley
Prickly sedge
Sea spleenwort
Sea rush
Stemless thistle
Soft trefoil

The following species were found in two to five tetrads:

Sand couch
Wild celery
Marram grass
Mountain everlasting
Lesser marshwort
Wormwood
Sea aster
Shore orache
Frosted orache
Lesser water plantain
Sea beet
Yellow-wort
Sea rocket
Calamint
Wood cudweed
Clustered bellflower
Hoary pepperwort
Spiked sedge
Slender thistle
Tufted sedge
Sand sedge
Mud sedge
Water whorl grass
Wallflower
Sea mouse-ear
Dwarf cornel

Melancholy thistle
Traveller's joy
Midland hawthorn
Rough hawksbeard
Houndstongue
Wall rocket
Lyme grass
Slender spike rush
Blue fleabane
Treacle mustard
Dwarf spurge
Small white fumitory
Yellow star of Bethlehem
Field gentian
Long-stalked cranesbill
Large-flowered hemp nettle
Sea milkwort
Sea sandwort
Opposite-leaved pondweed
Sea buckthorn
Elecampane
Mud rush
Venus' looking glass
Ivy duckweed
Gromwell
May lily
Spotted medick
Common melilot
Hemlock water dropwort
Yellow water lily
Green-winged orchid
Burnt-tip orchid
Wild parsnip
Wild parsley
Hawkweed oxtongue
Tasteless water pepper
Small pondweed
Reddish pondweed
Perfoliate pondweed
Intermediate wintergreen
Sea poa
Birdseye primrose
Hairy buttercup
Buckthorn
Great yellowcress
Grey bulrush
Houseleek
Eastern rocket
Unbranched bur-reed
Marsh stitchwort
Meadow rue
Lesser reedmace
Spring vetch
Purple milk vetch
Stagshorn clubmoss
Corn crowfoot
Hornwort
Marsh yellowcress
Henbane

The following species were found in six to ten tetrads:

Stinking mayweed
Slender parsley piert
Deadly nightshade
Flat-headed sedge
Tor grass
Wild cabbage
White bryony
Fingered sedge
Little mouse-ear
Good King Henry
Corn marigold
Pond water crowfoot
Frog orchid
Beaked hawksbeard
Early marsh orchid
Narrow-leaved marsh orchid
Floating scirpus
Wood fescue
Small-flowered willowherb
Winter aconite
Dyer's greenweed
Bloody cranesbill
Marsh St John's wort
Tutsan
Mountain St John's wort
Lesser twayblade
Juniper
Shoreweed
Bugloss
Gipsywort

Purple loosestrife
Peppermint
Tall melilot
Birdsnest orchid
White water lily
Spiny restharrow
Bee orchid
Bristly oxtongue
Pellitory of the wall
Water purslane
Long-leaved crowfoot
Lesser butterfly orchid
Flattened meadow grass
Great spearwort
Common wintergreen
Celery-leaved crowfoot
Mountain currant
Sweet briar
Bulrush
Sea club rush
English stonecrop
Lesser clubmoss
Sand spurrey
Greater chickweed
Sea arrowgrass
Globeflower
Corn salad
Common water crowfoot
Night-flowering catchfly
Narrow-leaved everlasting pea
White beak-sedge

Commonest

The following species have been recorded in at least 380 of the 396 tetrads; this indicates a 96% distribution in this area:

Common bent
Creeping bent
Sweet vernal grass
Daisy
Common mouse-ear
Field thistle
Marsh thistle
Spear thistle
Red fescue
Yorkshire fog
Soft rush
Broad-leaved plantain
Annual meadow grass
Self heal
Bracken
Creeping buttercup
White clover
Stinging nettle

SUGGESTED FURTHER READING

Baker, J.G. *North Yorkshire* (1906)

Belcher, H. *Scenery of the Whitby and Pickering Railway* (1836)

Carstairs, I. *The North York Moors National Park* (1978)

Clapham, A.R., Tutin, T.G. & Warburg, E.F. *Excursion Flora of the British Isles* (1981)

Fitter, A. *An Atlas of the Wild Flowers of Britain and Northern Europe* (1978)

Garrard, I. & Streeter, D. *The Wild Flowers of the British Isles* (1983)

Grigson, G. *The Englishman's Flora* (1975)

Hubbard, J.C.E. *Grasses* (1984)

Jermy, A.C., Chater, A.O. & David, R.W. *Sedges of the British Isles* (1982)

North York Moors National Park, Moorland Management – 1985-1990 (1991)

North York Moors National Park Plan – Second Review (1990)

Reynolds, B. *Whitby Wild Flowers* (1915)

Salisbury, Sir E. *Weeds and Aliens* (1964)

Scarborough Field Naturalists' Society. *The Natural History of the Scarborough District* (1953)

Spratt, D.A. & Harrison, B.J.D. *The North York Moors Landscape Heritage* (1989)

Stace, C. *New Flora of the British Isles* (1991)

GLOSSARY AND ABBREVIATIONS

Acid	soil or water with few basic minerals such as calcium and magnesium.
Agg.	an aggregate or group of closely related species or microspecies.
Alien	a plant not native to Britain; believed to have been introduced by man and now established in the wild.
Alkaline	soil or water which is not acid.
Alluvial	soil deposited by flowing water.
Annual	a plant which grows, flowers, fruits and dies off in one year.
Basic	non-acid or alkaline soil.
Base-rich	containing calcium and magnesium.
Biennial	a plant which takes two years to grow, flower, fruit and die.
Blanket bog	a bog on open or sloping ground, not in a valley, in areas of high rainfall.
Bog	an area of wet, acid moor, usually on deep peat.
Calcareous	base-rich soil formed over chalk or limestone, often supporting diverse plant communities.
Calcicole	a plant which requires a calcareous soil.
Calcifuge	a plant which requires a neutral to acid soil.
Carr	wet woodland (alder, willow, birch) usually with standing water.
Casual	a plant with erratic occurrence.
Epiphyte	a plant growing upon another plant for support but not obtaining nutrients from it.
Ericaceous	plants in the heather family (Ericaceae).
Eutrophication	a process of nutrient-enrichment occurring in water.
Fen	an area of wetland on calcareous to neutral (not acid) peat, usually low-lying in valley.
Flush	a wet area with seepage water dispersing over a broad area, not in a channel.
Glandular	any part of a plant which has small glands containing oil, resin or other liquid; often fragrant.
Glaucous	of bluish appearance.
Improved	arable and grassland which has been chemically sprayed to increase productivity. May have been ploughed and reseeded.
Ley	short-term grassland, ploughed and re-seeded in an arable crop rotation.
Marsh	an area of wetland on mineral (not peaty) soil.
Microspecies	plants differentiated by microscopic characteristics.

Native	plants that occur naturally in Britain and are not known to have been introduced by man.
Neutral	a soil neither very acid nor very basic.
Parasite	a plant which obtains all of its nutrients from another living plant.
Perennial	a plant which flowers and fruits each year and lives for several years.
Raised bog	a bog in which the peat has built up to form a convex dome.
Reseeding	a means of increasing productivity on grassland by ploughing, fertilising and drilling with a new seed mixture of productive grasses.
Rhizomatous	a plant with an underground stem bearing shoots which usually stores food and lasts for more than one season.
Saline	a damp or wet area with salt deposits.
Saprophyte	a plant which obtains its nutrients from dead organic matter.
Scrub	land dominated by shrubs, often an intermediate stage in reversion of grassland to woodland.
Set-aside	arable land which has been taken out of food production. A scheme aimed at reducing European food subsidies.
Slack	a water-logged valley or hollow usually on moorland.
sp.	species
spp.	more than one species.
ssp.	subspecies.
Tetrad	an area of land 2 x 2 kilometres sq, based on the national grid.
Unimproved	land which has not been intensively farmed by use of fertilisers, chemical sprays or reseeding.

INDEX OF ENGLISH NAMES

INDEX OF SCIENTIFIC NAMES